Dr. Henry J. Kowitz
Easton, Pa.

Family Reading Festival

STORIES AND POEMS TO READ TOGETHER

FAMILY READING FESTIVAL

Stories & Poems to Read Together

SELECTED AND EDITED BY

Frances Cavanah

ILLUSTRATED BY MAURICE BRÉVANNES

Prentice-Hall, Inc.

ENGLEWOOD CLIFFS, NEW JERSEY

OTHER BOOKS BY

Frances Cavanah

Two Loves for Jenny Lind

They Knew Abe Lincoln

We Came to America

Our Country's Story

Holiday Roundup

Real People Series
[EDITOR]

Library of Congress Catalog Card Number 58-9314

30285

TO

Muriel Fuller

editor and friend
for whose wise counsel
on this and other books
I shall be forever grateful

Acknowledgments

THE EDITOR wishes to express her thanks and appreciation for permission to use or reprint material copyrighted, or otherwise controlled, to:

Appleton - Century - Crofts, Inc., for "The Flower-Fed Buffaloes," from *Going to the Stars*, by Vachel Lindsay, copyright, 1926, D. Appleton & Company. Reprinted by permission of the publishers, Appleton-Century-Crofts, Inc.

Rowena Bastin Bennett for "Thanksgiving Magic," from *Child Life*.

The Bobbs-Merrill Company, Inc., for "Welcome, Grimalkin," from *Benjamin West and His Cat Grimalkin*, by Marguerite Henry and Wesley Dennis, copyright, 1947. Used by special permission of the publishers, The Bobbs-Merrill Company, Inc.

Brandt & Brandt for "God's World," from *Collected Poems*, Harper & Brothers, copyright, 1913, 1941, by Edna St. Vincent Millay; for "Prayer for a Better World," from *We Stand United and Other Radio Scripts*, by Stephen Vincent Benét, Rinehart and Company, Inc., copyright, 1942, by Stephen Vincent Benét.

Curtis Brown, Ltd., for "A New Song To Sing About Jonathan Bing," from *Jonathan Bing and Other Verses*, by Beatrice Curtis Brown, Oxford University Press. Reprinted by permission of the author. Copyright, 1936, by Beatrice Curtis Brown.

Gail Brook Burket for "Early American," "V. I. P.," and "Written with Stars," by permission of the author.

George T. Bye and Company for selection from *Farmer Boy*, by Laura Ingalls Wilder. Published by Harper and Brothers.

The Caxton Printers, Ltd., for "Paul Bunyan and the Popcorn Blizzard," from *Paul Bunyan Swings His Axe*, by Dell J. McCormick. Published by The Caxton Printers, Ltd., Caldwell, Idaho. Used by special permission of the copyright owners.

Elizabeth Coatsworth for "Danger!" from *Child Life*.

Padraic Colum for "The Man with the Bag," from *The Big Tree of Bunlahy*, published by The Macmillan Company.

Coward-McCann, Inc., for "The Sorcerer's Apprentice," reprinted by permission of Coward-McCann, Inc., from *More Tales from Grimm*, by Wanda Gág. Copyright, 1947, by Wanda Gág.

Crown Publishers, Inc., for "The Veneer of Silver," "The Blemish on the Diamond," and "A Rabbi for the Day," adapted from "The Parables of the Preacher of Dubno." From *A Treasury of Jewish Folklore*, edited by Nathan Ausubel. Copyright, 1948, by Crown Publishers, Inc. Used by permission of the publishers.

Ethel De Vito for "Letters from Dorothea," from *The Saturday Evening Post*.

Dial Press, Inc., for "Phaeton and the Chariot of the Sun," from *Stories of the Gods and Heroes*, by Sally Benson, copyright, 1940, by Sally Benson. Reprinted by permission of The Dial Press, Inc.

Dodd, Mead & Company, Inc., for "A Week of Sundays," reprinted by permission of Dodd, Mead & Company from *Tell Them Again Tales*, by Margaret and Mary Baker. Copyright, 1934, by Dodd, Mead & Company, Inc.

Mary Dickerson Donahey for "Lightfoot Has a Visitor" (original title "Rilla Solves a Mystery"), from *Child Life*.

Doubleday & Company, Inc., for "In the Garden of the Lord," reprinted by permission of Helen Keller and Doubleday & Company, Inc.

E. P. Dutton & Co., Inc., for "Ah Mee's Invention," from the book *Shen of the Sea*, by Arthur Bowie Chrisman. Copyright, 1925, by E. P. Dutton & Co., Inc. Renewal, 1953, by Arthur Bowie Chrisman; for "How Babe Got His Name," from the book *The Babe Ruth Story*, by Babe Ruth as told to Bob Considine. Copy-

Acknowledgments

right, 1948, by George Herman Ruth. Reprinted by permission of the publishers, E. P. Dutton & Co., Inc.

Dora W. Eastman for "Indian Prayer," from *The Soul of the Indian*, by Charles Eastman.

Edna Ferber for "The Fast," from *Fanny Herself*.

Aileen Fisher for "May Day," from *Child Life*.

Ilse F. Gilbert for "Bertram and the Troublesome Camel," from *Child Life*.

Harcourt, Brace and Company, Inc., for "Clever Manka," from *The Shoemaker's Apron*, copyright, 1920, by Parker Fillmore, renewed, 1948, by Louise Fillmore. Reprinted by permission of Harcourt, Brace and Company, Inc. For "Money in the Ice," from *Rufus M.*, by Eleanor Estes, copyright, 1943, by Harcourt, Brace and Company, Inc., and reprinted with their permission.

Harper & Brothers for "Kola," from *Thanks to Noah*, by George and Helen Waite Papashvily. Copyright, 1950, 1951, by George and Helen Waite Papashvily.

Cloyd C. Head for "Reflection" and "Saint Valentine," by Eunice Tietjens, from *Child Life*.

D.C. Heath and Company for "Ghost of the Lagoon," by Armstrong Sperry, from *Merry Hearts and Bold*, by Witty and others. Reprinted by special permission of D.C. Heath and Company.

Henry Holt & Co., Inc., for "The Apples of Iduna," from *Thunder of the Gods*, by Dorothy Hosford. Copyright, 1952, by Dorothy Hosford. For "Loveliest of Trees," from *A Shropshire Lad*, by A. E. Housman. Copyright, 1924, by Henry Holt and Company. For "The Linnet," from *Collected Poems, 1901-1918*, by Walter de la Mare. Copyright, 1920, by Henry Holt and Company. Copyright, 1948, by Walter de la Mare. For "Theme in Yellow," from *Chicago Poems*, by Carl Sandburg. Copyright, 1916, by Henry Holt and Company. Copyright, 1944, by Carl Sandburg. For "The Runaway," from *Complete Poems of Robert Frost*. Copyright, 1930, 1949, by Henry Holt and Company. Copyright, 1936, 1948, by Robert Frost. By permission of the publishers.

The Horn Book, Inc., for permission to use quotation from article by Elizabeth Coatsworth.

Houghton Mifflin Company for "Salt Water Tea," from *Johnny Tremain*, by Esther Forbes. Reprinted by permission of and arrangement with Houghton Mifflin Company, the authorized publishers.

Jack and Jill for "Why the Old Man Planted Trees," reprinted by special permission from *Jack and Jill*, copyright, 1946, by The Curtis Publishing Company. Permission is also granted by the author, Abraham Segal (Dan Murdoch).

Chiyono Sugimoto Kiyooka for "The Farmer Saint," from *Picture Tales from the Japanese*, by Chiyono Sugimoto, published by J. B. Lippincott Company.

Alfred A. Knopf, Inc., for "Mother to Son," reprinted from *The Dream Keeper*, by Langston Hughes, copyright, 1932, by Alfred A. Knopf, Inc. Used by permission of Alfred A. Knopf, Inc.

The late Robert Lawson for "Halloween," by Marie Lawson, from *Child Life*.

J. B. Lippincott Company for "A Kitten," from *Over the Garden Wall*, by Eleanor Farjeon. Copyright, 1933, 1951, by Eleanor Farjeon. "The Night Will Never Stay," from *Poems for Children*. Copyright, 1951, by Eleanor Farjeon. "Welcome to the New Year," from *Come Christmas*, by Eleanor Farjeon. Copyright, 1928, 1951, by Eleanor Farjeon. For "The Ugly Duckling," from *Hans Andersen: Forty Stories*, translated by M. R. James. Published by J. B. Lippincott Company.

Little, Brown & Company for "The Talkative Tortoise" and "The Flight of the Animals," from *The Fables of India*, copyright, 1955, by Joseph Gaer. For selection from *Mr. Popper's Penguins*, copyright, 1938, by Richard and Florence Atwater. For "Jungle Boy in New York" (original title "The Story of Saudin"), from *Land Below the Wind*, copyright, 1939, by Agnes Newton Keith. For "Eletelephony," from *Tirra Lirra*, copyright, 1932, by Laura E. Richards. For "The Hippopotamus," copyright, 1935, by Ogden Nash; "The Kitten," copyright, 1940, by Ogden Nash. From *Parents Keep Out*, by Ogden Nash. By permission of Little, Brown & Co.

Mrs. Hugh Lofting for "Animal Language," from *The Story of Doctor Dolittle*; copyright, 1920; published by J. B. Lippincott Co. Used by permission of Mrs. Lofting.

McGraw-Hill Book Company, Inc., for selection from *Halfway to Heaven*. Reprinted by permission from *Halfway to Heaven*, by Ruth Adams Knight, published by McGraw-Hill Book Company, Inc. Copyright, 1952, by Ruth Adams Knight. For "The Little Whistler," from *The Little Whistler*, by Frances Frost, published by Whittlesey House. Copyright, 1949, McGraw-Hill Book Company, Inc.

McIntosh & Otis, Inc., for "The White Man's Medicine," adapted from *Children of the Covered Wagon*, by Mary Jane Carr. Copyright, 1934, 1943, by Thomas Y. Crowell Company. Reprinted by permission of McIntosh & Otis, Inc., in behalf of Mary Jane Carr.

The Macmillan Company for "Pigeons or Peacocks?" from *Caddie Woodlawn*, by Carol Ryrie Brink. "The Secret Heart," from *Strange Holiness*, by Robert P. Tristram Coffin. "The Coin," from *Flame and Shadow*, by Sara Teasdale. "Something Told the Wild Geese," from *Branches Green*, by Rachel Field. Used with the

Acknowledgments

permission of The Macmillan Company.

Julian Messner, Inc., for "A Pig Named Dennis," reprinted by permission of Julian Messner, Inc., from *Grizzlies in Their Back Yard*, by Beth Day; copyright date November 19, 1956, by Beth Day.

M. S. Mill Co., Inc., for "The Loose that Gaid the Olden Geggs," from *My Tale Is Twisted*, by Colonel Stoopnagle. Copyright, 1945, by The Curtis Publishing Company. Copyright, 1945, 1946, by F. Chase Taylor. By permission of M. S. Mill Co., Inc.

William Morrow and Company, Inc., for "Beauty," from *I Am a Pueblo Indian Girl*, by E-Yeh-Shure. Copyright, 1939, by William Morrow and Company, Inc. By permission of William Morrow and Company, Inc.

Thomas Nelson & Sons for selection from *The Little Old Woman Who Used Her Head*, by Hope Newell, used by the permission of Thomas Nelson & Sons.

Plays, Inc., for "Paddy Boy" (original title "'Sure, Don't You Know?'"), copyright, 1953, by Aileen Fisher, reprinted from *Holiday Programs for Boys and Girls*, used by permission of Plays, Inc.

Rand McNally & Company for selection from *Brighty of the Grand Canyon*, by Marguerite Henry. Copyright, 1953, by Rand McNally & Company, publishers. For "The New Mother," from *They Knew Abe Lincoln*, by Frances Cavanah. Copyright, 1952, by Rand McNally & Company, publishers. For "A Horse for General Lee," (original title, "A Good Traveller"), from *24 Horses: A Treasury of Stories*, collected by Frances Cavanah and Ruth Cromer Weir. Copyright, 1950, by Rand McNally & Company, publishers. For "In Philadelphia, 1723," by Marjorie Knapp, from *Child Life*. For "How Arthur Became King," is from *King Arthur and His Knights*, by Maude Radford Warren, published by Rand McNally & Company.

Hamilton Richards for "The Golden Windows," by Laura E. Richards. Used by permission of Hamilton Richards, Trustee u/w Laura E. Richards.

Rinehart & Company, Inc., for "The Girl in the Picture: A Gypsy Adventure," adapted from *The Saturdays*, by Elizabeth Enright. Copyright, March 1941, by Elizabeth Enright Gillham.

Row, Peterson & Company for "Gudbrand-on-the-Hillside," by Gudrun Thorne-Thomsen, from *East o' the Sun and West o' the Moon*, revised edition, copyright, 1946, by Row, Peterson & Company. "How To Get What You Want for Christmas," by Aileen Fisher, from *Here Comes Christmas*, used by permission of the publisher.

Marion Plew Ruckel for "Abraham Lincoln," by Mildred Plew Meigs, from *Child Life*.

Mrs. Lew Sarett for "Four Little Foxes," from *Slow Smoke*, by Lew Sarett. Copyright, 1925, by Henry Holt and Company; copyright, 1953, by Lew Sarett. Reprinted by permission of Mrs. Lew Sarett.

John Schaffner for "Papa Was a Riot," by A. J. Ciulla, copyright, 1952, by *Everywoman's Magazine, Inc.* Reprinted by permission of the author and John Schaffner, agent for the author.

Charles Scribner's Sons for "The Piper at the Gates of Dawn," reprinted from *The Wind in the Willows*, by Kenneth Grahame (copyright, 1908, 1933, by Charles Scribner's Sons), with permission of the publisher. For "Man's Search for God," adapted by the author from *Augustus Caesar's World* (copyright, 1947, by Genevieve Foster), and *Birthdays of Freedom* (copyright, 1952, by Genevieve Foster), with the permission of Charles Scribner's Sons. "The Shooting Match at Nottingham Town" is from *The Merry Adventures of Robin Hood* by Howard Pyle, published by Charles Scribner's Sons.

Max Steele for "Ah Love! Ah Me!" from *Collier's*.

Dorothy Brown Thompson for "Back, Buster!" (original title, "Interpreter Needed") from *Child Life*.

James Thurber for "Many Moons," from the book *Many Moons*, published by Harcourt, Brace and Company. By permission of the author.

Nancy Byrd Turner for "Dark-Eyed Lad, Columbus," "Washington," and "The Flowers of Easter," from *Child Life*.

Viking Press, Inc., for "The Creation," from *God's Trombones*, by James Weldon Johnson. Copyright, 1927, by The Viking Press, Inc.; 1955 by Grace Nail Johnson. For "Firefly," from *Under the Tree*, by Elizabeth Madox Roberts. Copyright, 1922, by B. W. Huebsch, Inc.; 1950, by Ivor S. Roberts. Reprinted by permission of The Viking Press, Inc., New York.

Wake-Brook House and Florence Page Jaques for "The Pancake," from *There Once Was a Puffin, and Other Nonsense Verses for Children*, by Florence Page Jaques.

Albert Whitman & Co., for "Pecos Bill Busts Pegasus," from *Pecos Bill*, by James Cloyd Bowman. Used by permission of Albert Whitman & Co.

* * *

THE EDITOR wishes to thank the librarians of the Evanston Public Library and of the Curriculum Laboratory of Deering Library, Northwestern University, for their kindness and cooperation, and the following friends for the loan of books from their private libraries: Eloise Rue, school librarian; Lucile Pannell, former bookseller; and Helen Boyd, editor. I am grateful to Elsie Hunt, former chairman of the English Department, Nichols Public School of Evanston, for her suggestions. I also wish to thank Marjorie Thayer, Junior Book Editor of Prentice-Hall, Inc., and Muriel Fuller for their help.

Introduction

⟨ FAMILY READING FESTIVAL *is for parents and children to share.
Whether the stories and poems in this "*SEVEN BOOKS IN ONE*"
are read separately or aloud in a household group, the plan is to
provide interesting and varied reading for all the family; to give
every member selections culled both from the past and from the
best that many modern writers offer.*

*"The greatest books," said John Ruskin, "contain food for all
ages." There is less difference between good literature for young
people and for more mature persons than is often supposed. Children long ago appropriated such adult masterpieces as* Gulliver's
Travels *and* David Copperfield. *The swift-moving action of many
of our oldest myths, legends, and fables strikes a responsive chord
in modern boys and girls; yet these stories came into being to meet
the needs of older people as well as of the young. Certainly a book,
to be good enough for a child, must be interesting to his elders,
and those parents are fortunate who read with their children.*

*The pleasure of renewing acquaintance with such perennial
favorites as Tom Sawyer, Robin Hood, or the March Sisters and
Laurie in* Little Women *will be heightened by watching a younger
generation meet them for the very first time. There is a mutual
thrill of discovery in finding new favorites when the reading is
done aloud. A nonsense poem is twice as funny when several
people are laughing together. An adventure yarn is more exciting
when there is someone to share the suspense. An animal story, a
realistic tale of the present, a legend out of the past, the sayings
of a wise leader, or an account of a popular hero all take on added*

meaning when shared in the home; and everyone is richer for the experience. The act of sharing is in itself an enrichment. To read together is one way—and a very satisfying way—of creating closer family ties.

Every wise parent—or any wise older person who loves a child—has the same objective: to help him grow. To help him become a secure, happy, well-adjusted human being is the responsibility of the adults who for a few brief years have him in their care. This responsibility seems almost overwhelming in view of the problems he soon will be called upon to solve in a world more complicated than even we have known. It is for us to make him more aware of this world. We can help him to understand his neighbors, whether they live in the next block or on the other side of the earth. We can help him to think straight and to understand himself. No matter what may lie ahead for him, we can fortify him with the right ideas and strengthen his faith in those ideals which enabled earlier generations to meet the challenges of their times. We can supply him with examples of courage, so that he may learn to be courageous. We can help him to develop a taste for beauty. Nor must we forget that he needs to laugh. A sense of humor, the ability to see the funny side of things, will help him through many a trying situation.

A large order, perhaps, but to help us we have the wisdom and beauty of the past, both the immediate past and more distant times. We have instances of initiative and high courage, and knowledge is ours for the asking. All this may be found between the pages of our books which supplement living by making our lives richer and more enjoyable. He who likes to read has taken out insurance against boredom; he has grown a hedge against despair. Reading is a habit that pays lifelong dividends.

These dividends are to be reckoned both in pleasure and in accomplishment. History is filled with examples, and there are others all around us, of persons whose lives were changed or the mold of their careers set by their early reading. It was not only that they acquired the habit young, but what they read that counted. That is what always counts. A young reader who is given good books that satisfy his desire for experience, that give him a feeling of security, that inspire and entertain him, is less likely to turn to shoddy or vicious reading matter. Instead, one good book leads to another; new interests are formed; desirable character traits are strengthened. The parents who read with their sons and daughters are in a rare position to share their thoughts. By introducing good books into the family circle, everyone has a good time. The children see to that.

The purpose of Family Reading Festival is threefold: to entertain all the members of the family, to inspire them, to expand their horizons. Even the youngest ones have been remembered. Stories and poems that they will especially enjoy have been starred (*) in the Table of Contents. The humor or the fundamental truths that these stories set forth do not limit them to any one age group. Older readers like them too.

A single volume can never be a complete library, but one object of a collection such as this is to open doors. It is fervently hoped that, in addition to supplying many hours of pleasure, this anthology will stimulate interest in the complete books from which some of the selections are taken, and in other books which, in turn, will enrich the lives of their readers. Every child, like a flower, must do his own growing, but adults have the opportunity to prepare the soil and tend the plant. And it is a great privilege to be on hand to watch the blooming.

F.C.

Contents

I. THE BOOK OF THE FAMILY

II. THE BOOK OF ADVENTURE

Contents

III. THE BOOK OF ANIMALS

* Also of interest to younger readers.

Contents

IV. THE BOOK OF TALL TALES AND LAUGHTER

V. THE BOOK OF ENCHANTMENT

Fairy and Folk Tales

* Also of interest to younger readers.

Contents

Myths and Legends

VI. THE BOOK OF POETRY

Americans and America

The Comic Touch

* Also of interest to younger readers.

Contents

* Also of interest to younger readers.

[xvi]

Contents

VII. THE BOOK OF WISDOM

Fables and Allegories

* Also of interest to younger readers.

Contents

Wisdom of the Ages

Words to Remember

Prayers to Remember

* Also of interest to younger readers.

THE BOOK OF

The Family

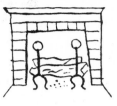

Introduction

⟨ THE YEARS *when we are slowly changing from children into men and women are a time to store up joy and laughter and wisdom, a time to get ready to meet whatever challenges the future may hold. To grow is to learn to understand ourselves and one another, to develop new interests, to want to know what lies around the corner, and to try to satisfy our curiosity. It involves a great deal more than adding inches. The happiest people never stop growing.*

The process is usually more interesting, however, in those who are young in years as well as in their hearts. More interesting but more painful, too. It is not easy to grow up. There are too many strange and bewildering behavior patterns to which the newcomer to our planet is expected to conform. The day will soon come when he must take his place in his community, in his country, and in the world, and he prepares for this day in his own family circle. The ideal preparation is a happy home where members have fun together, meet their problems with courage, and learn to give as well as to take. The boy, or girl, has a head start whose elders love and understand him and make him feel secure.

Children instinctively crave security, and they like stories that tell of satisfying family relationships. If the stories ring true, they reinforce what the child already knows, and he holds his own home all the dearer. If he has failed to find what he needs there, the right books can help to compensate for what he has missed. A sense of security is necessary to his well being, even if acquired vicariously.

Nor is a sense of security easy to acquire even in the so-called ideal home. Every young person feels lost at times. He may yearn for guidance but hesitate to ask for it. He may be striving toward an ideal that he can find no words to express. At such times many parents and teachers and older friends also feel lost. They do not know what to do. Many of them turn to books. The example of a fictitious character who is so true to life that he seems more real than some of our neighbors may resolve a problem more effectively than any amount of talking. A well-chosen story or an incident out of biography may prove to be the source of lifelong inspiration.

A number of our wisest and most popular writers, some of whose stories may be read in the following pages, have dipped into the treasury of their own family experiences. The classic example is Louisa May Alcott. Her Little Women *was the favorite of several generations. "It was almost the first book of its kind," said Cornelia Meigs in her fine biography,* Invincible Louisa, *"a direct, natural, truthful tale . . . It was just what girls had been starving for, although scarcely anyone knew it. Louisa did . . ."*

And Samuel Clemens knew what boys wanted! This was the same Sam, the prototype for the mischievous Tom Sawyer, *who grew up to write books under the pen name of Mark Twain. His mother served as the model for the sorely tried Aunt Polly.*

Among the other authors who are represented here, Laura Ingalls Wilder, Eleanor Estes, and Edna Ferber have also written stories that reflect their early lives. Carol Ryrie Brink's Caddie Woodlawn *is about her pioneer grandmother. Mary Jane Carr read the diaries of men and women who had traveled the Oregon Trail, and her account of the Indian father and the white one in "The White Man's Medicine" might easily have happened. The events described in "The New Mother" actually did happen—and to the young Abe Lincoln. His stepmother lavished on him love and understanding, and gave him some of the books that whetted his ambition. She made it possible for him to prepare, in his own home—humble cabin though it was—to meet the challenge of the future.*

A like preparation must be made by every child. In this, good books can play a vital and a joyous part.

Money in the Ice

❰ To THE Moffat children, who grew up during World War I, "making both ends meet" was a challenge to their sense of humor. Even seven-year-old Rufus took his turn at providing for the family with a dogged determination that was both tender and amusing.

SETTLEMENT HOUSE!" said Rufus in disgust. "Why do they call it *settlement* house?" He had come to the city cheerfully with Mama and Jane and Joey to watch their big sister, Sylvie, give a performance of *The Lollipop Princess*, in the Settlement House. He came because he expected to see Indians in a place with a name like that.

"Settlement House!" Rufus repeated. "I didn't see any Indians."

He was very disappointed. He had waited impatiently for today. Now, he thought, he would see the kind of house the settlers lived in, made of logs, where people who looked like Daniel Boone lived, and where there would be plenty of Indians about; friendly ones on the inside, and hostile ones on the outside. But these people were not Indians or pioneers either.

And the settlement house itself looked just like any other ordinary red brick house from the outside. Inside there were just rooms. There was just one big room with a stage in it. That's where the play was given. There was not a trace of an Indian! Not so much as a feather or a tomahawk!

"Why didn't you tell me this was just a house?" Rufus asked a little crossly. He and Mama, Jane, and Joey were picking their way up the street on the way to the trolley car. They were all walking gingerly on the ash-strewn pavements trying not to get cinders in their rubbers or to slip on a smooth spot. Sylvie had stayed behind in the Settlement House because she was giving *The Lollipop Princess* again tonight.

"Once I thought it meant Indians too," said Jane dreamily. "Stockades . . . blockades. But it doesn't."

Joey was silent. An uncomfortable thought had just struck him. The late afternoon was icy cold and the temperature might easily have fallen down around zero. And he or Mama or somebody should have remembered to turn off the water in the cellar before they left. Otherwise the pipes might have

[5]

frozen. And if they had frozen they might have burst! For a while he kept this possibility to himself.

"It's called a Settlement House," said Mama, "because the people who manage it try to settle newcomers to the country and tell them the ways of the land."

"Any newcomer is really a sort of a settler," added Jane.

"But if there aren't any Indians," said Rufus, still cross, and having to run to keep up with the rest of the family.

Joey took Rufus by the hand. "Well, fella," he said, to take Rufus' mind off the dismal disappointment he had had of not seeing any Indians, "well, you better stop thinking about Indians and think instead of whether the pipes busted or not!"

"Gracious!" exclaimed Mama. "Did we forget to turn off the water? How could we have, on a day like this?"

"'Cause it's daytime," said Jane. This was true. At night, before they went to bed, Mama or Joey turned the water off in the cellar in this zero weather, so the pipes would not freeze. But in the daytime there was usually somebody at home, running the water now and then and keeping the fires going.

They heard a trolley coming and hurried to the corner. Joey accidentally stepped on the heel of Jane's rubber and it slid off her shoe, but she managed to slither along on it and they did just barely catch the car. On the trolley it was beautifully warm.

"I can stand," said Rufus, for he considered it manly to hang on a strap in trolley cars. Of course he couldn't reach the straps, but he could stand without hanging on. There were seats enough for everybody, though, and Mama finally persuaded him to sit down too. Rufus soon became drowsy and he almost fell asleep. He heard Mama and Joey and Jane talking about the pipes.

"They needn't worry," he told himself. "If the pipes burst, I'll put my finger in the leak the way the boy did in 'The Leak in the Dike.' And I'll hold it there till help comes." He was too sleepy to tell them now. But he certainly was not going to fall asleep on this trolley the way babies do. Every time he felt his head wobble over side-

ways, he pulled himself up straight with a lurch and stared at the *Drink Moxie* ad.

Mama and Joey and Jane thought about the pipes. If only they had not burst! It was dreadful to have the pipes burst. The Moffats would have to call a plumber perhaps, and that cost a great deal of money. "Gee," Joey chided himself, "how did I forget?"

"We were all so excited about goin' to the play, we all forgot," said Jane.

"Well, maybe they didn't burst," said Joe. "I stoked the stoves good. That should've kep' the house warm enough."

"Ordinarily it would have," said Mama. "But this is bitter weather. And you know that kind of coal that we get nowadays isn't very good for our stoves."

Soft coal! Bituminous coal! That's the kind of coal they had to burn this year, for the good hard nut kind was scarce. When Mama started a fire with this coal, what a time she had! "By-two-minutes coal," she called it. "By two minutes the house will be full of smoke," she always said, making a joke of it.

The Moffats hated to get off the trolley where it was so warm. "Why couldn't we live on a trolley?" asked Jane, laughing.

"Sure. We could stretch out on the long seats and sleep," said Joe. "Rufe's practically asleep now."

"I'm not!" denied Rufus, sitting up straight with a jerk. "Just thinkin'. Where are we?"

"Goin' over the Cumberland Avenue bridge," said Jane. They all looked out over the snowy marshes. The sun had set, but there was still a wan wintry glow behind the heavy clouds in the west. "Those clouds look like mountains," said Jane. "You could think we were livin' in the mountains."

"That's night comin'," said Joe.

Now the trolley was swaying and sailing up Elm Street. Soon they would have to get off. In the town the streets seemed darker, for the great elm trees and the houses shadowed the sky. Just two more blocks and then they'd be at Ashbellows Place. Rufus was wide awake now and he was the one who pushed the bell. The trolley stopped and the Moffats stepped out into the cold.

"Br-r-r," said Mama.

The three children raced ahead. They would soon see whether or not the pipes had frozen. They slid up the street on the smooth icy stretches in the gutters, and then they turned into the narrow walk of their own yard. Both sides of the pavement leading to their porch were piled high with great banks of hard snow. "The Grand Canyon!" yelled Jane, her mind still on mountains.

Joey opened the door. The three children stood in the doorway and listened. They didn't hear one thing. This was encouraging, Rufus thought, for if the pipes had burst, surely they would hear water rushing in the cellar. But Joey said no, the pipes might have burst and the water frozen over the break. Or they might have frozen and not burst yet. That would not be quite so bad though, for he and Mama could thaw the pipes themselves with warm cloths and they need not call the plumber.

Joey led the way into the kitchen. Soon he had the lamps lighted. The fire in the stove had gone out! A fire made of this soft coal did not last and the house was very cold. Catherine-the-cat was sitting right on top of the stove to absorb the last bit of warmth there was in it. Nobody took off his coat or his mittens. And everybody held his breath as Joey went over to the sink. He turned the faucet on. The pipe shuddered but no water came. "Shucks!" said Joe. "It did freeze!" and he quickly turned the spigot off again.

Mama came in now. You could see everybody's breath even though they were in the house. Mama and Joey took the medium-sized lamp and went down to the cellar to investigate. Jane and Rufus stood at the top of the stairs and listened. They could hear Mama and Joey talking in low tones.

"Well," said Rufus, "did they bust?"

There was no answer. Mama and Joey were too busy, tapping the pipes here and feeling them there, to answer. Rufus and Jane stepped cautiously down one or two steps. These stairs did not have any backs to them and were really more like a ladder than a stairway. The unpaved cellar smelled of damp cold dirt.

"Did they bust?" Rufus demanded again.

"Yeh," came Joey's muffled voice.

"Bad?" asked Jane.

"No. A little break. Must have just happened," said Mama.

"Is there goin' to be a flood?" asked

Rufus, taking his mitten off and limbering up his forefinger.

"Nope," said Joe. "There's just a little water around the break. Jane, get some things to tie around the pipe."

Jane climbed to the head of the stairs where the rag bag hung on a nail. But Rufus felt his way up the stairs and into the kitchen and all the way out of the house. Rufus had a plan in his head. It was cold in the Moffats' house. The fire had gone out and the pipes had frozen. It was not at all nice there, thought Rufus. The first thing to do, of course, was to get the pipes fixed. Mama and Joey were taking care of that. The next thing was to fix the stove, but there wasn't anything in the house to start a fire with. And this was where Rufus' plan entered in. He knew of a certain new house that was being built over on Second Avenue. He figured he could get some shavings there to start a fire.

He first snatched an empty burlap bag from the back entry. Then he picked up his red sled, one of the low flat kind with round steel runners. And with his red plaid Mackinaw flapping open he took a good run and then belly-flopped across the hard snow that covered the Moffats' lawn and all the way down the street and across the lot to Elm Street.

In front of the drugstore he couldn't resist taking one or two good slides back and forth on the thick green ice that had piled up there. Many colors were reflected in the ice, red and blue ones from the big globes in the drugstore window and purple ones from the street lamp. "Well, I better go now and get the wood," said Rufus, and he made ready to take one last good slide.

He ran a way to gain momentum and then he flopped down on his sled. As he was skimming along the ice, his eyes watching the glassy surface go slipping by, he thought he saw something shiny, something shiny frozen in the ice. He thought it looked like money. It looked like a lot of money—not just two cents.

"Probably some old bottle tops," he told himself in order to keep his hopes under control. Nevertheless, he dragged his feet behind him so that he would slow up and he edged his sled backward toward the spot where he thought he had seen something shiny in the ice. He dug his toes and his fingers into the ice, getting a grip to pull himself backward. It might have been a mirage such as people see in the desert. They think they see something they want to see, like water or a city, when it isn't really there at all. But he hadn't even been thinking about money. He had been thinking only about getting the wood. Where were the shiny things? Maybe he had imagined them. No! There they were! There they were!

Rufus stopped his sled. He stopped right over the shiny things so he could look at them from between the front runners of his sled. He stared at them for a long, long time. They were money. They were not bottle tops. There were two quarters, three dimes, and two nickels, spread out, frozen solid beneath the surface of the ice. Rufus felt as though he were glued to this spot. He gazed at them, fascinated, taking them in. The coins were there, and they couldn't get away. Nobody else could get them either. He, Rufus, was on top of them on his own sled, nailing them down, laying claim to them like the miners in the Alaska gold fields.

For a long time Rufus was content just to look at the coins. The flickering street lamp made the shadows on the ice ripple like the sea, and Rufus studied the coins as he might study a little school of fish.

"Criminenty!" he murmured. He wiped his nose on the back of his black stocking mitten. "If it's only real," he said.

He closed his eyes for a second. Then he opened them, first one and then the other. The money was still there all right, two nickels, three dimes, and two quarters. And he saw them with both his eyes open and even with just one eye open. He could buy the dinner with this much money, he thought. He laughed to himself when he thought of how surprised all the Moffats would be when he staggered in with a load of food.

"How'm I gonna get it out?" he asked himself.

He didn't have his knife with him. If he went home for it, somebody else might come along, somebody who did have his knife with him, and dig up this money. "Let's see now," he muttered. He'd have to figure some way of getting this gold, this money, out of the ice.

Supposing he left his sled right over it, covering up the spot where the money lay embedded in the ice. No, that was a foolish idea. The sled would just attract attention and, besides, somebody might take his sled into the bargain, and he didn't want to lose that. "I know what," he said to himself. He took off his black stocking mitten and tossed it about three yards beyond the money. People would be so busy seeing his mitten and wondering what it was that they wouldn't see the money. "A decoy," he murmured, using a word he had heard Joey say lately.

Rufus hoped he wouldn't lose his mitten either, but certainly with all this much money at stake he would have to risk something. He wondered if he had placed it in the right spot. He backed off a few paces and studied the decoy. Maybe a few inches farther . . . He picked his mitten up, wiped his nose on the back of it again, and again tossed it carelessly down so it would look as though someone really had dropped it. He took one more look at the money. It was safe. It was frozen deeply in the ice and it must have been here for some days. So far no one else had seen it. Now he'd run quickly, get the ice pick and the chisel, his knife . . . quick . . .

That was what he did. He picked up his sled and tore. He belly-flopped up the street and across the empty lot so fast he didn't see Mr. Price coming until he was right up to him. Mr. Price had to leap into the air to avoid being knocked down.

When Rufus reached home, he could hear Mama and Joey still banging pipes down in the cellar. Janey was shaking down the cold ashes in the kitchen range, getting it ready for a new fire.

"I'll bring home some wood in a minute," Rufus yelled at her as he banged out of the house with the chisel and his knife. All the while he kept asking himself, "Are they safe?"

Fortunately it was really very dark now, although the lights in the drugstore window cast a glow that lighted up Rufus' mitten. Nobody had taken that anyway. If only nobody had taken the money. "Be there! Be there!" Rufus ordered, hardly daring to look. Now here was where the money should be, and here it was! Here it was! The same thing—two quarters, three dimes, and a couple of nickels. No one else had seen them. Rufus sat on his sled and he scraped and dug, chipped and filed, and finally he had them all out. He warmed the coins in his chubby, chapped fist.

While Rufus was standing in the red glow from the window, warming his money, Spec Cullom, the iceman, came along. What luck for him, out of all the people in Cranbury, to be the one to come along right now! Because in the wintertime Spec Cullom was also a plumber as well as the iceman. Not many people bought ice in the wintertime and a great many people needed help with their water pipes at this season. He had his plumbing kit with him right now, as a matter of fact. He stepped into the drugstore.

Rufus waited for Spec Cullom to come out. He looked in the drugstore window. The iceman was drinking a soda. Then he came out and he saw Rufus.

"Hello, fella," he said, starting to spar around a bit.

Rufus didn't spar back this time. His fist was full of money wanting to be spent. "Look," he said, wiping his nose on his sleeve. "I dug this up out of the ice."

"Lucky fella," said Spec Cullom, shoving his hat back on his head.

"How much of this money would it take to fix our pipe? It busted," said Rufus.

"How much do you think it's worth?" Spec asked.

Rufus looked at his money, studying what he was going to do with each piece. It was worth more than a nickel to have pipes fixed. He knew that. If he gave Spec one of the big pieces he might not have enough left to buy the supper. However, a pipe is important. He held up one of the quarters and looked at him anxiously.

But Spec shook his head. Reluctantly Rufus added the other quarter. Now he could buy hardly any supper. But Spec Cullom shook his head in disgust. "Five cents does it, fella," he said.

"A nickel?" asked Rufus incredulously. He picked one of these coins out and gave it to the iceman.

"That does it," said Spec, and he flipped the coin in the air, caught it, and stuck it in his pocket. "I'll drop right over," he added.

"Will you tell Mama I paid already?" asked Rufus.

"Right, Boss. So long!" And he winked at Rufus and hastened up the street with a careless, loose stride.

"S'long," said Rufus, looking after him admiringly and smiling to himself.

Then he crossed the street to the grocery store with as loose and careless a gait as he could muster with a sled to pull. Rufus laid all his money on the counter. He bought two packages of kindling wood, for of course he had given up the idea of going 'way over to Second Avenue after all that had happened. He bought a small sackful of good, hard nut coal. "Not that soft by-two-minutes kind," he said. "We have some of that." He bought some apples, some oranges, some eggs, and some potatoes, and he went home feeling like Santa Claus.

This time when he reached home Mama and Joey were in the kitchen, too. Somebody else was down in the cellar, bang-banging at the pipes, and Rufus knew who that was. Spec Cullom!

Joey and Mama had to heat some water to thaw out the pipes. "Now what am I goin' to start this old fire with?" Joey asked in perplexity. And right then was the time for Rufus to drag in his sledful of treasures.

"I found the money in the ice!" he yelled, jumping up and down so hard that Spec Cullom came dashing up the stairs to see what was wrong now.

Joey lost no time in making the fires, and Mama heated the water to thaw the pipes. It wasn't long before Spec had the break soldered together and then Mama went to the faucet to turn on the water.

Cr-unch! Cr-eak! Cr-rack! The water was trying to come through the ice.

Then with terrific spasms that shook the faucet the water did burst out of the pipe, first in rusty spurts and then in a good clear stream!

Spec Cullom left and Mama started to cook the supper. She made lots of apple fritters, using the supplies that Rufus had brought home. "Tell it again!" first one and then another asked Rufus. And he had to tell again the whole story of how he had found the money in the ice.

Naturally all the Moffats were excited about it.

"Imagine finding so much money in the ice!" marveled Jane, and she slid over the ice very carefully for some days, hoping she too would find a treasure. As for Rufus, he was the happiest of all. He went to bed that night right after supper, thinking about his luck. Finding the money in the ice more than made up for the disappointment about the Indians. He really felt like a hero. He hadn't had to hold his finger in the leak in the pipe. But he had come home with the money and everybody had had a good dinner. Furthermore, now the house was good and warm.

⟪ THE lively quartet in RUFUS M. and other books about the Moffats bear a decided resemblance to the family in which the author grew up in a New England town during World War I. Other books by Mrs. Estes include THE HUNDRED DRESSES, and GINGER PYE which won the Newbery Medal in 1952.

Pigeons or Peacocks?

⟨ JOHN WOODLAWN, *pioneer, liked to watch the flocks of pigeons that darkened the Wisconsin sky as they flew southward. They reminded him of the peacocks on the lawn of his English grandfather, Lord Woodlawn. As a boy, John had seen them only through the bars of an iron gate. His father, because of his marriage to a seamstress, had been disinherited.*

JOHN WOODLAWN sat behind a little table on which was spread the open letter which had come across the sea. His face was very grave.

"Children," he said, "we have come to a crossroad in our lives. Today I have received a letter from a source which I had thought closed to me. Once this letter could have meant a great deal to me, but now it has come almost too late."

"Oh, no, Johnny!" cried Mother quickly.

"Perhaps Mother is right," he went on. "The letter can still do much for us if we wish it. Children, an uncle, whom I have never seen, has died in England. He was Lord Woodlawn after my grandfather. Since his death, it appears that the family lawyers have spent some time in tracing his successor. At last they have found him. He turns out to be the son of a little seamstress. It seems, however oddly, that *I* may be the next Lord Woodlawn."

"You, Father!" the children cried. Clara, the oldest daughter, clasped her hands and said: "Oh, the big house with the peacocks, Father, will it be yours?"

"Yes, the big house with the peacocks, Clara," said Father slowly.

Caddie Woodlawn thought of the big house with the peacocks, too, and she tried to see in her mind just how it looked. But try as she would to see it clearly, the iron bars of a closed gate were always between, just as they had been when Father had first described it.

"There is one condition, however," continued Father, "which I must tell you about. The title and estates in England come to me only if I will give up my American citizenship and all my American connections and return to England to live. This requirement was a part of the late Lord Woodlawn's will, and if I do not wish to comply with it, the land and title

[13]

will pass on to another more distant relative who is living now in England."

"But, of course, you will," said Mother and Clara together.

"I suppose it would be foolish not to," said Father slowly, and he passed his hand across his forehead as though he were brushing away a cobweb or an unruly bit of hair. Then he folded the letter and put it back in the envelope and stood up, smiling. "In any case our decision must not be hasty," he said. "We must be sure that we are right."

"But it seems to me in a case like this that there can be only one right thing to do!" cried Mother warmly.

Father laid his hand on her arm, and looked deeply into her eyes. "Think,

Harriet. Think before you speak," he said.

"Couldn't we ever come back here to the farm?" asked Tom.

"No, Tom."

Caddie thought of her horse. "Would we have to leave Betsy and the other animals?"

"Yes, Caddie. Probably there would be many fine horses awaiting us in England."

"How soon would we have to go?"

"If we go, it will be soon."

"*If!*" cried Clara. "Father, how can you say an *if* to such a splendid thing!"

"It is only right to look at all the sides of an important question, Clara."

When they came out into the sunshine again, they were a little dazzled.

The parlor had been dark and cool, and, in the few moments they had stood there in dark coolness, the whole future had suddenly changed for the little Woodlawns. How strange, how unbelievable it was! No wonder they blinked at the sun, when they came out. But suddenly Tom saw something which brought him out of his daze. Hetty was setting off across the fields toward Maggie Bunn's.

"Bring her back," yelled Tom, and Caddie and Warren raced along with him to catch her.

They weren't long in overtaking her, and Tom said fiercely: "You hold your tongue, Hetty. Don't you go telling anyone we're English until you're good and sure."

"English?" said Hetty. "But we aren't English, Tom!"

"We will be if we go back there. Didn't you know that, you little silly?"

Hetty stopped struggling to be free, and looked earnestly from one face to another. "Will we? I thought we'd always be Americans. Then, I guess, I don't want to tell after all," she said, and the four of them went silently back to the house together.

That evening at supper, Mother and Annabelle, the young lady cousin from Boston who was visiting them, did most of the talking. Annabelle particularly was full of the most delightful plans for their life in England.

"Of course, you shall be presented to the Queen," she said, "and there will be balls and concerts and all manner of elegant things. Just think of the splendid clothes you can wear! The very latest fashions and all the hand-some noblemen simply languishing for dances with you. Oh, I do so envy you, you lucky girls! I do hope you will have me to visit you in England! Fancy an English lord coming from Dunnville! Was ever anything more absurd?"

Father said very little, and once, when Caddie glanced at him, she caught a troubled look in his eyes. It made the uncomfortable little ache in her own heart sharper.

After supper Caddie and the boys slipped out to the barn. Robert Ireton, the hired man, sat on a milking stool, tilted back against the barn, and strummed his banjo. Caddie sat on a loose pile of hay, her arms clasped around her knees. Above her the dark sky glittered and sparkled with thousands of stars. The milky way was a broad white path across the sky. There was the North Star and another star which she loved because it was so bright. She did not know its name, but she had always called it hers. There would be stars in England, but would they be so bright, so beautiful? The smell of clover and new hay tugged at her heart. Would anything in England smell as sweet? Caddie suddenly knew that she wanted the future, whatever it might hold, to be here in the country that she loved.

The members of the family appeared on time for breakfast the next morning, and everyone wore an air of strangeness and expectancy. They knew that today Father would make his decision about going back to England, and, until the decision was made, they felt ill at ease and somehow like a group of strangers sitting together at the familiar breakfast table. Caddie sat silent. She had dreamed last night about England. There had been peacocks and towers and moats, and it had seemed that the Woodlawn children were to be presented to the Queen, but then all of the others had vanished and only Caddie had gone on alone, and then she had found herself holding the hand of a little boy, and the little boy had been crying because he was hungry. And, when they had reached the Queen's palace, there had been a great barred gate, and through the gate they could see that the Queen had peacocks, too, but they could not get through the gate, and then soldiers had come and driven them away, and Caddie had wakened up and found that it was morning.

Father's voice broke through the memory of her dream. Caddie turned and looked at him, and she thought he was nicer sitting thus at the head of his simple table than he could ever be in any other place.

"I have been thinking," he said, "that you children are old enough to have some part in the decision which we must make today. It would hardly be fair for me alone, or for Mother and me, to say, without consulting you, either that you must give up your American citizenship and return to England or that you should remain here, giving up a good deal of money and a high position in England. After all, Mother and I have already lived a half of our lives, and they've been

worth the living, haven't they, Harriet?"

Mother smiled tremulously and nodded at him.

"But you young ones have all of your lives before you, and you already have some ideas of what you wish to make of them. It would be a pity for someone else to make a wrong decision for you. So I think it best that we should take a family vote. Since we are still on American soil and have always considered ourselves good Americans, we shall vote in the American way by written ballot. That is, each child shall decide for himself what he wishes to do. Then, without telling anyone else what he has decided, he shall write *Go* or *Stay* on a piece of paper which he shall then fold and place between the leaves of the family Bible in the parlor. We shall vote this afternoon at four o'clock, and, in the meantime, I want you to discuss it among yourselves and to ask Mother and me as many questions as you like. Above all, I want you to think each for yourself: 'What will be best for my future? Where shall I be most useful and happy?'"

"Shall I vote, too, Papa?" asked little Minnie, climbing onto Mr. Woodlawn's knee and looking earnestly into his face.

"Yes, you, too, little Minnie. Every Woodlawn shall vote except baby Joe, and his future we others must decide among us."

At mention of his name the baby bounced in his high chair and banged his spoon upon his tray.

"You and I shall not be allowed to

vote, baby Joe," said Annabelle, "but never you mind. You'll be a little English gentleman before the day is over, I'll be bound."

"Goo! goo!" said baby Joe and showed his two new teeth in a pink smile.

Then for a long time Father spoke to them quietly and earnestly, like an impartial judge, setting forth the advantages and the disadvantages of this move. He spoke of England more warmly than they had ever heard him speak before, picturing its beauties and the high place which they would be called to fill there. Then he spoke of America, and he did not say as many fine things of it as he had often said in the past, and Caddie knew why. It was because his heart belonged here in Wisconsin, and he did not wish to let his own preference prejudice his children. But he did speak briefly of the freedom which belonged to them in a new country, and he said that, although they might never be rich or famous in America, they would have the satisfaction of knowing that what they had they had made for themselves.

"An inherited fortune is never quite one's own," said Father slowly, "and yet I want you to understand that money and power are also great things, and that great good may come of them, if they are wisely handled."

Then he pushed back his chair from the table and took his hat and went out to see that the horses had a measure of oats.

"Do you think that Father wants to go back and be a lord?" asked Tom, as he and Caddie and Warren walked away to the lake.

"I guess he doesn't want us to know what he wants," said Caddie in a low voice. "He'd rather we made up our own minds."

"I can't see Father going back there where they treated him so badly once," said Tom. "Father's the kind of man who likes to do things for himself. I don't s'pose that English lords mend clocks and feed horses and put locks on guns for Indians, do you?"

"They don't have to!" shouted Warren.

"Well, Father doesn't *have* to either, but I think he'd miss it if he didn't do it."

"I think that Father likes to be at the front of things," said Caddie. "He likes to be free and help build new places. I think he'd rather go on West than go back to an old country where everything is finished."

"I would, too," said Tom. "I'd rather build a new mill in America than live in a castle in England that somebody who'd died hundreds of years ago had had the fun of building. That's how I feel."

"Me, too," said Warren.

"I guess we three'll vote the same," said Caddie, "but Mother and Clara and Hetty and Minnie will all be on the other side, and I don't know about Father. What he wants won't matter so much as what he thinks would be best for *us*. And, you know, he likes to make Mother happy."

They climbed onto the raft and Tom pushed off from shore. A cloud of gloom floated along with them as

[17]

they went down the lake on that bright August morning.

It was almost four o'clock, and the Woodlawn children had washed their hands and faces and smoothed their hair as if they were getting ready for a party.

"Just practicing up to be little lords and ladies," said Annabelle, who was as much excited as the rest of them, and even Tom was too distraught to answer her.

Caddie had gone off by herself to sit under a tree until Father should call her in to vote. She had closed her eyes, because the bees and birds and crickets sounded so much louder when she did, and it was fun to listen to them and try to tell from which direction each sound came. Soon, perhaps, she would be hearing English sounds. Suddenly a hot little hand was thrust into hers and she opened her eyes in surprise to see Hetty gazing earnestly into her face.

"Caddie, I'm going to vote like you do, did you know that?"

"How do you know how I'm going to vote?" asked Caddie. "We're not supposed to tell."

"Oh, I could guess that," said Hetty gravely. "You like it here better than anyplace, and so do I. I want to be an American."

Suddenly Caddie gave the round cheek a kiss. She had not remembered to kiss Hetty for a long time. "Hetty," she said, "no matter whether we go to England or stay in Wisconsin, let's be better chums, shall we?"

At four o'clock they went into the parlor and Father gave them all slips of paper exactly alike. There were pen and ink on the table beside the big Bible, and each member of the family wrote something on his or her slip, dried it, folded it, and placed it somewhere in the Bible. Father and Mother had slips of paper like the children, and they did the same. Minnie took the longest, because she had only just learned how to print and it had taken Hetty most of the morning to teach her how to print Go and Stay. But everyone waited quietly until she had finished.

"She must be writing Stay," whispered Hetty into Caddie's ear. "She can't do s and y very fast. Go wouldn't take her half so long, unless she's forgotten how."

Caddie's heart began to beat more quickly. What if Minnie did vote Stay? Hetty had voted to stay. That would make five on their side! Of course, Clara and Mother would be on the other side, and no one knew what Father would vote. Caddie knew that Mother's and Father's and even Clara's vote would count for more than theirs, because they were only the "young ones." Nevertheless for the first time today she began to hope. She found herself shivering with excitement.

Father took up the big Bible and looked through it until he had found eight slips of paper. He unfolded the first paper and in a low, clear voice read: "Stay."

One by one three more slips were unfolded and each one said Stay.

"Those are ours, I guess," whispered

Hetty, but Caddie squeezed her hand and said "Hush!" for Father was unfolding the fifth slip of paper.

"Go," read Father in the same steady voice.

Tom and Warren shuffled their feet restlessly. Tom seemed to hear Annabelle's sweet voice saying: "Practicing up to be little lords and ladies," and he kicked out viciously at a rag rug which his restless feet had scuffed into a roll.

Father unfolded the last three papers quickly and looked at them. Then he read them out: "Stay—stay—stay."

"Hooray!" yelled Warren.

But nobody else spoke for a moment. The solemnity of the occasion still held them spellbound.

"There is only one vote to go," said Father slowly.

"That one's mine!" cried Clara.

"Give it here and I'll tear it up. I don't want to go to England either!"

"But, Harriet," said Father gravely, taking Mother's hands, "you wanted to go, my dear. Are you doing this for my sake?"

"No, Johnny, I did it all for myself. We're all so happy here, and we might be wretched there. I never knew how much I loved it here until I had to choose—better than England—better than Boston! Home is where you are, Johnny!" Suddenly she burst into tears and flung herself into Mr. Woodlawn's arms.

"Hattie! Hattie! My little Harriet!" cried Father, holding her close and kissing her.

The children stood around with gaping eyes and mouths. Stranger even than an inheritance from England it was, to see Mother crying and Father kissing her.

⟨ MOST of the adventures related in the book CADDIE WOODLAWN *really happened to the grandmother of the author. "Gram was a fine storyteller," she said. "The stories I liked best were about her own childhood in Wisconsin. When my book was awarded the Newbery Medal in 1936, Caddie (then eighty-two years old) was as proud and happy as I was."*

Papa Was a Riot

THERE WAS nothing out of the ordinary in the way Mrs. Rhees made the announcement. It was in the quiet, businesslike monotone she always used. This one, however, gave me quick alarm. In my mind's eye, I could see Papa's eyes gleaming, his portly body quivering in eager anticipation. He could no more resist this opportunity to show off than could a Hollywood ham. Actually, there was no bigger ham in Hollywood or on the Broadway stage than was Papa, a shoemaker.

It wasn't that I didn't love Papa. You had to love him, whether you were related to him or not. He was kind and gentle and considerate, and everybody in the neighborhood had a good word for him.

"Students," Mrs. Rhees had announced, "our principal is sending out invitations to the parents of every pupil in school for our Loyalty Day Observances. I want you to urge them to attend. I am sending personal invitations to the fathers of all ninth graders to participate. A few words from them will round out our program. I know most of the fathers will be working, and some will not feel like appearing on our program. But if I can get

three or four who will agree to speak it will be sufficient."

I stole a glance at Spencer De Moss. He was smiling up at the teacher with that irritating smugness. His father was district attorney and a brilliant speaker. Madelaine Cotter's father was an alderman and wouldn't think of passing up a chance to pick up a stray vote here and there. But for the most part the teacher was going to get polite refusals.

Ordinarily Papa had no opportunity to come to the school functions. He worked every day. His shoe factory, however, was moving to larger quarters and Papa was enjoying a lengthy vacation. I couldn't picture Papa attending any affair without participating. I didn't want him attending this one because he was an exhibitionist and his English was so bad it was comedy.

It was Mr. Wright, our principal, who had thought of the idea for the Loyalty Day Observances. It was to be put on by the ninth grade. The war was still on and most of the families in the neighborhood had loved ones in the services. Carl, the oldest of our five boys, was overseas and in the thick of the fighting. Brother Victor would be called in two weeks. Mama was wearing a sick and worried look those days.

At the time I wasn't aware of what made Papa tick, the forces that determined his actions. His theatrics, I have come to realize, were the result of a naturally enthusiastic nature coupled with the severe training in Italian opera that Papa had as a youth, when he sang baritone for some small opera company in Italy. Needless to say, he was very popular in the neighborhood and very much in demand at social functions. No self-respecting family would think of holding a wedding reception without inviting Papa.

These wedding receptions followed the same general pattern. When the festivities had reached a climax, the band would stop playing, and the band leader would hold up his hands for silence.

"*Signore e signori,*" he would announce, "with much pleading and urging we have finally prevailed upon the good Don Nicola Barone to sing a few songs for us. I give you—Don Nicola Barone!"

Papa would swagger to the middle of the floor, the applause cascading all over the place. There was much laughter, too, at the notion that Papa needed pleading and urging to sing. Following Papa, almost like a faithful puppy, was the thin, bald, and mild-mannered Don Domenico, who would seat himself at a piano and strike a few chords of introduction. Then Papa would proceed to rattle every window in the place with that big baritone voice of

his. No matter what he sang, the crowd was wildly enthusiastic.

"Bravo, bravo!" they would cry. "Please, please, Don Nicola, another one." Papa would smile majestically, nod to Don Domenico, and launch into another inferno of sound.

When Papa thought he had sung enough, he'd hold up his hands for complete silence. It was the high point in his performance coming up, and the women would giggle, while the men would exchange knowing winks. Then began a flowery and highly complimentary talk by Papa, extolling the virtues of the groom and praising the beauty of the bride. This would produce a riot of laughter, and good-natured banter would fly about the hall. While Papa performed, Mama would sit on the sidelines watching, her brows knit in disapproval but her eyes laughing encouragement. Yes, Papa was a riot. What I didn't want was a riot at school.

I was home the night Papa read the letter from Mrs. Rhees. His eyes grew wide. "Grazia," he said in excitement, "see how my reputation as a speaker has reached the school!"

"You are the vain one," Mama sighed. "Has it not occurred to you, Nicola, that perhaps all fathers have received similar letters?"

"That is of no importance. I have been invited to speak and I will accept. Yes, I will astound them with my oratory. I will add new glory to the name of Barone."

Mama laughed good-naturedly. Papa went into his absurd jig step that was designed to amuse Mama. Soon both Papa and Mama were laughing heartily. To voice an objection to Papa's speaking at the Loyalty Day Observances at this time would have been no use at all. I hung desperately to the hope that Papa would forget or decide not to go through with it. I had my fingers crossed as I bided my time.

Two days later, in history class, the die was cast. We had put our books away, the lesson being over.

"In regard to the Loyalty Day Observances Friday," began Mrs. Rhees, "I have received four acceptances to my invitations to your fathers. The four who have agreed to speak are— Mr. Jacob De Moss, Mr. Arnold Cotter, Mr. Robert Furness, and—" there was a slight hesitation—"Mr. Nicola Barone. Will you thank these men for me?"

There was the usual murmur of voices after the announcement. I looked over at Spencer De Moss and he was wearing an infuriating grin. The day was long and practically unbearable.

That night I went into Sotile's Grocery Store to do some shopping for Mama. The bell over the door tinkled and Joe Sotile, Mr. Sotile's only son, looked up and waved good-naturedly. Joe was fullback on the football team. He was a hero to me.

"So your old man is gonna make a speech Friday! Boy, is he a character! He'll have them in stitches!"

"Silence, you!" roared Mr. Sotile, who was in the act of breaking up some spaghetti on wrapping paper for Donna Concetta.

"Do not criticize a fine man like Don Nicola," said Donna Concetta. "I did not know he was going to speak Friday. My Tony did not tell me. I am surely going now. With Don Nicola on the program, it will be a lively affair."

"Baloney!" answered Joe, startling me with his complete lack of respect for his elders. "Do you think that's a smart thing Mr. Barone is doing to embarrass the poor kid in front of all those people? Where does he get off making a speech when he can't even speak English right?"

"You are an insolent one and do not know what you are saying. You underestimate the intelligence of Nicola. I have confidence that he will know what to say, and when to say it, no matter what the circumstances."

Mr. Sotile was giving Joe a dirty look. "It is my fault," he apologized to Donna Concetta. "My son's bad manners reflect the looseness of my training of him. You know the old saying, 'An unweeded garden produces a poor crop.'"

"Oh, you are not alone, Don Pepe," replied Donna Concetta, "it is the times. We have that problem at home too. We parents would be further ahead if we raised hogs instead of children. That way, after they are grown, we can send them to market and realize a profit."

"That is true," agreed Mr. Sotile.

"Nuts," said Joe.

When I went home with the groceries, I was in a disturbed state of mind.

"Ricco," Mama called, "come here.

You have not been yourself lately. Is something wrong?" She put the back of her hand to my forehead to see if I was running a temperature.

"It's nothing, Mama," I answered. How could I tell her that I was ashamed of my father?

"Come with me, my son," she commanded. She sat me on the sofa next to her. "Now," she said, "tell me what this is all about."

Maybe I could make Mama see how absurd it was for Papa to speak at the school. "Mama," I began, "you know how kids are. If they get anything on you, they make life miserable for you."

Mama nodded.

"If someone in the family does something foolish, everybody in the family feels the shame of it. You understand, don't you, Mama?" I was pleading.

Again Mama nodded. Her voice was cold as she said, "You are trying to tell me something about your father speaking Friday, are you not, Ricco?"

I ignored the storm warnings and blundered on. "I will die of shame Friday if Papa speaks!"

"You," asked Mama with great suddenness, "ashamed of your father? I would never believe it. We have raised a viper in our midst. Go to bed, you ingrate. Your father has been too good to you. You do not deserve a father like that."

I went to bed feeling more discouraged than ever. Mama didn't understand. It was too much to hope for her to understand. She gave me the silent treatment for the rest of the week. But the affair on Friday wasn't bothering Papa in the least. If he had been asked to advise the President, I believe he would have done so without blinking an eye.

Friday finally came around. The classes came and went. Though I wished the day were over, I hated each passing minute because it brought me closer to the assembly hall.

I was amazed at the response of the parents. The hall was jammed. Good-naturedly, many consented to stand. I couldn't help thinking bitterly that Papa was going to put on his act before a standing-room-only crowd.

Looking around, I spotted Mama sitting with complete strangers down front. Several rows back I spied Donna Concetta sitting with Mr. Sotile. It seemed the whole neighborhood was there.

The Murphy Post Band was entertaining with some old favorites and stirring marches. The program started with the pledging of allegiance to the flag. Then the band played "The Star-Spangled Banner" while we all sang. Our ninth grade certainly did itself proud. Little Madelaine had recited a poem with stirring effect. My buddy, Tommy Gelfo, surprised everyone with a recitation no one thought him capable of. Then there was a barbershop quartet that sang patriotic songs with nice effects. The grown-up audience was receiving us with enthusiasm. We topped all efforts with a well-rehearsed play on a historical theme. It went off smoothly, and Mrs. Rhees was grinning from ear to ear.

While the stagehands were clearing the stage, the Murphy Post Band went to work again and entertained with more music. Then Mr. Wright went to the center of the stage and introduced Mr. Robert Furness.

Mr. Furness was a building contractor whose boy Jimmy was in our grade. He was a tall, lanky man in tweeds. His delivery was smooth and easy. He made a good speech filled with sage advice. It left the audience in a thoughtful mood, which is what Mr. Furness had set out to do.

Next, Mr. Wright introduced Madelaine Cotter's father. Mr. Arnold Cotter was fat and bald, with the eloquence of a practical politician. His speech was slick. The applause was generous and he certainly did his political cause no harm that day. When Mr. Jacob De Moss strode to the center of the stage, I took a long and careful look. He was handsome and he was dignified. Here was one of the finest speakers of our time. The mood created by him and by the other fine speakers was deadly serious. Papa was going to shatter that mood with a resounding crash.

Now Mr. Wright was introducing Papa, and Papa was striding toward the stage. I grew cold all over and slid down in my seat. I closed my eyes. Hearing him was bad enough, but to see the violent gestures would be too much. I prayed hard that it would soon be over. Here it comes, I thought, the television comedian. He'll have them rolling in the aisles.

Papa's voice came to me, and with a shock I realized it wasn't quite what I expected. His voice was no whisper by any means; it had carrying power. But it was restrained and rather gentle. The accent was there. It was so thick you could slice it, but Papa was giving it a surprising charm. I sat up and opened my eyes. I felt myself thaw out. I looked Papa over as if seeing him for the first time. He was all dignity and sincerity. It came to me—Papa's been around!

Then I gave real attention to what he was saying. I won't attempt to quote him verbatim; that would be impossible. He was saying in effect: "I regret that my limited knowledge of the English language forbids my saying to you the things my heart wishes to say. There are so many mutual anxieties I would like to share with you, so many fears, so many hopes, so many suggestions for the present and future. Fortunately, the very capable speakers before me have said these things in grand style. There are, however, two languages that are universal—the language of music and the language of prayer. When these two are combined, a thing of beauty is created. With your permission, I would like to sing for you a prayer set to music. We all realize the urgent need for spiritual guidance in these troubled times and we are all familiar with 'The Lord's Prayer.' I sing for you 'The Lord's Prayer.'"

Don Domenico was climbing the steps to the stage. He went to the piano without a word. He struck a few chords of introduction. I thought, Papa's going to blast them out of their seats! But again I was wrong.

Papa caressed the lyrics of that yearning, pleading song with all the care of a diamond cutter. He had his voice well in check. There was beauty in it beyond belief. As he mouthed each note, making a gem of it, it came to me that he was truly a great singer. And he was my father! There was a tightness in my throat and a pressure on my chest that I recognized as pride.

Many things were clear then. I recognized the Papa who in my selfishness had been a stranger—the Papa who paced the floor nights when he could not sleep, staring out into the street, not seeing, but thinking of Carl overseas—where he might be, what he was doing, if he was well, and if he was alive. Then I thought of Papa's visits to our bedroom when he thought we were all asleep, staring at us one at a time. As I listened to Papa singing, I felt thoroughly humble. Mama was right! I didn't deserve such a father.

Papa let his voice out just a trifle, sending golden note after golden note.

It sent a shiver down my spine. He drew the closing notes out tenderly; they came like angels treading on cobwebs. His *Amen* was beautiful.

Though I couldn't see, I could hear, and what I heard was absolute silence. They don't like him, I thought; they're sitting on their hands! I was growing angry and I wanted to stand up and tell the crowd what I thought of them. But slowly the applause came. It rose to thunder. Everybody was standing up and clapping furiously.

I felt a hand on my shoulder. When I turned to look back, there was Mrs. Rhees. "Ricco," she managed to say—her voice had an odd catch—"what a great man your father is. You must be very proud."

I could only nod. Speech was impossible for me. And it was just as well, for what I wished to say could not be put in words.

The Fast

FANNY BRANDEIS was a strange mixture of tomboy and bookworm. The spiritual side of her was groping and feeling its way about as does that of any little girl whose mind is exceptionally active, and whose mother is unusually busy. It was on the Day of Atonement, known in the Hebrew as Yom Kippur, in the year following her father's death, that that side of her performed a rather interesting handspring.

Fanny had never been allowed to fast on this, the greatest and most solemn of Jewish holy days. So it was in the face of her mother's disapproval that Fanny, making deep inroads into the steak and fried sweet potatoes at supper on the eve of the Day of Atonement, announced her intention of fasting from that meal to supper on the following evening. She had just passed her plate for a third helping of potatoes. Her brother, Theodore, one lap behind her in the race, had entered his objection.

"Well, for the land's sakes!" he protested. "I guess you're not the only one who likes sweet potatoes."

Fanny applied a generous dab of butter to an already buttery morsel, and chewed it with an air of conscious virtue.

"I've got to eat a lot. This is the last bite I'll have until tomorrow night."

"What's that?" exclaimed Mrs. Brandeis sharply.

"Yes, it is!" hooted Theodore.

Fanny went on conscientiously eating as she explained. "Bella Weinberg and I are going to fast all day. We just want to see if we can."

"Betcha can't," Theodore said.

Mrs. Brandeis regarded her small daughter with a thoughtful gaze. "But that isn't the object of fasting, Fanny—just to see if you can. If you're going to think of food all through the Yom Kippur services—"

"I sha'n't!" protested Fanny passionately. "Theodore would, but I won't."

"Wouldn't any such thing," denied Theodore. "But if I'm going to play a violin solo during the memorial service, I guess I've got to eat my regular meals."

Theodore sometimes played at temple on special occasions. The little congregation, listening to the throbbing rise and fall of the fifteen-year-old boy's violin playing, realized vaguely that here was something disturbingly, harrowingly beautiful. They did not know that they were listening to genius.

Molly Brandeis, in her second-best dress, walked to temple Yom Kippur eve, her son at her right side, her daughter at her left. The Brandeis' seat was well toward the rear. This enabled them to get a complete picture of the room in its holiday splendor. Fanny drank it in eagerly, her dark eyes soft and luminous. The bare, yellow-varnished wooden pews glowed with the reflection from the chandeliers. The seven-branched candlesticks on either side of the pulpit were entwined with smilax. The red plush curtain that hung in front of the Ark on ordinary days, and the red plush pulpit cover, too, were replaced by gleaming white satin edged with gold fringe. How the rich white satin glistened in the light of the electric candles! Fanny Brandeis loved the lights and the gleam and the music, so majestic and solemn. The sheer drama of the thing got her.

In fact, the thing she had set herself to do today had in it very little of religion. Mrs. Brandeis had been right about that. It was a test of endurance, as planned. Fanny had never fasted in all her healthy life. She would come home from school to eat formidable stacks of bread and butter, enhanced by brown sugar or grape jelly, and topped off with three or four apples from the barrel in the cellar. Two hours later she would attack a supper of fried potatoes and liver and tea and peach preserves and more stacks of bread and butter. She liked good things to eat, this sturdy little girl, as did her friend, that blonde and creamy

person, Bella Weinberg. The two girls exchanged meaningful glances during the evening service.

The service was brief. Rabbi Thalmann and his congregation would need their strength for tomorrow's trial. The Brandeises walked home through the soft September night, and the children had to use all their Yom Kippur dignity to keep from scuffing through the piled-up drifts of crackling autumn leaves. Theodore went to the cellar and got an apple, which he ate with what Fanny considered an unnecessary amount of scrunching. It was a firm, juicy apple, and it gave forth a cracking sound when his teeth met in its white meat. Fanny, after regarding him with gloomy superiority, went to bed.

She woke early, with a heavy feeling. Early as it was, Molly Brandeis had tiptoed in still earlier. Looking down at her strange little daughter, she wondered just how much determination lay back of the broad white brow. She had said little to Fanny about this feat of fasting, and she told herself that she disapproved of it. But in her heart she wanted the girl to see it through, once attempted.

Fanny's nostrils dilated to that most tantalizing of smells—the aroma of simmering coffee. It carried with it visions of hot, brown breakfast rolls, and eggs, and butter. Fanny loved her breakfast. She turned over now, and decided to go to sleep again. But she could not. She got up and dressed slowly and carefully.

She put on clean, crisp underwear, and did her hair expertly. She slipped an all-enveloping pinafore over her head, that the new silk dress might not be crushed before church time. She thought that Theodore would surely have finished his breakfast by this time. But when she came downstairs he had just begun. An egg, all golden and white and crispy brown at the frilly edges, lay on his plate. Fanny passed the breakfast table just as he plunged his fork into the egg yolk. She caught her breath sharply, and closed her eyes. Then she turned and fled to the front porch.

But the real struggle was to come later. They went to temple at ten, Theodore with his beloved violin tucked carefully under his arm. Bella Weinberg was waiting at the steps.

"Did you?" she asked eagerly.

"Of course not," replied Fanny disdainfully. "Do you think I'd eat old breakfast when I said I was going to fast all day?" Then, with sudden suspicion, "Did you?"

"No!" stoutly.

They entered and took their seats. All during the sermon Fanny sat and dreamed and watched the shadow on the window of the pine tree that stood close to the temple. From time to time Bella would turn to bestow upon her a look intended to convey intense suffering. Fanny stonily ignored these mute messages. They offended something in her, though she could not tell what.

At the noon intermission she did not go home to the tempting dinner smells. She wandered off through the little city park and down to the river, where she sat on the bank and felt

very virtuous and spiritual, and hollow. She was back in her seat when the afternoon service was begun.

The memorial service was to begin shortly after three, and lasted almost two hours. At quarter to three Bella slipped out through the side aisle, beckoning mysteriously to Fanny. Fanny looked at her mother.

"Run along," said Mrs. Brandeis. "The air will be good for you. Come back before the memorial service begins."

Fanny and Bella met, giggling, in the vestibule.

"Come on over to my house for a minute," Bella suggested. "I want to show you something."

The Weinberg house, a great, comfortable, well-built home, with encircling veranda and a well-cared-for lawn, was just a scant block away. They skipped across the street, down the block, and in the back door. The big sunny kitchen was deserted. The house seemed very quiet and hushed. Bella led the way to the butler's pantry that was as large as the average kitchen. And there, ranged on platters and baking boards and on snowy-white napkins, was that which made Tantalus' feast seem a dry and barren snack. The Weinbergs had baked.

It is the custom in the household of Atonement Day fasters of the old school to begin the evening meal, after the twenty-four hours of abstainment, with coffee and freshly baked coffee cake of every variety. There were to be sisters and brothers and out-of-town relations as guests at the evening meal, and Mrs. Weinberg had outdone her-self.

"Oh!" exclaimed Fanny in a sort of agony and delight.

"Take some," said Bella, the tempt-ress.

The pantry was fragrant as a garden with spices and the melting, delectable perfume of brown, freshly baked dough, sugar-coated. There was one giant platter devoted wholly to round, plump cakes with puffy edges, in the center of each a sunken pool that was all plum, bearing on its bosom a snowy sifting of sugar. There were others whose centers were apricot, pure mol-ten gold in the sunlight. There were speckled expanses of cheese kuchen, the golden-brown surface showing rich cracks, through which one caught glimpses of the lemon-yellow cheese beneath—cottage cheese that had been beaten up with eggs and spices and sugar and lemon. Flaky crust rose, jag-gedly, above this plateau. There were cakes with jelly, cinnamon kuchen, and cunning cakes with almond slices nestling side by side.

Fanny Brandeis gazed, hypnotized. As she gazed Bella selected a plum tart and bit into it—bit generously, so that her white little teeth met in the very middle of the oozing red-brown juice and one heard a little squirt as they closed on the luscious fruit. At the sound Fanny quivered all through her plump and starved little body.

"Have one," said Bella generously. "Go on. Nobody'll ever know. Any-way, we've fasted long enough for our age. I could fast till suppertime if I wanted to, but I don't want to."

She swallowed the last morsel of the plum tart, and selected another—ap-ricot, this time—and opened her moist red lips. But just before she bit into it, she selected its counterpart and held it out to Fanny. Fanny shook her head slightly. Her hand came up in-voluntarily.

"Go on," urged Bella. "Take it. They're grand! M-m-m-m!" The first bite of apricot vanished between her rows of sharp white teeth. Fanny shut her eyes as if in pain. She was fighting the great fight of her life. She was to meet other temptations, and perhaps more glittering ones, in her lifetime, but to her dying day she never forgot that first battle between the flesh and the spirit, there in the sugar-scented pantry—and the spirit won. Fanny turned sharply, like a soldier, and marched blindly out of the house, down the back steps, across the street, and so into the temple.

The evening lights had just been turned on. The little congregation, re-laxed, weary, weak from hunger, many of them, sat rapt and still, except at those times when the prayer book de-manded spoken responses. Fanny slid very quietly into the seat beside Mrs. Brandeis, and slipped her moist and cold little hand into her mother's warm, work-roughened palm. Bella, the guilty, came stealing in, a pink-and-gold picture of angelic virtue. Fanny, looking at her, felt very aloof, and clean, and remote.

Molly Brandeis seemed to sense what had happened.

[29]

"But you didn't, did you?" she whispered softly.

Fanny shook her head.

Rabbi Thalmann was seated in his great carved chair. His eyes were closed. The wheezy little organ in the choir loft at the rear of the temple began the opening bars of Schumann's "Traümerei." And then, above the cracked voice of the organ, rose the clear, poignant wail of a violin. Theodore Brandeis had begun to play.

You know the playing of the average boy of fifteen—that nerve-destroying, uninspired scraping. There was nothing of this in the sounds that this boy called forth from the little wooden box and the stick with its taut lines of catgut. Whatever it was—the length of the thin, sensitive fingers, the turn of the wrist, the articulation of the forearm, the something in the brain, or all these combined—Theodore Brandeis possessed that which makes for greatness. You realized that as he crouched over his violin to get his cello tones.

As he played today the little congregation sat very still, and each was thinking of his ambitions and his failures, of the duty left undone, of the hope deferred; of the wrong that was never righted. It felt the salt taste on its lips. It put up a furtive hand to dab at its cheeks, and saw that the one who sat in the pew just ahead was doing likewise. This is what happened when this boy of fifteen wedded his bow to his violin. And he who makes us feel all this has that indefinable, magic, glorious thing known as Genius.

When it was over, there swept through the room that sigh following tension relieved. Rabbi Thalmann passed a hand over tired eyes, then rose and came forward to the pulpit. He began, in Hebrew, the opening words of the memorial service, and so on to the prayers in English, with their words of infinite humility and wisdom.

"Thou hast implanted in us the capacity for sin, but not sin itself!"

Fanny stirred. She had learned that a brief half hour ago. The service marched on, a moving and harrowing thing. The Amens rolled out with a new fervor from the listeners. They came to that gem of humility, the mourners' prayer; the ancient and ever-solemn Kaddish prayer. There is nothing in the written language that, for sheer drama and magnificence, can equal it as it is chanted in the Hebrew.

As Rabbi Thalmann began to intone it in its monotonous repetition of praise, there arose certain black-robed figures from their places and stood with heads bowed over their prayer books. These were members of the congregation from whom death had taken a toll during the past year. Fanny rose with her mother and Theodore, who had left the choir loft to join them. The little wheezy organ played very softly. Fanny felt a hot haze that blurred her vision. Her shoulders shook with a sob. She felt her mother's hand close over her own that held one side of the book. The prayer, that was not of mourning but of praise, ended with a final crescendo from the organ. The silent black-robed figures were seated.

Over the little, spent congregation hung a glorious atmosphere of detachment. These Jews, listening to the words that had come from the lips of the prophets in Israel, had been on this day thrown back thousands of years, to the time of the destruction of the temple. Fanny Brandeis was shaken by it. Her head ached (that was hunger) and her hands were icy. Rabbi Thalmann, there on the platform, seemed somehow very far away.

The long service swept on to its close. Suddenly organ and choir burst into a paean. Doctor Thalmann raised his arms. The congregation swept to its feet with a mighty surge. Fanny rose with them, her face very white in its frame of black curls, her eyes luminous. She raised her face for the words of the ancient benediction:

"May the blessing of the Lord our God rest upon you all. God bless thee and keep thee. May God cause His countenance to shine upon thee and be gracious unto thee. May God lift up His countenance unto thee, and grant thee peace."

The Day of Atonement had come to an end. It was a very quiet, subdued, and spent little flock that dispersed to their homes. Fanny walked out with scarcely a thought of Bella.

"Bet you're hungry!" from Theodore.

"I was, but I'm not now."

She had intended to tell of the trial in the Weinbergs' pantry. But now something within her—something fine, born of this day—kept her from it. But Molly Brandeis guessed something of what had happened. She had felt a great surge of pride, had Molly Brandeis, when her son had swayed the congregation with the magic of his music. She kissed him good night with infinite tenderness and love. But she came into her daughter's tiny room after Fanny had gone to bed, and leaned over and put a cool hand on the hot forehead.

"Fanchen, doesn't it make you feel happy and clean to know that you were able to do the thing you started out to do?"

"Umhmph," replied Fanny drowsily.

"Only," Molly Brandeis was thinking aloud now, quite forgetting that she was talking to a very little girl, "only, life seems to take such special delight in offering temptation to those who are able to withstand it. I don't know why that's true, but it is. I hope —oh, my little girl, my baby—I hope—"

But Fanny never knew whether her mother finished that sentence or not. She remembered waiting for the end of it, to learn what it was her mother hoped. And she had felt a sudden, scalding drop on her hand where her mother bent over her. And the next thing she knew it was morning, with mellow September sunshine.

⟨ IN *her autobiography* A PECULIAR TREASURE *Edna Ferber has told how, at the age of thirteen, she decided to fast during the Day of Atonement. This story is taken from her book* FANNY HERSELF.

The White Man's Medicine

⟨[THIS story, adapted from CHILDREN OF THE COVERED WAGON, tells of a thrilling episode in the adventures of the Stephen Company. The company was named for Jim Stephen, captain of one of the wagon trains that made the long, dangerous journey over the Oregon Trail nearly a century ago.

THE WAGONS wheeled to a level place within sight of the sturdy walls of Fort Laramie. At the fort, where Captain Stephen and Henri Devine, the French-Canadian guide, went to report the arrival of the company, Devine was greeted by a trader named Bissonette, an old friend of his. The news that the trader gave them of Indian feeling toward the white travelers was disquieting. Bissonette knew the Indians as well as he knew his own people, and Devine was certain that his friend didn't speak idly when he warned them that travel among the red men of this section was dangerous. Captain Stephen decided not to frighten the women and children with word of the danger ahead, but to hold a council of the men that night.

That afternoon, when the work of making camp was over, Michael O'-Reilly took several of the children to visit the fort, a picturesque place always of great interest to emigrants.

Michael lifted Myra, Dr. Dean's little six-year-old daughter, to his shoulder and carried her there with many a gallop and leap. Their gay laughter was drowned by the queerest chorus imaginable—shouting and talking of men and women, yelping and barking of dogs, laughter and chattering of children. They paused outside the fort gate, while a camp of Dakota Indians, who had just crossed the river, came by with their whole camp equipment.

The Indians arrived on horseback and on foot, several hundred of them. Warriors, their powerful bodies daubed with brilliant colors, galloped proudly by, followed by their squaws. Horses and ponies, dripping wet from their plunge in the river, raced along. Small boys, their naked, copper-colored bodies gleaming in the sun, darted wildly among the many dogs. Myra clapped her small hands, laughing in delight. Her blue sunbonnet had fallen back, and her hair was a golden shimmer in the sunlight.

Suddenly a splendid horse was pulled up in front of the little party at the fort gate. A tall Indian, beautifully built, as were most of the Dakotas, stared fixedly down at Myra. He stared, as if entranced, and the child looked up at him, smiling, unafraid.

Angered by the steady stare of the Indian, Michael drew the little girl from his shoulder and held her in his arms. The Indian spoke in his native tongue which, of course, Michael couldn't understand; but when he pointed to a group of horses, held by a young brave nearby, and then at Myra, it was clear that he was offering to trade the horses for Myra.

"Get along with you!" Michael shouted angrily. "You'd better be minding your own business!"

Without thinking what he did, one of the boys laughed at Michael's outburst. The big Indian stiffened indignantly. Several others drew rein, hemming the little group in. The fort gate was opened quickly. Bissonette came out, followed by Captain Stephen and Henri Devine. The fort official spoke soothingly to the red men, who listened in frowning silence. After a few moments they rode away.

"That redskin wanted to trade horses for Myra!" sputtered Michael.

"He is a powerful Dakota chief, Wolf's Brother," said Bissonette. "He thought he was honoring you by offering a trade. It's too bad anyone laughed. An Indian hates ridicule. Every one of those braves would have been on you in a flash if Wolf's Brother had given the word. They worship him."

"Well, he knows now that we don't want to trade, anyway," Michael said. "Faith, they have children enough of their own without wantin' one of ours."

The incident at the gate was soon forgotten by the boys in the interest of going through the fort; but it was not forgotten by the Dakota chief, as they were to learn to their sorrow.

The image of the little white girl, blue eyes laughing fearlessly, hair a crown of golden glory, stayed in the mind of Chief Wolf's Brother. "Little Daughter of the Rising Sun," he named her, and the conviction that she was a gift from the gods took hold of him. Plainly, for all the world to see, he thought, the gods had set their mark on her. Had they not taken bits of the heavens to make her eyes? Had they not wreathed her head in sunlight? And where—the chief's heart lifted at the thought—where could be found a more desirable mate for Young War Eagle, his son, who already, at the age of eight, was giving promise of becoming a notable chief?

He would make the whites another offer for the child. If they rejected his offer—the chief's face darkened—if they refused the honor he held out to them, he would take the child by force, and with her he would take many scalps . . .

Wolf's Brother wasn't long in acting. After the evening meal, when the emigrants were gathered about campfires, the guards brought word to Captain Stephen: "A band of seven Indians coming on horseback. All dressed up in their best beads and feathers."

Bissonette, who had come over from the fort, went forward with Captain Stephen to meet the Indians.

"It's Wolf's Brother!" exclaimed the Frenchman. "He's coming to make another bid for the little girl. You'll have to handle this thing carefully. Tell him that you are honored by his offer, and try to make him forget it. Offer gifts to him and flatter him, but get the child out of sight."

Word was sent to the mothers to put all the children to bed at once; a chief was calling and the children might annoy him! So the little pioneers were bundled off to bed in the wagons, astonished and protesting. Myra cried with disappointment; but Jim, Captain Stephen's ten-year-old son, knew what it was all about. His father had told him. A chief had come to bargain for Myra and they were hiding her away from him. Jim's heart beat double time with excitement. If only he could stay up with the men! But his father's orders had to be obeyed, so he tried to content himself with peering through the canvas and straining his ears to catch bits of the talk.

"Golly, Jim!" Jerry, his seven-year-old cousin, leaned against his shoulder, whispering. "Did you see the feathers on his head! Golly! Do you think he's an Indian giant, Jim?"

The chief was an impressive figure. Over six feet tall, broad-shouldered, slim-hipped, he moved with a graceful ease that was surprising and pleasing to see. His head was dressed in an elaborate bonnet of eagle feathers, the tails of the bonnet extending almost to the ground. Solemn greetings were exchanged, and Captain Stephen, through Bissonette, invited the callers to sit at the campfire and smoke the pipe of friendship. What thoughts were in the white men's minds as they complied with this rule of Indian etiquette—Dr. Dean, Myra's father; Captain Stephen, Henri Devine, and the subcaptains of the wagon train—all realizing what the visit of the chief might mean, and not one daring to betray the emotions that surged in his heart!

When the pipe had gone the rounds, Wolf's Brother came directly to the point. As he spoke to the Frenchman, one of the braves went outside the encampment, returning in a few moments with three splendid horses, one of which had a bundle tied on its back. In silence the watchers waited while the brave untied the buckskin thongs that held the bundle in place. He laid at the chief's feet a beautiful white buffalo robe and a curious object that Devine recognized as a whistle made from the wing bone of a war eagle, an article held in reverence by the Indians who thought it to possess great power. With an eloquent gesture the chief indicated the robe, the whistle, and the horses. Bissonette spoke slowly, carefully:

"Chief Wolf's Brother says that his visit is more than a friendly call. He comes, directed by the gods, to trade with the white men."

Bissonette paused, and looked at Dr. Dean. The doctor felt his heart give a bound that was painful. He knew what was coming. The interpreter continued:

"Chief Wolf's Brother offers the greatest gifts in his power to give in exchange for the golden-haired child, Little Daughter of the Rising Sun. He promises on his unbreakable honor to care for her as he would care for a beloved daughter, and to rear her carefully as a bride for his only son, Young War Eagle, who will be a great and powerful chief one day."

Again the Frenchman paused. Watching him intently, Captain Stephen saw a warning expression in his eyes. He continued:

"Chief Wolf's Brother says that the three horses he offers are the fleetest in the land. The robe of the white buffalo is sacred. It will cover the white men from the evil spirit in their perilous journey through the mountains. The whistle made from the wing bone of the great war eagle will be a sign to all members of the Sioux nation that the men who carry it are friends who have earned the right to their protection. With these aids the journey ahead of the white men will be safe. Without them—each mile will be fraught with great peril. Chief Wolf's Brother awaits the white chief's decision."

Then the white men understood! Truly this chief was well named, brother of the wolf. He was clever and cruel. In exchange for Myra he guaranteed the wagon train safe passage through Sioux territory. He would send word along the trail that the train was not to be molested. But if the emigrants refused to surrender the child, he would turn loose on them the poison of his wrath. They would be harried and hounded at every turn, and what chance would they have against the savage hordes the chief could turn against them?

In the silence that followed, while Captain Stephen was searching his mind for just the right words, Dr. Dean stepped forward.

"I am the child's father," the doctor said. "I ask the right to reply to the chief."

They stood facing each other, in the leaping light of the fire, piercing black eyes meeting steady blue eyes in a look that was like the crossing of swords. Dr. Dean spoke in a calm voice:

"Chief Wolf's Brother, a father himself, will understand a father's feeling for his child. Would the chief trade his son for anything the white men could offer? Would any threat of personal harm move him to give up his Young War Eagle forever? We appreciate the value of the gifts the great chief offers. We know that he means to honor us—but I would not trade my little daughter, nor allow her to be traded, for anything anyone could offer! Men do not sell their flesh and blood! Chief Wolf's Brother will understand."

While the doctor spoke, and while Bissonette interpreted his speech, not a man of the campfire group so much as stirred. They seemed not to breathe, so motionless they were. It was the chief's turn to speak. What would he reply to Dr. Dean? But the chief did not speak. He motioned to a brave who wrapped up the buffalo robe and the eagle wing bone whistle, and bound them on the horse's back. Then, without a word, Chief Wolf's Brother and his men started away toward their horses. Bissonette called to them:

"Wolf's Brother! The white chief asks you to wait. He has a gift of tobacco for you and your camp."

The chief turned his head and flashed a look of scorn at the white men.

"The white chief may keep his tobacco!" he said, and he and his young men rode out of the encampment.

The men sat late around the fire that night, talking in low voices. Dr. Dean had done the right thing, the only thing he could do. But they felt themselves caught in a cruel trap from which there was no escape. They had to travel through the country of the Dakotas for many days. They must put themselves and their dear ones at the mercy of men without mercy. What chance had they? They talked until the moon was low in the sky and the stars were small and white.

When Myra's father had appealed to the chief's love for his own child, he had touched the only tender chord in the stern heart of Wolf's Brother. All the chief's strongest affection and fondest hopes were centered in Young War Eagle. When Wolf's Brother pictured his son's future, he saw him as a mighty chief, a power not only among the Dakotas, but one held in respect by other tribes as well. He took jealous care that nothing was left

undone to prepare the boy for his glorious future.

At eight years Young War Eagle's well-built body was as hard as iron. Every morning of his life he had had a dip in cold water to toughen him. He had been trained to stand without flinching while his naked body was lashed with branches, to strengthen his endurance. He had learned, while still a baby, that to cry in pain or anger, or to show fear, was unworthy of a chief. He had never been sick in his life, and for all his stern rearing he was as happy-hearted as a lark. Every day, he thought, was a glorious adventure. Life was good. He worshiped his father, and the chief's heart gloried in the love of his son.

So, when Dr. Dean, looking so earnestly into the chief's eyes, had asked, "Would Chief Wolf's Brother trade his son for anything the white men could offer?" the word-arrow had gone straight to its mark. But his very love for Young War Eagle, and his fanatical ambition to provide for the boy's triumphant future, made him determined to have, at all cost, this Little Daughter of the Rising Sun to rear as the young chief's bride should be reared. So he closed his heart to the white father's appeal. He would not answer—in words!

The dark face of Wolf's Brother brightened a bit as he and his braves rode toward the camp of circled tepees. Young War Eagle would be riding out to meet him. The boy watched for his father's homecomings, and his eyes were always first to sight the tall figure of the returning chief. He would be riding out soon, his sturdy figure erect on his prancing pony.

A frowning line appeared between the chief's black eyes. The boy did not come. And then his ears caught a sound that chilled his blood. It was the voice of Many Stars, the ancient medicine man. He was chanting the medicine song for the nearly dead.

Two figures rose from the shadows and came toward the riders. One was the figure of Spirit Wind, a young mystic whom Many Stars was training to take his own place as chief medicine man of the tribe, when he was dead. The other figure was that of Truth Teacher, the old camp crier.

"Speak!" The chief had brought his horse to a standstill and was waiting for them.

Spirit Wind spoke: "Young War Eagle was thrown from a wild horse. He is stricken by a deep sleep. Many Stars works over him now in the medicine tepee, but, alas! His sleep is like the sleep of death." The young man's voice held the somber cadence of the death chant.

A moment later, in the maroon-colored medicine tepee, when Chief Wolf's Brother looked down on his son, lying prostrate on a medicine robe between the fire and Many Stars' platform shrine, he saw that the sleep that held the boy was, indeed, like the sleep of death. Young War Eagle's forehead was icy to the touch, and his breath was so faint that it did not stir his breast. Near the door of the tepee crouched White Antelope, his mother. She bit her lips to keep back the cry that rose to them, while about the

boy's pallet Many Stars and Spirit Wind circled in a medicine dance, chanting their weird song.

The mother and father watched all night, while Spirit Wind fed the fire and joined his aged master in the medicine rites. Several times the old man laid his hand on the boy's heart, expecting to find it stilled; but the strong young constitution held up. It was weakening gradually, and the medicine man, who had seen many die, knew that before the morning's sun was high in the heaven, the boy's spirit would leave his body. A changed note crept into his song of petition. He was getting ready to begin the death chant.

Bissonette had not slept well. All night he had turned and tossed while his mind had wrestled with the problem of how to win Chief Wolf's Brother from his determination to take the little white girl. *Mon Dieu!* thought the weary Frenchman, why couldn't these white people stay at home? He knew of another case like this, a case where a chief had taken a fancy to a white child and kidnaped him. The child had been carried into the mountains and was never seen again by his parents. That there had been other such cases he knew, for he had seen children in isolated Indian camps, whose blue eyes, blond hair and regular features told plainly that no Indian blood ran in their veins.

When daylight came Bissonette arose, determined to make a supreme effort to turn the stubborn chief from his dark purpose. But his hope was dashed by the news that met him when he rode into the Dakota camp. Young War Eagle's injury lent new gravity to the problem. If the boy died, the Indians would certainly lay the disaster to some evil power invoked by the white men. It might lead to a massacre. Bissonette groaned in despair as he turned back toward Fort Laramie. What was to be done now?

Suddenly a thought that had the power of inspiration leaped into his mind. There might be a chance, even now! It would be a desperate chance, but this whole thing was desperate. He turned his horse toward the wagon camp and rode at top speed. When he rode back a short time later, Dr. Dean rode with him. The doctor's face was pale and grim. Bissonette explained, as they rode side by side, frequently lapsing into his native French in his haste and excitement:

"If you can save him, everything may be won. If you fail—well, things can't be much worse than they are now. The boy is dying, they say, but it may be that Many Stars is mistaken. Chief Wolf's Brother knows me and will listen to me, at any rate. I'll try to convince him that you can cure the boy."

Dr. Dean didn't speak. His thoughts raced ahead of their horses to the tepee where the chief's son lay close to death. The boy had been thrown from a wild horse, likely striking on his head. He had lain all night in a stupor. Perhaps the skull was fractured. Even if the chief did give him permission to try, would it be possible to save the boy after that long neglect? What was he going into—he, a

white man, mistrusted, hated, by the Indians—working directly against the medicine man, who was revered and idolized by the tribe? His medical skill, with all the odds against it, pitted against a belief that was as old as creation, whose origin no man knew! But no! The thought came with the comfort of firmly spoken words. He was not relying on his medical skill alone. His faith, his belief in the mercy of an Almighty Father, would come to his assistance now, and that faith need not be pitted against the faith of the Indians. Did they not worship, in their different ways, the same Great Spirit? Strength and calmness came to Dr. Dean then. He lost all feeling of fear and knew only a great eagerness to do all he could to save the young life that was ebbing away.

When the white men drew near the medicine tepee, they found that the boy had been carried outside. This was in accordance with a beautiful belief. The Indians, loving nature, believed it the right of every man to die under the roof of heaven, the open sky. Young War Eagle lay on a white buffalo robe. His mother was prostrate on the earth nearby. Chief Wolf's Brother was meeting his sorrow standing, as befitted a man and a chief.

Dr. Dean's eyes sought the boy's face anxiously. He still lived. The doctor clenched his teeth and dug his fingernails into his palms, in his anxiety to get to work, to shield that flickering flame of life. Every second was vital.

Bissonette stepped to Wolf's Brother's side and spoke earnestly.

The chief looked at him dully, at first, seeming not to know nor care what he was talking about. But suddenly, he wheeled and faced Dr. Dean. Something terrible and savage leaped into the black eyes. It was evident that Bissonette had judged correctly. Wolf's Brother already associated this misfortune that had befallen him with the white strangers.

Dr. Dean met the savage eyes fairly. He had forgotten all fear of personal danger in his pity for this afflicted father, and his sincerity, his desire to help, showed in his eyes and spoke to the chief's heart. The savage eyes softened and a look of appeal filled them. Wolf's Brother turned to Bissonette and listened carefully.

"The white medicine man has come to help you, Chief Wolf's Brother!" Bissonette was saying. "He has a powerful medicine. It has called back many as near the threshold of death as your son is. Let him try his medicine, Wolf's Brother! Young War Eagle should live many more years. He should be a powerful chief. Let the white medicine man work with Many Stars. Are not two more powerful than one?"

The chief looked questioningly at Many Stars. He was torn between the desire to try the white man's medicine and the fear of going against the wishes of his tribe's honored wise man. The Frenchman addressed his appeal to the ancient medicine man:

"Many Stars, wise one! You prayed and, lo, the gods have answered your prayer! See, they have sent this white medicine man with a wonderful new medicine! He will teach you how to use it, and your people will honor you more than they have yet honored you! Do you consent, Many Stars?"

White Antelope rose from the ground and held out her arms in supplication. "Oh, Many Stars, consent!" she implored. "Take this help the gods have sent to you!"

The old man considered for a moment. The boy was marked for death. Nothing could save him now. Sometimes, when one as dearly loved as Young War Eagle was loved died, the tribe turned against the medicine man and killed him. It would be wise to have this white man to blame, when the youth's spirit passed. Then the people could vent their grief on him. Let the white man try—and fail! Many Stars made a submissive gesture. The chief stepped back. The way was clear for Dr. Dean.

The doctor was at work on Young War Eagle instantly. His hands went searchingly over the black head. He lifted the closed lids and peered into the dull eyes. He took note of pulse and breathing, and he was satisfied that there was no fracture. The boy suffered from a severe concussion, he decided. If he had been properly cared for at first, he would have responded well; but now—well, he was still alive and that was all. He carried his patient back into the medicine tepee, and laid him near the smoldering fire. While he administered a powerful stimulant, the fire was built up and rocks were heated to pack around the chilled body. The fight against death had begun. It would be a hard one.

At times, it seemed to Dr. Dean that it was not this strange Indian child he fought to save, but his own little Myra. As he worked, he prayed. White Antelope and her sister, a quiet, intelligent woman, heated stones at the doctor's orders, and chafed Young War Eagle's limbs, as he directed. Once, in the late afternoon, White Antelope's hand touched the boy's head caressingly, brushing back the dark hair. It was a mother gesture, tender and wistful. Dr. Dean saw then what he had been hoping for. The sick boy's eyelids fluttered. His eyes opened for an instant and closed wearily. The doctor's heart sang with joy. This was the first evidence of returning consciousness. The deathlike sleep that had held Young War Eagle since his fall was loosening its grip.

There was every reason to hope, now, that the battle would be won.

That night Dr. Dean stayed with his patient, fearing to trust him even to the care of White Antelope and her sister. Toward morning the boy opened his eyes again and called his mother by name. White Antelope bent over him, speaking low, what words Dr. Dean did not know. He knew only that they were the right words, for Young War Eagle smiled on hearing them, sighed, and went to sleep. The doctor knew then that the boy would recover. Pale with weariness, he rode back to the encampment. Captain Stephen and Michael came out to meet him, one question on their lips: Chief Wolf's Brother—Myra? Dr. Dean shook his head.

"I don't know," he answered wea-rily. "The boy will live, but the chief hasn't said a word to me."

That question remained unanswered for a week.

Captain Stephen had planned to lay over in the shadow of Fort Laramie for only three days, long enough for his people to trade at the fort and rest, before heading out across the desert. The fear of being overtaken by early blizzards in the mountains was what prompted his haste to be on; but Dr. Dean couldn't leave Young War Eagle until his recovery was well assured. He didn't want to leave until Chief Wolf's Brother had promised that he wouldn't attempt to take Myra. So there was nothing to do but wait.

The captain was worried by the delay. "This is one of the trials of the trail that we didn't count on," he said ruefully to Henri Devine.

"It is," agreed the guide. "And, still, wasn't the boy's accident providential for us? These Indians carry out what they have their minds set on— if they can. Wolf's Brother would have taken Myra Dean if he had had to massacre the whole outfit to do it."

"And how do we know that he hasn't changed his mind about that?"

Devine was silent. The injured boy was making steady improvement. Dr. Dean called to see him every day, and waited hopefully for a word of gratitude from Chief Wolf's Brother, a word that did not come. So a week went by, and the Stephen company could wait no longer. Dr. Dean sought out the chief to take leave of him, taking Bissonette along to interpret for him.

"Young War Eagle will be up and around soon," said Dr. Dean. "My medicine is no longer needed in the camp of Chief Wolf's Brother. I must go with my people who are anxious to be on the way. They have delayed their journey several days that I might be with the chief's sick son. Tomorrow, at sunup, we shall take our way on the trail. Good-by, Chief Wolf's Brother!"

The chief took the doctor's outstretched hand, but he said nothing and his expression was unreadable. There was a gleam in his eyes, but whether it was friendly or sinister Dr. Dean could not tell.

He felt tired and sick at heart as he rode toward the wagon encampment. Was all his effort in vain? When he slipped wearily from his saddle, Myra left her play and ran to meet him, talking excitedly of the Indian camp that she and Jerry were making of twigs and clay. He laid his hand on her sunny head and spoke cheerily to her, but to himself he groaned:

"Myra, child, if we get out of this scrape with our lives—and yours—I'll see that your hair is dyed as black as midnight!"

On the afternoon of their last day at the fort, Bissonette rode into the wagon camp with a summons from Chief Wolf's Brother. Captain Stephen, Devine, and Dr. Dean went to answer the mysterious order. In reply to the captain's question Bissonette said that he had no idea what the chief had in mind. He had sent for the men, that was all he could say.

The dark face of Wolf's Brother did not relieve the suspense of the white men, when he met them at the entrance to his tepee.

It was the first time Captain Stephen and Dr. Dean had been in the tepee of a chief, and, anxious though they were, they couldn't resist an interested look about. The place was very clean and orderly. White Antelope was a good housekeeper. The only furnishings were beds made of piles of buffalo robes and back rests of woven willow, covered with robes. The chief seated his guests in a semicircle, indicating where each should sit. Many Stars and Spirit Wind were there, and were seated in honored places. Chief Wolf's Brother took up his long, finely decorated pipe and filled it carefully with a mixture of tobacco and dried red willow. He placed a tuft of straw on the tobacco and held the pipe out for Many Stars to light. Rising, the chief offered the lighted pipe to the sun, the father of all things, and to the earth, the mother; then he passed it to the guest on his left.

One after the other, each in his turn, the men smoked briefly. They were surprised to see, while the pipe was being passed, that a crowd was gathering outside the tepee. All the men and women of the camp came quietly, their moccasined feet stirring the grass as lightly as wind. They sat on the ground and waited expectantly, those in the foreground peering under the lifted bottom of the tepee.

Captain Stephen and Dr. Dean exchanged nervous glances. Had the Indians gathered to witness their execution? But the voice of the chief commanded their instant attention. Chief

Wolf's Brother was speaking in a low, musical voice that was vibrant with emotion. The white men were astonished and fascinated by the light that illumined his dark face when he spoke, softening the stern features wonderfully. Bissonette interpreted the chief's words:

"My heart is filled with gratitude to my white brothers who have done for me a service that I can never repay. I and my people will not forget how your great white medicine man came in answer to the prayers of our honored medicine man, Many Stars, and persuaded the Great Spirit to spare the life of my son, Young War Eagle. I will prove to you that a chief does not forget!"

In the silence that followed these words, the chief unwrapped a bundle that Spirit Wind laid before him, and once again the white buffalo robe and the mystic whistle were displayed to the white men. At the same time, a brave approached the tepee leading the beautiful horses that Wolf's Brother had brought to the wagon encampment on that memorable night when he had come to bargain for Myra. The chief resumed his speech:

"Accept, White Brothers, these offerings of thanksgiving! They will serve you in your long travel across the desert and through the mountains. The story of your service to Wolf's Brother will run before you like the wind, and these gifts will be a sign to the children of the great Dakota family that you have claim to their friendship."

A low-voiced chorus of approval went up from the listeners outside the tepee.

In the great relief that they felt at the lifting of their long suspense, the white men had difficulty in replying to Wolf's Brother's courtly speech, but a reply was expected of each of them, so each of them did his best to please. Dr. Dean felt more like giving three cheers than making a formal speech, and Captain Stephen was almost overpowered by the desire to jump on his horse and ride to the wagon encampment with the wonderful news of the chief's gratitude. But the occasion was too solemn for anything but very formal demonstration, and after the speeches were made, Captain Stephen presented gifts that he had brought with him—tobacco for the men to mix with their ground red willow and beads for White Antelope and her sister. Many Stars brought the festivity to an end with a prayer, and dusk was gathering when the Indians and white men parted.

That night, when the silence of sleep held the Stephen company, Dr. Dean went to the edge of the camp, where the sentinels kept their solitary watch, and stood for a long time, looking in the direction of Wolf's Brother's circled tepees. There he had fought and won the hardest, strangest battle of his life. He was glad to be leaving the place forever.

"All's well!" The report of the weary guard, giving up his post to the midnight relief, echoed in the doctor's heart:

"All's well."

A Colt of His Own

⟨[THE hero of this story from FARMER BOY was the author's husband, Almanzo Wilder, who spent his boyhood on an old-fashioned farm in New York State nearly a century ago. His father raised fine horses but would not allow his son to touch the colts. Almanzo yearned to have one of his own.

FATHER HAD so much hay that year that the stock could not eat it all, so he decided to sell some of it in town. Almanzo Wilder sat at the supper table, wishing he did not have to go back to school. He thought about figuring, and he was thinking so hard that words came out of his mouth before he knew it.

"Thirty bales to a load, at two dollars a bale," he said. "That's sixty dollars a lo—"

He stopped, scared. He knew better than to speak at table, when he wasn't spoken to.

"Mercy on us, listen to the boy!" Mother said.

"Well, well, well, son!" said Father. "I see you've been studying to some purpose." He drank the tea out of his saucer, set it down, and looked again at Almanzo. "Learning is best put into practice. What say you ride to town with me tomorrow, and sell that load of hay?"

"Oh, yes! Please, Father!" Almanzo almost shouted.

He did not have to go to school next morning. He climbed high up on top of the load of hay, and lay there on his stomach and kicked up his heels. Father's hat was down below him, and beyond were the plump backs of the horses. He was as high up as if he were in a tree.

The load swayed a little, and the wagon creaked, and the horses' feet made dull sounds on the hard snow. The air was clear and cold, the sky was very blue, and all the snowy fields were sparkling.

Just beyond the bridge over Trout River, Almanzo saw a small black thing lying beside the road. When the wagon passed, he leaned over the edge of the hay and saw that it was a pocketbook. He yelled, and Father stopped the horses to let him climb down and pick it up. It was a fat black wallet.

Almanzo shinnied up the bales of hay and the horses went on. He looked at the pocketbook. He opened it, and it was full of bank notes. There was nothing to show who owned them.

He handed it down to Father, and Father gave him the reins. The team seemed far below, with the lines slanting down to the hames, and Almanzo felt very small. But he liked to drive. He held the lines carefully and the horses went steadily along. Father was looking at the pocketbook and the money.

"There's fifteen hundred dollars here," Father said. "Now who does it belong to? He's a man who's afraid of banks, or he wouldn't carry so much money around. You can see by the creases in the bills, he's carried them some time. They're big bills, and folded together, so likely he got them all at once. Now who's suspicious, and stingy, and sold something valuable lately?"

Almanzo didn't know, but Father didn't expect him to answer. The horses went around a curve in the road as well as if Father had been driving them.

"Thompson!" Father exclaimed. "He sold some land last fall. He's afraid of banks, and he's suspicious, and so stingy he'd skin a flea for its hide and tallow. Thompson's the man!"

He put the pocketbook in his pocket and took the lines from Almanzo. "We'll see if we can find him in town," he said.

Father drove first to the Livery, Sale, and Feed Stable. The liveryman came out, and sure enough Father let Almanzo sell the hay. He stood back and did not say anything, while Almanzo showed the liveryman that the hay was good timothy and clover, clean and bright, and every bale solid and full weight.

"How much do you want for it?" the liveryman asked.

"Two dollars and a quarter a bale," Almanzo said.

"I won't pay that price," said the liveryman. "It isn't worth it."

"What would you call a fair price?" Almanzo asked him.

"Not a penny over two dollars," the liveryman said.

"All right, I'll take two dollars," said Almanzo quickly.

The liveryman looked at Father, and then he pushed back his hat and asked Almanzo why he priced the hay at two dollars and a quarter in the first place.

"Are you taking it at two dollars?" Almanzo asked. The liveryman said he was. "Well," Almanzo said, "I asked two and a quarter because if I'd asked two, you wouldn't have paid but one seventy-five."

The liveryman laughed, and said to Father, "That's a smart boy of yours."

"Time will show," Father said. "Many a good beginning makes a bad ending. It remains to be seen how he turns out in the long run."

Father did not take the money for the hay; he let Almanzo take it and count it to make sure it was sixty dollars.

Then they went to Mr. Case's store. This store was always crowded, but Father always did his trading there, because Mr. Case sold his goods cheaper than other merchants. Mr. Case said, "I'd rather have a nimble sixpence than a slow shilling."

Almanzo stood in the crowd with Father, waiting while Mr. Case served firstcomers. Mr. Case was polite and friendly to everybody alike; he had to be, because they were all customers. Father was polite to everybody, too, but he was not as friendly to some as he was to others.

After a while Father gave Almanzo the pocketbook and told him to look for Mr. Thompson. Father must stay in the store to wait his turn; he could not lose time if they were to get home by chore time.

No other boys were on the street; they were all in school. Almanzo liked to be walking down the street, carrying all that money, and he thought how glad Mr. Thompson would be to see it again.

He looked in the stores, and the barber shop, and the bank. Then he saw Mr. Thompson's team standing on a side street, in front of Mr. Paddock's wagon shop. He opened the door of the long low building, and went in.

It was warm in the building, and there was a good smell of shavings and leather and paint. Beyond the stove two workmen were making a wagon, and another was painting thin red lines on the red spokes of a new buggy. The buggy glistened proudly in black paint. Long curls of shavings lay in heaps, and the whole place was as pleasant as a barn on a rainy day. The workmen whistled while they measured and marked and sawed and planed the clean-smelling wood.

Mr. Thompson was arguing about the price of a new wagon. Almanzo decided that Mr. Paddock did not like Mr. Thompson, but he was trying to sell the wagon. He figured the cost with his big carpenter's pencil, and soothingly tried to persuade Mr. Thompson.

"You see, I can't cut the price any further and pay my men," he said. "I'm doing the best I can for you. I guarantee we'll make a wagon to please you, or you don't have to take it."

"Well, maybe I'll come back to you, if I can't do better elsewhere," Mr. Thompson said suspiciously.

"Glad to serve you any time," said Mr. Paddock. Then he saw Almanzo, and asked him how the pig was getting along. Almanzo liked big, jolly Mr. Paddock; he always asked about Lucy, his pig.

"She'll weigh around a hundred and fifty now," Almanzo told him. Then he turned to Mr. Thompson and asked, "Did you lose a pocketbook?"

Mr. Thompson jumped. He clapped a hand to his pocket, and fairly shouted.

"Yes, I have! Fifteen hundred dollars in it, too. What about it? What do you know about it?"

"Is this it?" Almanzo asked.

"Yes, yes, yes, that's it!" Mr. Thompson said, snatching the pocketbook. He opened it and hurriedly counted the money. He counted all the bills over twice, and he looked exactly like a man skinning a flea for its hide and tallow.

Then he breathed a long sigh of relief, and said, "Well, this durn boy didn't steal any of it."

Almanzo's face was hot as fire. He wanted to hit Mr. Thompson.

Mr. Thompson thrust his skinny hand deep into his pants pocket and hunted around. He took out something.

"Here," he said, putting it into Almanzo's hand. It was a nickel.

Almanzo was so angry he couldn't see. He hated Mr. Thompson; he wanted to hurt him. Mr. Thompson called him a durn boy, and as good as called him a thief. Almanzo didn't want his old nickel. Suddenly he thought what to say.

"Here," he said, handing the nickel back. "Keep your nickel. I can't change it."

Mr. Thompson's tight mean face turned red. One of the workmen laughed a short jeering laugh. But Mr. Paddock stepped up to Mr. Thompson, angry.

"Don't you call this boy a thief, Thompson!" he said. "And he's not a beggar, either! That's how you treat him, is it? When he brings you back your fifteen hundred dollars! Call him a thief and hand him a nickel, will you?"

Mr. Thompson stepped back, but Mr. Paddock stepped right after him. Mr. Paddock shook his fist under Mr. Thompson's nose.

"You measly skinflint!" Mr. Paddock said. "Not if I know it, you won't! Not in my place! A good, honest, decent little chap, and you— For a cent I'll— No! You hand him a hundred of that money, and do it quickly! No, two hundred! Two hundred dollars, I say, or take the consequences!"

Mr. Thompson tried to say something, and so did Almanzo. But Mr. Paddock's fists clenched and the muscles of his arms bulged. "Two hun-

dred!" he shouted. "Hand it over, quick! Or I'll see you do!"

Mr. Thompson shrank down small, watching Mr. Paddock, and he licked his thumb and hurriedly counted off some bills. He held them out to Almanzo. Almanzo said, "Mr. Paddock—"

"Now get out of here, if you know what's healthy! Get out!" Mr. Paddock said, and before Almanzo could blink he was standing there with the bills in his hand, and Mr. Thompson slammed the door behind himself.

Almanzo was so excited he stammered. He said he didn't think Father would like it. Almanzo felt queer about taking all that money, and yet he did want to keep it. Mr. Paddock said he would talk to Father; he rolled down his shirt sleeves and put on his coat and asked, "Where is he?"

Almanzo almost ran, to keep up with Mr. Paddock's long strides. The bills were clutched tight in his hand. Father was putting packages into the wagon, and Mr. Paddock told him what had happened.

"For a cent I'd have smashed his sneering face," Mr. Paddock said. "But it struck me that giving up cash is what hurts him most. And I figure the boy's entitled to it."

"I don't know as anyone's entitled to anything for common honesty," Father objected. "Though I must say I appreciate the spirit you showed, Paddock."

"I don't say he deserved more than decent gratitude for giving Thompson his own money," Mr. Paddock said. "But it's too much to ask him to stand

and take insults, on top of that. I say Almanzo's entitled to that two hundred."

"Well, there's something in what you say," said Father. Finally he decided, "All right, son, you can keep that money."

Almanzo smoothed out the bills and looked at them: two hundred dollars. That was as much as the horse buyer paid for one of Father's four-year-olds.

"And I'm much obliged to you, Paddock, standing up for the boy the way you did," Father said.

bank. Almanzo could just look over the ledge at the cashier sitting on his high stool with a pen behind his ear. The cashier craned to look down at Almanzo and asked Father:

"Hadn't I better put this down to your account, sir?"

"No," said Father. "It's the boy's money; let him handle it himself. He won't learn any younger."

"Yes, sir," the cashier said. Almanzo had to write his name twice. Then the cashier carefully counted the bills, and wrote Almanzo's name in a little book.

"Well, I can afford to lose a customer now and then, in a good cause," said Mr. Paddock. He asked Almanzo, "What are you going to do with that money?"

Almanzo looked at Father. "Could I put it in the bank?" he asked.

"That's the place to put money," said Father. "Well, well, well, two hundred dollars! I was twice your age before I had so much."

"So was I. Yes, and older than that," Mr. Paddock said.

Father and Almanzo went to the

He wrote the figures $200 in the book, and he gave the book to Almanzo.

Almanzo went out of the bank with Father, and asked him: "How do I get the money out again?"

"You ask for it, and they'll give it to you. But remember this, son; as long as that money's in the bank, it's working for you. Every dollar in the bank is making you four cents a year. That's a sight easier than you can earn money any other way. Any time you want to spend a nickel, you stop and think

[47]

how much work it takes to earn a dollar." . . .

Almanzo squirmed. He was thinking that he had more than enough money to buy a little colt. He could break a little colt of his own; he could teach it everything. Father would never let him break one of his colts.

"Father!" Almanzo exclaimed.

"Yes, son?"

"Can I? Can I really tell you what I want?"

"Yes, son," Father encouraged him.

"I want a colt," Almanzo said. "Could I buy a colt all my own with some of that two hundred dollars, and would you let me break him?"

Father's beard slowly widened with a smile. "Son, you leave that money in the bank."

Almanzo felt everything sinking down inside him. And then suddenly, the whole world was a great, shining, expanding glow of warm light. For Father went on: "If it's a colt you want, I'll give you Starlight."

"Father!" Almanzo gasped. "For my very own?"

"Yes, son. You can break him, and drive him, and when he's a four-year-old you can sell him or keep him, just as you want to. We'll take him out on a rope, first thing tomorrow morning, and you can begin to gentle him."

⟨ Almanzo *later went* West *to live, and the record of how he and Laura Ingalls met and married may be read in* The Little Town on the Prairie *and* These Happy Golden Years. *Mrs. Wilder's "Little House" books about the adventures of her own family brought our country's pioneer past vividly to life.*

The New Mother

INSIDE THE cabin the only light came from a feeble fire in the mammoth fireplace. The dirt floor felt cold under her moccasined feet, as Sarah Lincoln paused in the doorway. Tom, her husband, cleared his throat in some embarrassment. He had only recently married the Widow Johnson, and he knew this home was not what she and her three children had expected.

"Sally, Abe, this is your new mammy," he called. "I've been back to Kaintuck to git myself a wife."

It was then that Sarah, peering through the gloom, saw the Lincoln children. They huddled on low stools near the fire, looking up at her out of frightened gray eyes. Sarah gasped at the sight of their thin soiled clothing, their dark matted hair, their pinched gray faces smudged with soot.

"Howdy!" She tried to smile, but they only huddled closer together. "Don't you want to meet my young-'uns?"

"Mamma, I don't like it here," said Johnny Johnson.

"Sh!" Sarah warned. She nudged Betsy and Mathilda, who stopped staring long enough for each to make an awkward curtsy. Sally, after one glance at their pretty linsey-woolsey dresses and neat leather moccasins, tried to hide her bare toes under the stool. Abe said, "Howdy," somewhere down inside his stomach.

From the moment Sarah laid aside her hood and shawl, things began to happen in the Lincoln cabin. First, she announced cheerfully, she and Sally would have some victuals on the table, quicker than anyone could say "Jack Robinson." Tom went out to the wagon to unhitch the horses, and when he came back he was carrying a slab of bacon and a comb of honey.

Dennis Hanks, an older cousin who made his home with the Lincolns, brought in some firewood. Abe and Mathilda started for the spring, swinging the water pail between them. A few minutes later Sally had forgotten her soiled dress and her bare feet, as she and Betsy mixed batter and set corn bread to bake on the hearth.

Keep 'em busy. Git 'em working together, said Sarah to herself. They'll soon forget they're shy.

Soon the magic smell of frying bacon filled the air. The table was rather crowded with eight people gathered around it, but no one seemed to mind. Under the influence of a hearty meal, Sally and her stepsisters chattered like

[49]

old friends. Only Abe ate in silence, his eyes on the slab of bark which served him as a plate.

"I declare," said Dennis, as he sopped up some of the golden honey on his corn bread. "I ain't et like this since Cousin Nancy died."

Abe jumped up and started for the cabin door. A little choking sound escaped him.

Tom tried to hide his embarrassment in a show of anger. "Abe Lincoln, you set right down and finish your corn bread."

Abe shook his head. "I—I can't, Pa."

Tom was on his feet now. "This is a purty way to treat your new ma—after she goes and gits all these good victuals ready. You clean up your plate, or I'll give you a hiding."

The young Johnsons gasped. Sally, twisting the hem of her dress, cast an appealing glance at her new stepmother.

Sarah's heart seemed to turn over. Abe looked so miserable and scared. He was frightened not only of his father but of the strange woman who had come, without warning, to take his mother's place. She never would get next to him if Tom was not careful.

"Please, let the boy be," she said.

"I won't stand for him treatin' you that way."

Sarah smiled, more brightly than she felt. "Abe and I'll have plenty of chance to git acquainted. I reckon all of us are through."

She arose, her hands on her hips, surveying the dirty room. "Thar's a sight o' things to be done here before we unpack my plunder from the wagon. Fust, I'll need lots of hot water. Who wants to go to the spring?"

Her glance rested on Abe.

"I'll go, ma'am." He grabbed the wooden bucket and made his escape.

Abe made several trips to the spring that afternoon. Each pailful of water was poured into one of the huge iron kettles over the fireplace. Higher and higher roared the flames, and when Sarah wasn't asking for more water, she was asking for more wood. She would hear the steady chop-chop of Abe's ax in the clearing. Every few minutes, it seemed, he was bringing in a fresh armful of wood. His woebegone expression was giving way to one of curiosity—curiosity at all the strange goings on in the Lincoln cabin.

For even Dennis was working. Under Sarah's direction he washed the cabin walls, while the girls scrubbed the table, the few three-legged stools. Not since Nancy died had the cabin had such a thorough going over.

At length Sarah climbed the peg ladder to peer into the loft. "Tssch! Tssch!" she said when she saw the cornhusks and dirty bearskins on which the boys had been sleeping. "Take 'em out and burn 'em, Tom."

"Burn 'em?" he protested.

"Burn those kivers on the bed downstairs, too. We're startin' fresh in this house."

Tom sighed, but did as he was asked.

Within a few hours the cabin fairly shone. Then came the most remarkable occurrence of that remarkable afternoon—the unloading of Sarah Lincoln's plunder.

"Tom, you oughter git the walnut

bureau in fust," she suggested. "I'm most perticular about that."

With much heaving and grunting Tom and Dennis carried in the bureau, setting it in the place of honor against the wall opposite the bed. "This-here bureau cost forty-five dollars," Tom announced in an undertone.

Forty-five dollars! Abe gasped. Sarah saw him run a finger over the shining dark wood. She noticed his startled expression when he saw his reflection in the little mirror which she hung above the bureau. Most likely he had never seen a looking glass before.

The wagon yielded other pieces of furniture—a larger table, chairs with real backs, a spinning wheel, a big chest filled with clothes. Mrs. Lincoln's pots and pans shone. Her pewter dishes were spotless.

Most remarkable of all were the feather beds. One was laid on the pole bed in the corner. Another was placed on a clean bearskin in another corner to provide a sleeping place for the girls. The third was carried to the loft. Sarah handed Abe one end of a homespun blanket. "If you'll help me spread these blankets, you and Dennis can turn in. I reckon you won't mind if Johnny bunks with you."

"Yes'm—I mean, no'm," said Abe. She saw his look of astonishment when he felt the warmth of soft wool between his fingers. It had been a long time since he had slept under a blanket. He almost smiled as he punched his fist into the feather bed.

Within a few minutes gentle snores could be heard coming from the loft. The three girls on the makeshift bed in the corner were already asleep. Sarah sank down into one of her own chairs before the fire, a pile of sewing in her lap.

Thar's nothin' wrong with Sally that soap and water and a little lovin' won't fix, she thought. Did my heart good to hear her call me Mamma, jes' like my own young'uns. But Abe—

Sarah paused to thread her bone needle.

Abe's harder to figure out, she went on talking to herself. Thar's a lonesome place in his heart. Still a little skittish of havin' a new mammy, I reckon. Jes' have to be patient.

The bearskin at the door was pushed aside and Tom entered, his arms filled with wood. He started to dump the whole armful on the floor near the fireplace. Then, seeming to think better of it, he arranged the logs in a neat pile.

"By cracky"—he gave a look around the room—"you sure did a heap of fixin' here today."

Sarah laughed softly. "Why, Tom, we ain't started yit. You won't know the place when we git through. I reckon you and Dennis will want to split and smooth some logs and lay a puncheon floor. Folks shouldn't live on a dirt floor, not this day and age."

There was a look of distress, almost of anguish, on Tom's face as his wife continued to outline the changes she expected in the cabin. "But, Sairy!" he protested.

"Yes, Tom?" Sarah looked up from her sewing.

Under her level gaze, he began to squirm. "Nothin' much. I jes' figured maybe Dennis and I'll go huntin' tomorrow. That slab of bacon is all the meat we have."

The next morning Sarah was pleased to have the men out of the house. "Abe," she said, "today I aim to make you two young'uns look more human."

Abe looked startled, but at his step-mother's request he carried several pails of water from the spring. He poured it into the kettles to boil. He dragged a big wooden tub inside. Then mumbling something about having to chop more wood, he disappeared through the door. Sarah smiled as the sharp, steady sound of his chopping was borne to her on the crisp air.

Two hours later she stood in the doorway watching the girls trip gaily down the path. Sally, her hair in two neat pigtails, was wearing her step-mother's shawl over one of Betsy's dresses. She was taking her new sisters to call on one of the neighbors.

Sarah shaded her eyes with her hand and peered off into the woods. "Abe! Oh, Abe," she shouted.

The only answer was the sound of an ax biting into wood—faster and faster.

"You heerd me, Abe," she called.

He came then, reluctantly. Leaving his ax by the door, he edged into the room.

"Sally's had her bath," said Sarah firmly. "Now I've got a tub of good hot water and a gourdful of soap waitin' for you. Skedaddle out of those old clothes and throw 'em in the fire—"

"I—I ain't got any others." Abe looked terrified.

Sarah laughed. "I don't aim to pluck your feathers without giving you some new ones. I set up late last night, cut-ting down a pair of Mr. Johnson's old pants. I got one of his shirts, too."

Abe slowly started taking off his shirt. He walked toward the fire, edging along the wall, keeping as far away as possible from the tub of hot water.

"That tub won't bite," Sarah reminded him. "Now I'm a-goin' down to the spring. When I git back, I want you to have yourself scrubbed all over."

Abe stuck one toe into the water, said "Ouch!" and drew it out again. Finally, screwing up his courage, he put in his whole foot. He put in his other foot. Then he sat down in the tub. By the time Sarah returned he was standing before the fire dressed in the cut-down trousers and homespun shirt of the late Mr. Johnson.

Sarah surveyed him critically. "You look different already. Those trousers look a mite too big, but you'll soon grow into 'em."

Abe was somewhat surprised to find how good it felt to be clean. "Thank you, ma'am. Now I reckon I'd better finish my chopping."

"No," said Sarah. "You set yourself down on that stool and let me git at your hair."

Sarah not only washed his hair but some of the places Abe himself had overlooked. His neck had not had such a scrubbing for more than a year. He submitted silently, only screwing up his eyes a little tighter when Sarah dug in behind his ears. But when she opened the top drawer of the bureau and took out a haw comb and a pair of scissors, he jumped up in alarm.

"Thar's no call to be skeered," she told him, with another look at his mop of unruly black hair. "I'm jes' goin' to cut away some of that brush heap on top your head."

"Then how folks know I'm me?" he asked plaintively.

"What you mean, Abe?"

"When we came to Indiany, Pappy marked off our claim by pilin' brush along the boundary lines. He said he wanted everyone to know this here was our farm. I figured that brush heap atop of me is my boundary line. How folks know I'm Abe Lincoln, if you clear it away?"

It was the first time Sarah had heard him say more than "Yes'm" or "No'm," and such a long speech took her by surprise. Was he joking? It was hard to tell, he was such a solemn-looking boy. Or was he still frightened? He sat quietly as she snipped off lock after lock of the unruly black hair. She tried not to pull, but once he said, "Ouch!" She patted his shoulder and waited a moment before she attacked the next tangle.

"Thar!" she said at last. "It's all over. S'pose you mosey over to the lookin' glass and tell me if that's Abe Lincoln you see."

He gazed at his reflection, a pleased expression in his eyes. "It's Abe, I reckon. I still ain't the purtiest boy in Pigeon Creek. On t'other hand, thar ain't quite so much of me to be ugly, now you cleared away the brush heap."

Suddenly he grinned, and Sarah laughed in relief. "You're a caution, Abe. Smart, too. Had much schoolin'?"

Abe shook his head, serious again. "I've just been to school by littles."

"Have you a mind to go again?"

"There ain't any school since Master Crawford left. Anyhow, Pappy don't set much store by eddication."

Sarah looked at him sharply. "Can you read?"

"Yes'm. But I haven't any books."

"Now, that's peculiarsome," said Sarah. "You can read and you haven't any books. I have books and can't read."

Abe stared at her, amazed. "You have books?"

She walked over to the bureau and came back carrying four worn-looking little volumes. "Books are a right good thing to have, so I brung 'em along. You set yourself down thar at the table and I'll show you."

Abe, his brown cheeks flushed with pleasure, spelled out the titles: "*Rob-in-son Cru-soe, Pil-grim's Prog-ress, Sin-bad the Sail-or, Ae-sop's Fa-bles.* Oh, ma'am, this-here book is one Master Crawford told us about."

Sarah sat down beside him and turned the pages. "The stories look like little bitty ones. Could you read one of 'em to me, Abe?"

The book was open to the story of "The Crow and the Pitcher." Abe, his shorn head bent above the page, began to read. " 'A crow was almost dead of—of th-thirst, when he found a p-pitcher with a little water in the bottom.' "

It had been so long since Abe had seen a book that he stumbled over a few of the words, but he gained more confidence as he went along. " 'The crow reached in his bill to take a drink. He tried and tried, but he could not reach the water. He was al-most ready to give up, when he had an i-dea. He picked up a peb-ble in his bill and dropped it into the pit-cher. He picked up an-other pebble and an-other. . . .

" 'With every pebble that he dropped, the water in the pitcher rose a little high-er. At last the water rose so high that the crow could reach it with his bill. He took a long drink, and so was a-ble to q-q-quench his thirst and save his life.' "

"You read right well," said Sarah.

Abe laughed delightedly. "It says something else here. 'Mor-al,' " he read. " 'Little by little does the trick.' "

Abe took the book closer to the fire-place where it was easier to see the words. He read story after story, pausing only now and then to throw another log on the fire. As Sarah went about her household tasks, she watched him closely, a puzzled frown in her honest gray eyes. Abe was different from what her John would ever be. He was different from any boy she had ever seen. She pulled a chair closer to the fire and picked up her knitting. "Which story do you like best?" she asked.

Abe looked up with a start. "The one about the smart crow that filled up the pitcher with pebbles so he could git himself a drink."

"That story sorta reminds me of you," she told him.

"How come, ma'am?"

"Didn't that Mr. Aesop say, 'Little by little does the trick'? Wall, you go to school by littles. Each time you l'arn something. I figure those little bits of l'arnin' are like pebbles. Keep on pilin' 'em up higher, and you'll make something of yourself."

Abe shook his head. "I reckon I won't ever git to go to school agin."

"I wouldn't say that. Lots of new folks are a-comin' to Pigeon Creek, and the more folks, the more likely another schoolmaster is to come."

"But Pappy says I already know how to read and write and cipher. He says I have more eddication than he ever had. I—I can't help it, ma'am. I want to know more'n Pappy knows."

"Your pappy's a good man," said Sarah, "and the next time a school keeps in these parts, I'm a-goin' to ask him to let you and the other young'uns go. That's a promise, Abe."

Again Abe could only stare.

"Meanwhile, you can l'arn right smart jes' by reading these-here books."

"I can read 'em—any time I like?"

"I'm a-giving 'em to you to keep."

"Oh, Mamma," said Abe. The name slipped out as though he had always been used to saying it.

Only the fire crackling softly on the hearth broke the long silence. "You're my boy now, Abe," said Sarah softly, "and I'm a-goin' to help you all I can."

Abe did not answer. He did not need to. His shining eyes told Sarah all she wished to know. And he had called her Mamma of his own free will.

⟪ This story is from THEY KNEW ABE LINCOLN, a book based on the personal recollections of people who knew the young Abe Lincoln.

MARK TWAIN

Tom Sawyer Attends His Funeral

❐ TOM felt he had been unjustly punished by Aunt Polly, with whom he lived; Joe Harper had a similar grievance against his mother. The chums found a small log raft and persuaded Huck Finn, the town waif, to run away with them. Not far from town, in the Mississippi River, there was an uninhabited island, and they decided to go there and be pirates.

THE BOYS found plenty of things to be delighted with. They discovered that Jackson's Island was about three miles long and a quarter of a mile wide, and that the shore it lay closest to was only separated from it by a narrow channel hardly two hundred yards wide. They took a swim, so it was close upon the middle of the afternoon when they got back to camp. They fared sumptuously upon cold ham, and then threw themselves down in the shade to talk. But the talk soon began to drag. The stillness, the solemnity that brooded in the woods, and the sense of loneliness, began to tell upon the spirits of the boys. They fell to thinking. A sort of undefined longing crept upon them. This took dim shape, presently—it was budding homesickness. But they were all ashamed of their weakness, and none was brave enough to speak his thought.

For some time now, the boys had been dully conscious of a peculiar sound in the distance.

"What is it!" exclaimed Joe.

"I wonder," said Tom in a whisper.

"Tain't thunder," said Huckleberry in an awed tone, "becuz thunder—"

"Hark!" said Tom. "Listen."

They waited a time that seemed an age, and then the same muffled boom troubled the solemn hush.

"Let's go and see."

They sprang to their feet and hurried to the shore, where they parted the bushes on the bank and peered out over the water. The little steam ferryboat was about a mile below the village, drifting with the current. Her broad deck seemed crowded with people. There were a great many skiffs rowing about or floating with the stream in the neighborhood of the ferryboat. Then a great jet of white smoke burst from the ferryboat's side. As it expanded and rose in a lazy cloud, that same dull throb of sound was borne to the listeners again.

"I know now!" exclaimed Tom. "Somebody's drownded!"

"That's it!" said Huck. "They done that last summer, when Bill Turner got drownded. They shoot a cannon over the water, and that makes him come up to the top."

"By jings, I wish I was over there now," said Joe.

"I do, too," said Huck. "I'd give heaps to know who it is."

The boys still listened and watched. Presently a revealing thought flashed through Tom's mind.

"Boys, I know who's drownded—it's us!"

As twilight drew on, the ferryboat went back to her accustomed business and the skiffs disappeared. The pirates returned to camp. They were jubilant with vanity over their new grandeur and the illustrious trouble they were making. They caught fish, cooked supper and ate it. But when the shadows of night closed them in, they gradually ceased to talk, and sat gazing into the fire. Tom and Joe could not keep back thoughts of certain persons at home who were not enjoying this fine frolic as much as they were.

As the night deepened, Huck began to nod and presently to snore. Joe followed next. Tom lay upon his elbow for some time, watching the two intently. At last he got up cautiously, on his knees, and went searching in the grass among the flickering reflections flung by the campfire. He picked up and inspected several large semicylinders of the thin white bark of a syca-

more, and finally chose two which seemed to suit him. Then he knelt by the fire and painfully wrote something upon each of these with his "red keel." One he rolled up and put in his jacket pocket, and the other he put in Joe's hat and removed it to a little distance from the owner. Then he tiptoed his way cautiously among the trees till he felt that he was out of hearing, and straightway broke into a run in the direction of the sand bar. A few minutes later, he was in the shoal water of the bar, wading toward shore . . .

Tom Sawyer flew along unfrequented alleys, and shortly found himself at his aunt's back fence. He climbed over and approached the "ell," for a light was still burning there. There sat Aunt Polly, his brother Sid, his sister Mary, and Joe Harper's mother, grouped together, talking. They were by the bed, and the bed was between them and the door. Tom went to the door and began to softly lift the latch. He pressed gently, and the door yielded a crack. He continued pushing cautiously, and quaking every time it creaked, till he judged he might squeeze through on his knees.

"What makes the candle blow so?" said Aunt Polly. Tom hurried up. "Why, that door's open, I believe. Go 'long and shut it, Sid."

Tom disappeared under the bed just in time.

"But as I was saying," said Aunt Polly, "he warn't *bad*, so to say, only mischeevous. Only just giddy, and harum-scarum, you know. He warn't any more responsible than a colt. *He* never meant any harm, and he was the best-hearted boy that ever was"—and she began to cry.

"It was just so with my Joe, always full of his devilment, and up to every kind of mischief, but he was just as unselfish and kind as he could be. Laws bless me, to think I went and whipped him for taking that cream, never once recollecting that I throwed it out myself because it was sour. And I never to see him again in this world!" And Mrs. Harper sobbed as if her heart would break.

"Yes, yes, yes, I know just how you feel, Mrs. Harper. I know just exactly how you feel. No longer ago than yesterday noon, my Tom took and filled the cat full of Pain-killer medicine, and I did think the cretur would tear the house down. And God forgive me, I cracked Tom's head with my thimble, poor boy, poor dead boy."

But this memory was too much for the old lady, and she broke entirely down. Tom was snuffling now himself. He began to have a nobler opinion of himself than ever before.

He went on listening, and gathered by odds and ends that it was conjectured at first that the boys had got drowned while taking a swim. It was believed that the search for the bodies had been a fruitless effort merely because the drowning must have occurred in mid-channel. The boys, being good swimmers, would otherwise have escaped to shore. This was Wednesday night. If the bodies continued missing until Sunday, all hope would be given over, and the funerals would be preached on that morning. Tom shuddered.

Mrs. Harper gave a sobbing good night and turned to go. Then with a mutual impulse the two bereaved women flung themselves into each other's arms and had a good, consoling cry, and then parted. Aunt Polly was tender far beyond her wont, in her good night to Sid and Mary. Sid snuffled a bit and Mary went off crying.

Aunt Polly knelt down and prayed for Tom so touchingly, and with such measureless love in her old trembling voice, that he was weltering in tears again long before she was through.

He had to keep still long after she went to bed, for she kept making brokenhearted ejaculations from time to time and tossing restlessly. But at last she was still, only moaning a little in her sleep. Now the boy stole out, rose gradually by the bedside, shaded the candlelight with his hand, and stood regarding her. His heart was full of pity for her. He took out his sycamore scroll and placed it by the candle.

But something occurred to him, and he lingered, considering. His face lighted with a happy solution of his thought; he put the bark hastily in his pocket. Then he bent over and kissed the faded lips. . . .

When the Sunday-school hour was finished the next Sunday, the bell began to toll, instead of ringing in the usual way. It was a very still Sabbath, and the mournful sound seemed in keeping with the musing hush that lay upon nature. None could remember when the little church had been so full before. There was finally a waiting pause, and then Aunt Polly entered, followed by Sid and Mary, and then by the Harper family, all in deep black.

As the service proceeded, the clergyman drew such pictures of the graces, the winning ways, and the rare promise of the lost lads, that every soul there felt a pang in remembering that he had persistently seen only faults and flaws in the poor boys. The minister related many a touching incident in the lives of the departed, which illustrated their sweet, generous natures; and the people remembered with grief that at the time they occurred they had seemed rank rascalities, well deserving of the cowhide. The congregation became more and more moved, till at last the whole company broke down and joined the weeping mourners, the preacher himself giving way to his feelings and crying in the pulpit.

There was a rustle in the gallery, which nobody noticed. A moment later the church door creaked. The minister raised his streaming eyes above his handkerchief and stood transfixed. First one and then another pair of eyes followed the minister's, and then almost with one impulse the congregation rose and stared. The three dead boys came marching up the aisle, Tom in the lead, Joe next, and Huck, a ruin of drooping rags, sneaking sheepishly in the rear! They had been hid in the unused gallery listening to their own funeral sermon!

Aunt Polly, Mary, and the Harpers threw themselves upon their restored ones, smothered them with kisses and poured out thanksgivings, while poor Huck stood abashed and uncomfortable. He started to slink away, but Tom seized him.

"Aunt Polly, it ain't fair. Somebody's got to be glad to see Huck."

"And so they shall. I'm glad to see him, poor motherless thing!" And the loving attentions Aunt Polly lavished upon him were the one thing capable of making him more uncomfortable than he was before.

Suddenly the minister shouted at the top of his voice: "Praise God from whom all blessings flow—SING!—and put your hearts in it!"

And they did. "Old Hundred" swelled up with a triumphant burst, and while it shook the rafters Tom Sawyer the Pirate looked around upon the envying juveniles about him and confessed in his heart that this was the proudest moment of his life. . . .

Tom with his brother pirates had paddled over to the Missouri shore on a log, at dusk on Saturday, landing five or six miles below the village. They had slept in the woods at the edge of the town till nearly daylight, and had then crept through back lanes and alleys and finished their sleep in the gallery of the church.

At breakfast Monday morning, Aunt Polly and Mary were very loving to Tom and very attentive to his wants. There was an unusual amount of talk. In the course of it Aunt Polly said:

"Well, I don't say it wasn't a fine joke, Tom, but it is a pity you could be so hardhearted as to let me suffer so. If you could come over on a log to go to your funeral, you could have come over to give me a hint some way that you warn't dead, but only run off."

"I wish now I'd thought," said Tom in a repentant tone, "but I dreamed about you anyway. That's something, ain't it?"

"It ain't much—a cat does that much—but it's better than nothing. What did you dream?"

"Why, Wednesday night I dreamed that you was sitting over there by the bed, and Sid was sitting by the wood-box, and Mary next to him."

"Well, so we did. So we always do. I'm glad your dreams could take even that much trouble about us."

"And I dreamt that Joe Harper's mother was here."

"Why, she *was* here! Did you dream any more?"

"Oh, lots. But it's so dim now."

"Well, *try* to recollect, can't you?"

"Somehow it seems to me that the wind—the wind blowed the—the—"

"Try harder, Tom! The wind did blow something. Come!"

Tom pressed his fingers on his forehead. "I've got it now! I've got it now! It blowed the candle!"

"Mercy on us! Go on, Tom, go on!"

"And it seems to me that you said, 'Why, I believe that that door—' "

"Go on, Tom!"

"Just let me study a moment, just a moment. Oh, yes, you said you believed the door was open."

"As I'm sitting here, I did! I never heard the beat of that in all my days! Don't tell me there ain't anything in dreams. Sereny Harper shall know of this before I'm an hour older. I'd like to see her get around *this* with her rubbage 'bout superstition. Go on, Tom!"

"Oh, it's all getting just as bright as day now. Next you said I warn't *bad*,

only mischeevous and harum-scarum, and not any more responsible than—than—I think it was a colt."

"And so it was! Well, goodness gracious! Go on, Tom!"

"And then you began to cry."

"So I did. So I did. Not the first time, neither. And then—"

"Then Mrs. Harper she began to cry, and said Joe was just the same, and she wished she hadn't whipped him for taking cream when she'd throwed it out her own self—"

"Tom! The sperrit was upon you!"

"And then there was a whole lot of talk 'bout dragging the river for us, and 'bout having the funeral Sunday, and then you and old Mis' Harper hugged and cried, and she went."

"It happened just so, as sure as I'm a-sitting in these very tracks. Tom, you couldn't told it more like, if you'd 'a' seen it! And *then* what? Go on, Tom!"

"Then I thought you prayed for me. And you went to bed, and I was so sorry that I took and wrote on a piece of sycamore bark, We *ain't dead—we are only off being pirates*, and put it on the table by the candle. You looked so good, laying there asleep, that I thought I went and leaned over and kissed you."

"Did you, Tom, *did* you! I just forgive you everything for that!" And she seized the boy in a crushing embrace that made him feel like the guiltiest of villains.

The children left for school, and the old lady to call on Mrs. Harper. What a hero Tom was become! He did not go skipping and prancing, but moved with a dignified swagger as became a pirate.

But when he reached home, the first thing his aunt said to him was: "Tom, I've a notion to skin you alive!"

"Auntie, what have I done?"

"Well, you've done enough. Here I go over to Sereny Harper, like an old softy, expecting I'm going to make her believe all that rubbage about that dream, when, lo and behold, she'd found out from Joe that you was over here and heard all the talk we had that night. Tom, I don't know what is to become of a boy that will act like that. It makes me feel so bad to think you could let me go to Sereny Harper and make such a fool of myself."

This was a new aspect of the thing. His smartness of the morning had seemed to Tom a good joke before, and very ingenious. It merely looked mean and shabby now. He hung his head.

"Auntie, I know now it was mean, but I didn't mean to be mean. I didn't, honest. And besides, I didn't come over here to laugh at you that night."

"What did you come for, then?"

"It was to tell you not to be uneasy about us, because we hadn't got drownded."

"I'd give the whole world to believe that. But it ain't reasonable; because, why didn't you tell me, child?"

"Why, you see, when you got to talking about the funeral, I just got all full of the idea of our coming and hiding in the church, and I couldn't somehow bear to spoil it. So I just put the bark back in my pocket."

"What bark?"

"The bark I had wrote on to tell you we'd gone pirating. I wish now you'd waked up when I kissed you."

"What did you kiss me for, Tom?"

"Because I loved you so, and you laid there moaning and I was so sorry."

The words sounded like truth. The old lady could not hide a tremor in her voice when she said:

"Kiss me again, Tom! And be off with you to school now."

The moment he was gone, she ran to a closet and got out the ruin of a jacket which Tom had gone pirating in. Then she stopped, with it in her hand, and said to herself:

"No, I don't dare. Poor boy, I reckon he's lied about it, but it's a blessed, blessed lie, there's such a comfort come from it. I hope the Lord, I *know* the Lord will forgive him, because it was such goodheartedness in him to tell it. But I don't want to find out it's a lie. I won't look."

She put the jacket away, and stood by musing a minute. Twice she put out her hand to take the garment again, and twice she refrained. Once more she ventured, and this time she fortified herself with the thought: "It's a good lie, it's a good lie, I won't let it grieve me." So she sought the jacket pocket. A moment later she was reading Tom's piece of bark through flowing tears and saying, "I could forgive the boy, now, if he'd committed a million sins!"

◖ You will want to read of Tom's further adventures in the book itself and in the sequel, THE ADVENTURES OF HUCKLEBERRY FINN.

Jo Meets Apollyon

⟨[Meg, Jo, Beth, and Amy March of Little Women, drawn from members of the author's family, liked to act out the allegory of Pilgrim's Progress. Like Christian, in his travels toward the Celestial City, each girl carried her special "burden." Jo's was a fiery temper, symbolized by the wicked "Apollyon" whom she must meet and overcome.

Girls, where are you going?" asked Amy, coming into her older sisters' room one Saturday afternoon, and finding them getting ready to go out, with an air of secrecy which excited her curiosity.

"Never mind; little girls shouldn't ask questions," returned Jo sharply.

Now if there is anything mortifying to our feelings, when we are young, it is to be told that. Amy bridled at this insult and determined to find out the secret, if she teased for an hour. Turning to Meg, who never refused her anything very long, she said coaxingly, "Do tell me! I should think you might let me go, too. Beth is fussing over her piano, and I haven't got anything to do, and am so lonely."

"I can't, dear, because you aren't invited," began Meg; but Jo broke in impatiently, "Now, Meg, be quiet, or you will spoil it all. You can't go, Amy; so don't be a baby, and whine about it."

"You are going somewhere with Laurie, I know you are."

"Yes, we are. Now do be still."

"I know! I know! You're going to the theater to see The Seven Castles!" she cried, adding resolutely, "And I shall go. Mother said I might see it. I've got my rag money, and it was mean not to tell me in time."

"Just listen to me a minute, and be a good child," said Meg soothingly. "Mother doesn't wish you to go this week, because your eyes are not well enough yet to bear the light of this fairy piece. Next week you can go with Beth and Hannah."

"I don't like that half as well as going with you and Laurie. Please let me; I've been shut up with this cold so long, I'm dying for some fun. Do, Meg! I'll be ever so good," pleaded Amy, looking as pathetic as she could.

"Suppose we take her. I don't believe Mother would mind, if we bundle her up well," began Meg.

"If she goes, I shan't! And if I don't, Laurie won't like it; and it will be very rude, after he invited only us, to go and drag in Amy. I should think she'd hate to poke herself where she isn't wanted," said Jo crossly.

Her tone and manner angered Amy, who began to put her boots on, saying, in her most aggravating way, "I *shall* go. Meg says I may; and if I pay for myself, Laurie hasn't anything to do with it."

"You can't sit with us, for our seats are reserved, and you mustn't sit alone; so Laurie will give you his place, and that will spoil our pleasure. Or he'll get another seat for you, and that isn't proper, when you weren't asked. You shan't stir a step; so you may just stay where you are," scolded Jo, crosser than ever, having just pricked her finger in her hurry.

Sitting on the floor, with one boot on, Amy began to cry, and Meg to reason with her, when Laurie called from below, and the two girls hurried down, leaving their sister wailing; for now and then she forgot her grown-up ways, and acted like a spoilt child. Just as the party was setting out, Amy called over the banisters, in a threatening tone, "You'll be sorry for this, Jo March."

"Fiddlesticks," returned Jo, slamming the door.

They had a charming time, for *The Seven Castles of the Diamond Lake* was as brilliant and wonderful as heart could wish. But, in spite of the comical red imps, sparkling elves, and gorgeous princes and princesses, Jo's pleasure had a drop of bitterness in it. The fairy queen's yellow curls re-minded her of Amy; and between the acts she amused herself with wondering what her sister would do to make her "sorry for it." She and Amy had had many lively skirmishes in the course of their lives, for both had quick tempers. Amy teased Jo, and Jo irritated Amy, and semi-occasional explosions occurred, of which both were much ashamed afterwards. Although the older, Jo had the least self-control, and had hard times trying to curb the fiery spirit which was continually getting her into trouble.

When Jo and Meg got home, Amy was reading in the parlor. She assumed an injured air, as they came in, and never lifted her eyes from her book or asked a single question. Perhaps curiosity might have conquered resentment, if Beth had not been there to inquire and receive a glowing description of the play. On going up to put away her best hat, Jo's first look was toward the bureau; for, in their last quarrel, Amy had soothed her feelings by turning Jo's top drawer upside down on the floor. Everything was in its place, and Jo decided Amy had forgiven and forgotten her wrongs.

There Jo was mistaken; for the next day she made a discovery which produced a tempest. Meg, Beth, and Amy were sitting together, late in the afternoon, when Jo burst into the room, looking excited and demanding breathlessly, "Has any one taken my book?"

Meg and Beth said "No," at once, and looked surprised. Amy poked the fire, and said nothing. Jo saw her color rise, and was down upon her in a minute.

"Amy, you've got it!"

"No. I haven't."

"You know where it is, then!"

"No, I don't."

"That's a fib!" cried Jo, taking her by the shoulders, and looking fierce enough to frighten a much braver child than Amy.

"It isn't. I haven't got it, don't know where it is now, and don't care."

"You know something about it, and you'd better tell at once, or I'll make you," and Jo gave her a slight shake.

"Scold as much as you like, you'll never see your silly old book again," cried Amy, getting excited in her turn.

"Why not?"

"I burnt it up."

"What! My little book I was so fond of, and worked over, and meant to finish before Father got home? Have you really burnt it?" said Jo, turning very pale, while her eyes kindled and her hands clutched Amy nervously.

"Yes, I did! I told you I'd make you pay for being so cross yesterday—"

Amy got no farther, for Jo's hot temper mastered her. She shook Amy till her teeth chattered in her head, crying in a passion of grief and anger: "You wicked, wicked girl! I never can write it again, and I'll never forgive you."

Meg flew to rescue Amy, and Beth to pacify Jo, but Jo was quite beside herself. With a parting box on her sister's ear, she rushed out of the room up to the old sofa in the garret, and finished her fight alone.

The storm cleared up below, for Mrs. March came home, and, having heard the story, soon brought Amy to a sense of the wrong she had done her sister. Jo's book was the pride of her heart, and was regarded by her family as a literary sprout of great promise. It was only half a dozen little fairy tales, but Jo had worked over them patiently, hoping to make something good enough to print. She had just copied them with great care, and had destroyed the old manuscript, so that Amy's bonfire had consumed the loving work of several years. To Jo it was a dreadful calamity, and she felt that it never could be made up to her. Beth mourned as for a departed kitten, and Meg refused to defend her pet. Mrs. March looked grave and grieved, and Amy felt that no one would love her till she had asked pardon for the act which she now regretted more than any of them.

When the tea bell rang, Jo appeared, looking so grim and unapproachable that it took all Amy's courage to say meekly: "Please forgive me, Jo. I'm very, very sorry."

"I never shall forgive you," was Jo's stern answer, and from that moment she ignored Amy entirely.

No one spoke of the great trouble, not even Mrs. March, for all had learned by experience that when Jo was in that mood words were wasted. The wisest course was to wait till some little accident, or her own generous nature, softened Jo's resentment. It was not a happy evening; for, though they sewed as usual while their mother read aloud, something was wanting, and the sweet home peace was disturbed. They felt this most when singing time came;

for Beth could only play, Jo stood dumb as a stone, and Amy broke down, so Meg and Mother sang alone.

As Jo received her good-night kiss, Mrs. March whispered gently: "My dear, don't let the sun go down upon your anger; forgive each other, help each other, and begin again."

Jo wanted to lay her head down on that motherly bosom, and cry her grief and anger all away, but she felt so deeply injured that she really *couldn't* quite forgive yet. So she winked hard, shook her head, and said, gruffly because Amy was listening: "It was an abominable thing, and she don't deserve to be forgiven." . . .

Amy was much offended that her overtures of peace had been repulsed, and began to wish she had not humbled herself; to feel more injured than ever, and to plume herself on her superior virtue in a way which was particularly exasperating. Jo still looked like a thundercloud, and nothing went well all day. Meg was pensive, Beth *would* look grieved and wistful, and Amy kept making remarks about people who were always talking about being good, and yet wouldn't try.

"Everybody is so hateful, I'll ask Laurie to go skating. He is always kind and jolly, and will put me to rights, I know," said Jo to herself, and off she went.

Amy heard the clash of skates, and looked out with an impatient exclamation: "There! She promised I should go next time, for this is the last ice we shall have. But it's no use to ask such a crosspatch to take me."

"Don't say that; you *were* very naughty, and it *is* hard to forgive the loss of her precious little book. But I think she might do it now, and I guess she will, if you try her at the right minute," said Meg. "Go after them. Don't say anything till Jo has got good-natured with Laurie. Then take a quiet minute, and just kiss her, or do some kind thing, and I'm sure she'll be friends again."

"I'll try," said Amy; and, after a flurry to get ready, she ran after the friends who were just disappearing over the hill.

It was not far to the river, but both were ready before Amy reached them. Jo saw her coming, and turned her back. Laurie did not see, for he was carefully skating along the shore, sounding the ice, for a warm spell had preceded the cold snap.

"I'll go on to the first bend, and see if it's all right, before we begin to race," Amy heard him say, as he shot away in his fur-trimmed coat and cap.

Jo heard Amy panting after her run, stamping her feet and blowing her fingers, as she tried to put her skates on. But Jo never turned and went slowly zigzagging down the river, taking a bitter, unhappy sort of satisfaction in her sister's troubles. As Laurie turned the bend, he shouted back: "Keep near the shore; it is not safe in the middle."

Jo heard, but Amy was just struggling to her feet and did not catch a word. Jo glanced over her shoulder, and the little demon she was harboring said in her ear: "No matter whether she heard or not, let her take care of herself."

Laurie had vanished round the bend. Jo was just at the turn, and Amy, far behind, was striking out toward the smoother ice in the middle of the river. For a minute Jo stood still, with a strange feeling at her heart. Then she resolved to go on, but something held and turned her around, just in time to see Amy throw up her hands and go down, with the sudden crash of rotten ice, the splash of water, and a cry that made Jo's heart stand still with fear. She tried to call Laurie, but her voice was gone. She tried to rush forward, but her feet seemed to have no strength in them; and, for a second, she could only stand motionless, staring, with a terror-stricken face, at the little blue hood above the black water. Something rushed swiftly by her, and Laurie's voice cried out:

"Bring a rail; quick, quick!"

How she did it, she never knew; but for the next few minutes she worked as if possessed, blindly obeying Laurie. Lying flat, he held Amy up by his arm and hockey stick till Jo dragged a rail from the fence. Together they got the child out, more frightened than hurt.

"Now then, we must walk her home as fast as we can; pile our things on her, while I get off these confounded skates," cried Laurie, wrapping his coat round Amy, and tugging at the straps.

Shivering, dripping, and crying, they got Amy home; and, after an exciting time of it, she fell asleep, rolled in blankets, before a hot fire. During the bustle Jo had scarcely spoken but had flown about, looking pale and wild, with her dress torn and her hands cut and bruised by ice and rails. When

Amy was comfortably asleep, the house quiet, and Mrs. March sitting by the bed, she called Jo to her, and began to bind up the hurt hands.

"Are you sure she is safe?" whispered Jo, looking remorsefully at the golden head, which might have been swept away from her sight forever under the treacherous ice.

"Quite safe, dear. She is not hurt and won't even take cold, I think, you were so sensible in covering and getting her home quickly."

"Laurie did it all; I only let her go. Mother, if she *should* die, it would be my fault." Jo dropped down beside the bed in a passion of penitent tears, telling all that had happened, bitterly condemning her hardness of heart.

"It's my dreadful temper! I try to cure it; I think I have, and then it breaks out worse than ever. Oh Mother, what shall I do? what shall I do?"

"Watch and pray, dear; never get tired of trying; and never think it is impossible to conquer your fault," said Mrs. March, drawing the blowzy head to her shoulder, and kissing the wet cheek so tenderly that Jo cried harder than ever.

"You don't know; you can't guess how bad it is! It seems as if I could do anything when I'm in a passion; I get so savage, I could hurt anyone, and enjoy it. Oh Mother, do help me!"

"I will, my child, I will. Don't cry so bitterly, but remember this day, and resolve, with all your soul, that you will never know another like it. Jo, dear, we all have our temptations, some far greater than yours, and it often takes us all our lives to conquer them. You think your temper is the worst in the world; but mine used to be just like it."

"Yours, Mother? Why, you are never angry!" For the moment, Jo forgot remorse in surprise.

"I've been trying to cure it for forty years, and have only succeeded in controlling it. I am angry nearly every day of my life, Jo, but I have learned not to show it."

"Mother, are you angry when you fold your lips tight together, and go out of the room sometimes, when people worry you?" asked Jo, feeling nearer and dearer to her mother than ever before.

"Yes, I've learned to check the hasty words that rise to my lips. When I feel that they mean to break out against my will, I just go away a minute, and give myself a little shake, for being so weak and wicked," answered Mrs. March, with a sigh and a smile, as she smoothed and fastened up Jo's disheveled hair.

"How did you learn to keep still? That is what troubles me, for the sharp words fly out before I know it."

"Your father helped me, Jo, and I have a better friend, even than Father, to comfort and sustain me. My child, the troubles and temptations of your life may be many, but you can over-come and outlive them all if you learn to feel the strength and tenderness of your Heavenly Father as you do that of your earthly one. The more you love and trust Him, the nearer you will feel to Him, and the less you will depend on human power and wisdom. . . ."

Jo's only answer was to hold her mother close, and, in the silence which followed, the sincerest prayer she had ever prayed left her heart without words; for in that sad, yet happy hour, she had learned not only the bitter-ness of remorse but the sweetness of self-denial and self-control. Amy stirred, and sighed in her sleep; and, as if eager to begin at once to mend her fault, Jo looked up with an expression on her face which it had never worn before.

"I let the sun go down on my anger; I wouldn't forgive her, and today, if it hadn't been for Laurie, it might have been too late! How could I be so wicked?" said Jo, half aloud, as she leaned over her sister, softly stroking the wet hair scattered on the pillow.

As if she heard, Amy opened her eyes, and held out her arms, with a smile that went straight to Jo's heart. Neither said a word, but they hugged one another close, in spite of the blan-kets, and everything was forgiven and forgotten in one hearty kiss.

⟨ A STORY about Apollyon from PILGRIM'S PROGRESS may be found in the Book of Wisdom.

THE BOOK OF

Adventure

Introduction

⟨ ADVENTURE IS *the ingredient that adds zest to life—or to a book. Young readers crave it. The world into which they have been born is a strange, fascinating place, one they have had little time to explore. In their desire for new experiences they frequently turn to reading and to watching television and moving pictures. Boys and girls like to identify themselves with characters that do things; just as they themselves want to do things in real life. They want action. Fortunate is the child who finds it between the covers of a book, for there is a sense of permanency in the printed word that other forms of communication lack. A good story seems better each time it is read, and some of the world's masterpieces, the ones that have been remembered the longest, have been adventure tales.*

The Bible is filled with such stories. The most popular legends have centered around some colorful figure, such as King Arthur or Robin Hood, whose exploits have captured the imagination of succeeding generations. We still enjoy the old tales retold by Washington Irving, our first American storyteller. He began to gather these tales during his boyhood rambles through the countryside.

"I even journeyed one long summer's day to the summit of the most distant hill," he said, "whence I stretched my eye over many a mile and was astonished to find how vast a globe I inhabited."

Irving did what other writers of good adventure tales have done. He introduced interesting characters doing interesting things in interesting places. He enabled his readers to see more than they otherwise might have seen. He expanded their horizons.

"*The writer [who writes for children],*" *said Elizabeth Coatsworth, whose story "Danger!" appears in this book, "has come upon something in life which has amused or delighted or surprised him. 'Look!' he exclaims . . . . Each book is merely an enlargement of that exclamation 'Look!'*"

Particularly is this true of an adventure story. In Esther Forbes's "Salt Water Tea" we see the Boston Tea Party through the eyes of her youthful hero, Johnny Tremain. In "The Girl in the Picture" Elizabeth Enright has said, in effect, "Let us look at a gypsy caravan near Paris some eighty years ago."

Armstrong Sperry first heard of the South Seas in the hairraising yarns told by his seafaring great-grandfather. The old seaman was always talking of Bora Bora, that far-off island where he had once been shipwrecked.

"That was the purtiest little island I ever did see," he told the boy. "I hope you'll see it for yourself someday, young'un."

Armstrong Sperry not only saw it; he helped others to see it. When he grew up, he sailed for the South Seas, and out of his interest in the Polynesian people he wrote and illustrated several books. In his short story of Bora Bora the reader shares in the suspense of meeting "The Ghost of the Lagoon."

Not all adventures happen in distant places. Sights we take for granted because they are so familiar may seem glamorous and exciting to one who views them for the first time. Electricity is no novelty to an average American. Riding in an elevator is an experience most of us have had. But to Saudin, a boy from the jungles of North Borneo who visited New York, the elevator was a little room that miraculously could move up and down. The city at night was a "very great village with a thousand lights." When he returned to Borneo, he told his story to Agnes Newton Keith.

"His attitude," she said, "was that of a Marco Polo who scarcely expects his words to be believed."

A good adventure yarn makes it possible for each of us to be a Marco Polo. We may visit other places or share vicariously in the events of other times. We may discover that there are adventures to be had close by. But in all the stories the authors have said "Look!" They have pushed back the horizon for us a little farther.

ESTHER FORBES

Salt Water Tea

⟪ AFTER *Johnny Tremain, orphaned apprentice to a Boston silversmith, burned his hand, he had to find other work. Through Rab, an older boy who set type for the Weekly Observer, a patriotic newspaper, he obtained a job delivering papers. One night late in 1773 the friends were invited to a meeting of a secret organization known as the Observers.*

JOHNNY TREMAIN looked about through the haze of tobacco smoke. Sam Adams was standing at the far end of the room.

"Gentlemen," he said, "tonight we have made our decision—and know the method by which the detested tea can be destroyed, if the ships are not allowed to return. Here we have with us two of exactly—ah—the sort of boys or young men we intend to use for our great purpose. Two boys in whom we have implicit trust. If it is the wish of the assembled club members, I suggest we approach them with our proposition tonight . . . enlist their aid. Twenty days will be up before we know. We'd best get on with our plans."

The members once more took their seats. All agreed the boys were to be told.

"First," Adams said to the boys, "raise your right hands. Swear by the great name of God Himself never, for as long as you live, to divulge to anyone the secret matters now trusted to you. Do you so swear?"

The boys swore . . .

"There's no chance—not one—those ships will be allowed to return. The mass meetings which will be held almost daily demanding the return of the tea are to arouse public opinion and to persuade the world we did not turn to violence until every other course had been blocked to us. When the twenty days are up, on the night of the sixteenth of December, those ships are going to be boarded. That tea will be dumped in Boston Harbor. For each ship, the *Dartmouth*, the *Eleanor*, and the brig, the *Beaver*, we will need thirty stout, honest, fearless men and boys. Will you be one, Rab?"

He did not say Rab and Johnny, as the younger boy noticed. Was this because he thought Johnny too cripple-handed for chopping open sea chests—

or merely because he knew Rab was older?

"Of course, sir."

"How many other boys could you find for the night's work? Strong and trustworthy boys—for if one pound of tea is stolen, the whole thing becomes a robbery—not a protest."

Rab thought.

"Eight or ten tonight, but give me a little time so I can feel about a bit and I can furnish fifteen or twenty."

"Boys who can keep their mouths shut?"

"Yes."

Paul Revere said, "I can furnish twenty or more."

"Not one is to be told in advance just what the work will be, nor who the others are, nor the names of the men who instigated this tea party— that is, the gentlemen gathered here tonight. Simply, as they love their country and liberty and hate tyranny, they are to gather in this shop on the night of December sixteenth, carrying with them such disguises as they can think of, and each armed with an ax or hatchet."

"It will be as you say." . . .

Both the boys were in their truckle beds. The loft still smelled of tobacco and the spices of the punch.

Johnny moved restlessly on his bed.

"Rab . . . those boys you promised. Am I one?"

"Of course."

"But my hand . . . What will we have to do?"

"Chop open tea chests. Dump tea in the harbor."

"Rab?"

"Hummmmm?"

"How can I ever . . . chop?"

"You've twenty days to practice in. Logs in back yard need splitting."

"Rab . . ."

But the older boy was asleep.

Johnny was so wide awake he couldn't close his eyes. Old Meeting clock struck midnight. He was thinking of those tea ships, the *Dartmouth*, the *Eleanor*, the *Beaver*, great white sails spread softly, sweeping on and on through the night to Boston. Nearer, nearer . . .

Next morning Johnny was up and out in the back yard early. At first it seemed impossible to hold an ax in a left hand, steady it with his bad right. He gritted his teeth and persevered. Rab set type, pulled proofs as usual. But often he was gone from home, and Johnny knew he was "feeling about" for those fifteen to twenty boys he had promised. Would the others go and Johnny be left behind? He could not bear the thought, and Rab had promised him that in twenty days he might learn to chop.

Almost every day and sometimes all day, the mass meetings at Old South Church went on. Tempers grew higher and higher. Boston was swept with a passion it had not known since the Boston Massacre three years before. Sometimes the boys slipped over to Griffin's Wharf. By the eighth of December the *Eleanor* had joined the *Dartmouth*. These were strange ships. They had unloaded their cargoes—except the tea. The Town of Boston had ordered them not to unload the tea and the law stated they could not leave until they had unloaded. Nor would the Governor give them a pass to return to England. At Castle Island the British Colonel Leslie had orders to fire upon them if they attempted to sneak out of the harbor. Johnny saw Rotch, the twenty-three-year-old Quaker who owned the *Dartmouth*, running about in despair. The Governor would not let him leave. The Town would not let him unload. Between them he was a ruined man. He feared a mob would burn his ship.

There was no mob, and night and day armed citizens guarded the ships. They would see to it that no tea was smuggled ashore and that no harm was done to the ships. Back and forth paced the guard. Many of their faces were familiar to Johnny. One day even John Hancock took his turn with a musket on his shoulder, and the next night he saw Paul Revere.

Then on the fifteenth, the third of the tea ships arrived. This was the brig, the *Beaver*.

The next day, the sixteenth, Johnny woke to hear the rain drumming sadly on the roof, and soon enough once more he heard all the bells of Boston cling-clanging, bidding the inhabitants come once more, and for the last time, to Old South to demand the peaceful return of the ships to England.

By nightfall, when the boys Rab had selected began silently to congregate in the office of the *Observer*, behind locked doors, the rain stopped. Many of them Johnny knew. When they started to assume their disguises, smootch their faces with soot, paint them with red paint, pull on nightcaps, old frocks, torn jackets, blankets with holes cut for their arms, they began giggling and laughing at each other. Rab could silence them with one look, however. No one passing outside the shop must guess that twenty boys were at that moment dressing themselves as "Indians."

Johnny had taken some pains with his costume. He had sewed for hours on the red blanket Mrs. Lorne had let him cut up and he had a fine mop of feathers standing upright in the old knitted cap he would wear on his head, but when he started to put on his disguise, Rab said no, wait a minute.

Then he divided the boys into three groups. Beside each ship at the wharf they would find a band of men. "You," he said to one group of boys, "will join the boarding party for the *Dartmouth*. You for the *Eleanor*. You for the *Beaver*." Each boy was to speak softly to the leader and say, "Me Know You," for that was the countersign. They would know the three leaders because each of them would wear a white handkerchief about the neck and a red string about the right wrist. Then he turned to Johnny.

"You can run faster than any of us. Somehow get to Old South Church. Mr. Rotch will be back from begging once more the Governor's permission for the ships to sail within a half hour. Now, Johnny, you are to listen to what Sam Adams says next. Look you. If Mr. Adams then says, 'Now may God help my country,' come back here. Then we will take off our disguises and each go home and say nothing. But

[73]

if he says, 'This meeting can do nothing more to save the country,' you are to get out of that crowd as fast as you can, and as soon as you get into Cornhill begin to blow upon this silver whistle. Run as fast as you are able back here to me and keep on blowing. I'll have boys posted in dark corners, close enough to the church, but outside the crowd. Maybe we'll hear you the first time you blow."

About Old South, standing in the streets, inside the church, waiting for Rotch to return with the very last appeal that could be made to the Governor, was the greatest crowd Boston had ever seen—thousands upon thousands. There was not a chance, not one, Johnny could ever squirm or wriggle his way inside, but he pushed and shoved until he stood close to one of the doors. Farther than this he could not go—unless he walked on people's heads. It was dusk already.

Josiah Quincy's voice rang out from within. "I see the clouds roll and the lightning play, and to that God who rides the whirlwind and directs the storm, I commit my country . . ."

The words thrilled Johnny, but this was not what he was waiting for, and it was not Sam Adams speaking. He was bothered with only one thing. Quincy had a beautiful carrying voice. It was one thing to hear him and another Sam Adams, who did not speak well at all.

The crowd made way for a chaise. "Rotch is back! Make way for Rotch!" Mr. Rotch passed close to Johnny. He was so young he looked almost ready to cry. This was proof enough that the

Governor had still refused. Such a turmoil followed Rotch's entry, Johnny could not hear any one particular voice. What chance had he of hearing Sam Adams' words? He had his whistle in his hand, but he was so jammed into the crowd about the door that he did not believe he would be able to get his hand to his mouth.

"Silence." That was Quincy again. "Silence, silence, Mr. Adams will speak." Johnny twisted and turned and brought the whistle to his lips.

And suddenly there was silence. Johnny guessed there were many in that crowd who, like himself, were hanging on those words. Seemingly Mr. Adams was calmly accepting defeat, dismissing the meeting, for now he was saying, "This meeting can do nothing more to save the country."

Johnny gave his first shrill blast on his whistle, and he heard whistles and cries seemingly in all directions, Indian war whoops, and "Boston Harbor a teapot tonight!" "Hurrah for Griffin's Wharf!" "Salt-water tea!" "Hi, Mohawks, get your axes and pay no taxes!"

Johnny was only afraid all would be over before Rab and his henchmen could get to the wharf. Still shrilling on the whistle, he fought and floundered against the tide of the crowd. It was sweeping toward Griffin's Wharf, he struggling to get back to Salt Lane. Now he was afraid the others would have gone on without him. After all, Rab might have decided that Johnny's legs and ears were better than his hands—and deliberately let him do the work that best suited him. Johnny pushed open the door.

Rab was alone. He had Johnny's blanket coat, his ridiculous befeathered knitted cap in his hands.

"Quick!" he said, and smootched his face with soot, drew a red line across his mouth running from ear to ear. Johnny saw Rab's eyes through the mask of soot. They were glowing with excitement. His lips were parted. His teeth looked sharp and white as an animal's. In spite of his calm demeanor, calm voice, he was charged and surcharged with a will to action, a readiness to take and enjoy any desperate chance. Rab had come terrifyingly alive.

They flung themselves out of the shop.

"Roundabout!" cried Rab. He meant they would get to the wharf by back alleys. "Come, follow me."

He flew up Salt Lane in the opposite direction from the waterfront. Now they were flinging themselves down back alleys (faster and faster). Once they had a glimpse of a blacksmith shop and other "Indians" clamoring for soot for their faces. Now slipping over a back-yard fence, now at last on the waterfront, Sea Street, Flounder Alley. They were running so fast it seemed more like a dream of flying than reality.

The day had started with rain and then there had been clouds, but as they reached Griffin's Wharf the moon, full and white, broke free of the clouds. The three ships, the silent hundreds gathering upon the wharf, all were dipped in the pure white light. The crowds were becoming thousands, and there was not one there but guessed what was to be done, and all approved.

Rab was grunting out of the side of his mouth to a thickset, active-looking man, whom Johnny would have known anywhere, by his walk and the confident lift of his head, was Mr. Revere. "Me Know You."

"Me Know You," Johnny repeated this countersign and took his place behind Mr. Revere. The other boys, held up by the crowd, began arriving, and more men and boys. But Johnny guessed that many who were now quietly joining one of those three groups were acting on the spur of the moment, seeing what was up. They had blacked their faces, seized axes, and come along. They were behaving as quietly and were as obedient to their leaders as those who had been so carefully picked for this work of destruction.

There was a boatswain's whistle, and in silence one group boarded the *Dartmouth*. The *Eleanor* and the *Beaver* had to be warped in to the wharf. Johnny was close to Mr. Revere's heels. He heard him calling for the captain, promising him, in the jargon everyone talked that night, that not one thing should be damaged on the ship except only the tea, but the captain and all his crew had best stay in the cabin until the work was over.

Captain Hall shrugged and did as he was told, leaving his cabin boy to hand over the keys to the hold. The boy was grinning with pleasure. The "tea party" was not unexpected.

"I'll show you," the boy volunteered,

"how to work them hoists. I'll fetch lanterns, mister."

The winches rattled and the heavy chests began to appear—one hundred and fifty of them. As some men worked in the hold, others broke open the chests and flung the tea into the harbor. But one thing made them unexpected difficulty. The tea inside the chests was wrapped in heavy canvas. The axes went through the wood easily enough—the canvas made endless trouble. Johnny had never worked so hard in his life . . .

Mr. Revere whispered to him. "Go get brooms. Clean um' deck."

Johnny and a parcel of boys brushed the deck until it was clean as a parlor floor. Then Mr. Revere called the cap-tain to come up and inspect. The tea was utterly gone, but Captain Hall agreed that beyond that there had not been the slightest damage.

It was close upon dawn when the work on all three ships was done. And yet the great, silent audience on the wharf, men, women, and children, had not gone home. As the three groups came off the ships, they formed in fours along the wharf, their axes on their shoulders. Then a hurrah went up and a fife began to play. Standing quietly in the crowd, Johnny saw Sam Adams, pretending to be a most innocent bystander. . . .

As they started marching back to the center of town, they passed the

Coffin House at the head of Griffin's Wharf. A window opened.

"Well, boys," said a voice, so cold one hardly knew whether he spoke in anger or not, "you've had a fine, pleasant evening for your Indian caper, haven't you? But mind . . . you've got to pay the fiddler yet." It was the British Admiral Montague.

"Come on down here," someone yelled, "and we'll settle that score tonight."

The Admiral pulled in his head and slapped down the window.

Johnny and Rab knew, and men like the Observers knew that the fiddler would have to be paid. . . .

Next day, all over Boston, boys and men, some of them with a little paint still showing behind their ears, were so lame they could scarce move their fingers, but none of them—not one—told what it was that had lamed them so. They would stand about and wonder who "those Mohawks" might have been, or what the British Parliament might do next, but never say what they themselves had been doing, for each was sworn to secrecy.

Only Paul Revere showed no signs of the hard physical strain he had been under all the night before. Not long after dawn he had started on horseback for New York and Philadelphia with an account of the Tea Party. He could chop open tea chests all night, and ride all day.

⟪ OF the stirring events that led to the Battle of Lexington, and of the part played by boys like Johnny Tremain, you may read in Esther Forbes's novel of that title. This book was awarded the Newbery Medal in 1944. PAUL REVERE AND THE WORLD HE LIVED IN won the Pulitzer Prize.

The Girl in the Picture

⟨ THE four Melendy children lived in New York City. By pooling their allowances, they found that each of them could have an especially fine Saturday every four weeks. When her Saturday came, Randy (short for Miranda) visited an art gallery to see an exhibit of paintings from abroad. And here she ran head-on into an unexpected adventure.

THE GALLERY was hushed and dim after the bright, sharp street. "Catalog, miss?" said a man at a little desk. His eyeglasses flashed in the dimness.

"Thank you," Randy said, and took one of the little folders he offered; then, almost on tiptoe, she stepped into the main room of the gallery. There were a lot of people looking at the pictures and talking to each other as if they were in church, low-voiced and serious. One of the people she knew, and at the sight of her Randy's heart sank. It was old Mrs. Oliphant—"the Elephant," Randy's brother Rush called her behind her back—who really was old because she had known Father's father way back in the last century. She was a big, tall old lady with a lot of furs that smelled of camphor, and a great many chains around her neck that got caught on each other. She was nice, Randy supposed, but so far away in her oldness and

dignity. She hoped Mrs. Oliphant wouldn't notice her.

Pretty soon she forgot about everything but the pictures. There was a nice one of a girl in an old-fashioned dress playing the piano. If she looked at a picture long enough, without being interrupted, Randy could make it come alive sometimes; and now she could almost hear the music the girl in the picture was playing.

"Marvelous substance," murmured a hushed voice behind her, and another hushed voice replied, "Unbelievable resilience in the flesh tones!"

Gee whiz, thought Randy, are they talking about the picture? And she moved on to the next one, a field all burning yellow in the sunshine. You could tell it was twelve o'clock noon on a summer day; probably July. Randy could nearly smell the heat. She was having a good time. She looked at all the pictures: fat ladies bathing in a brook, a girl with opera glasses, apples and pears on a blue plate, a man in a boat, two dead rabbits, and then all of a sudden she came to the picture that was hers, her very own one.

Randy was always finding things that belonged to her in a special way, though ownership had nothing to do with it. Now she had found the picture. The catalog told her that the picture was called *The Princess*, that it had been painted by someone named Jules Clairon in the year 1881. In the picture a girl about Randy's age was sitting on a garden wall and looking out over an enormous city. She had a solemn little face. Her long hair hung to the sash of her old-fashioned dress, and among the potted chrysanthemums at her feet sat a black poodle with a red bow on top of his head. On either side the clipped plane trees were almost bare, and in the distance the huge city was spread in a dusky web of blue and gray. A day had come and gone, years ago, and still it was alive. I wish I'd known that girl, Randy thought.

She felt a touch on her shoulder that brought her back to her own world with a start. The Elephant, darn it, thought Randy crossly. Just when I was getting right into that picture, too.

"Well, well! What are you doing here?" inquired Mrs. Oliphant in her deep cavernous voice with its faint foreign accent. She whacked Randy's shoulder absent-mindedly. "You seem very interested in this picture, Miranda."

"I think it's beautiful," Randy said, sloping her shoulder out from under Mrs. Oliphant's hand as tactfully as she could.

"It isn't so beautiful as I remembered it," observed Mrs. Oliphant, regarding it with a frown. "But then I haven't seen it for sixty years. Not since I was eleven years old."

"Eleven years old!" repeated Randy. It was impossible that Mrs. Oliphant had ever been eleven. "Not since the day it was finished," the old lady explained. "You see, I was the girl in the picture."

"You!" cried Randy, amazed. Her mouth dropped open half an inch.

"That's I at the age of eleven," said Mrs. Oliphant, very pleased at Randy's surprise. "Not much to look at, was I?"

"I think you looked nice." Randy considered the girl in the picture. "Interesting and, well, nice. I was just wishing I'd known that girl."

"And how she would have loved knowing you. Sometimes she was very lonely," said Mrs. Oliphant. "Unfortunately she disappeared long, long ago."

Randy looked up at her companion's face. What she said was true. The face was so old, crossed with a thousand lines, and the dark, fiery eyes were overhung by such severe black brows that every trace of the little girl she had once been had vanished with the past.

"What was that big city in the distance?"

"It was Paris," said the old lady with a sigh.

"Who was the dog?"

"Tartuffe, we called him. He was a

selfish old beast, and very dull company." Mrs. Oliphant shook her head and laughed, remembering. Then she looked about her questioningly. "Who is with you, Miranda? I don't see any of your family."

"I'm all alone," Randy told her.

"Alone? How old are you, child?"

"Ten," said Randy.

Mrs. Oliphant shook her head again. "When I was your age such a thing was unheard of. What a lucky girl you are! Well, since we are both alone, why don't you come with me and have a cup of tea, or an ice-cream soda, or a chocolate marshmallow sundae, or whatever you prefer?"

Randy was beginning to like Mrs. Oliphant very much. "I'd love to," she said.

Surrounded by an aura of camphor and Eau de Cologne, and with all her chains jingling, the old lady swept splendidly from the gallery. Randy followed in her wake, like a dinghy behind a large launch. After they had walked a block or two, they came to a large hotel. They entered a room full of little tables, gilt chairs, and mirrors. A waiter led them to a table by a long window. After a period of deliberation, it was decided that the old lady would have tea and toast, and Randy would have vanilla ice cream with chocolate sauce.

"And, François, bring some *petits fours*, also."

Randy did not know what "*petits fours*" meant, but she did not like to ask.

"Ah, yes," said Mrs. Oliphant when she had uncoiled from her layers of furs, taken off her gloves, and arranged her necklaces. "My childhood was a very different thing from yours."

"Tell me about it," said Randy. Then "please," as an afterthought.

"Would you like to hear the whole story?"

"Yes, yes, please, the whole story," begged Randy, giving an involuntary bounce on the hard chair. She loved to be told stories.

"Well, it's a long time ago," said the old lady. "Before you were born, even before your father was born, imagine it! The garden in the picture was the garden of my father's house in Saint-Germain near Paris. It was an old house even then, tall and narrow and gray, with patches of ivy. The inside of it was stuffy and dark and full of furniture. My mother had died when I was born and my father's business kept him in Paris all day, so I was brought up by my aunts and an English governess. They gave me my lessons, too. I was never allowed to go to school. The aunts were all maiden ladies years older than my father. They always wore black, and spoke in quiet polite voices except when shouting at *Tante Amelie*, the deaf aunt, who carried a great curved ear trumpet like the tusk of an elephant. Ah, here is the tea."

François arranged the feast before them. *Petits fours* turned out to be the most wonderful little cakes in frilled paper collars: pink, and pale yellow, and chocolate, with silver peppermint buttons on top. Randy's eyes glittered with such enthusiasm that the old lady was delighted. "You shall have some to take home to the other children. François, please bring us a boxful of *petits fours* to take home."

"That will be wonderful," Randy said, not quite with her mouth full, but almost. "Please tell me some more."

"Very well," said her friend. "The English governess was also elderly. Her name was Miss Buff-Towers and she was related in some way to an earl, a fact she was very proud of and never forgot. I knew no children. If it hadn't been for the garden I might have gone mad from boredom.

"This garden was very large, enclosed by a high wall, and shaded by old chestnut trees that bloomed every spring in great cornucopias of popcorn. There was a tiny bamboo jungle, and a summerhouse with a wasp's nest, and two enormous mossy statues: one of Diana, and one of Apollo. In the distance the whole of Paris lay spread out like a map: golden in the morning, blue in the dusk, shining like a thousand fires at night.

"One September evening when I was eleven years old I had gone into the garden, and was sitting in my usual place on the wall looking at the city and hoping dinner would be ready soon. I heard steps on the little gravel path behind me and, turning, saw my father and another gentleman, a friend whom he had brought home for dinner. I stood up respectfully and was introduced to Monsieur Clairon. He was a tall man with a brown beard and pleasant eyes. I had a feeling, looking at him, that he was more alive than most people.

" 'Your daughter makes me think of the princess in a fairy tale who looks out of her tower at the world,' he told my father. 'Someday I would like to paint her just as she was: sitting on that wall.'

"I was flattered and self-conscious, but only for a moment. 'We mustn't make her vain, Jules,' said my father in a stately voice. 'That plain little face was never meant for Art.'

"Dinner, for once, was fun. Monsieur Clairon told jokes and stories, everybody laughed, and each story was repeated in loud brays for *Tante* Amelie.

" 'I've been making sketches at the carnival down the street,' he told me. 'I can never resist carnivals. This one has a camel and a dancing bear as well as the usual carrousel and fortune-tellers. It makes good pictures. You've seen it, I suppose, mademoiselle?' He turned to me.

" 'No, monsieur,' I said sadly. I knew there was a carnival somewhere in the town. Bursts of music had been drifting over the wall all day.

" 'But you must see it!' Monsieur Clairon insisted. 'It leaves at midnight. I should be happy to take you this evening—'

" 'Heaven forbid, Jules,' said my father, with a distressed smile. 'Gabrielle would come home with smallpox or whooping cough or measles or all three.'

" 'And so dreadfully dirty!' added Miss Buff-Towers.

" 'Someone might even kidnap her!' said my *Tante* Marthe, who always expected the worst.

[81]

" 'It's out of the question,' stated my father firmly.

"For the first time since I was a tiny child I dared to defy the collective opinion of my aunts, father, and governess.

" 'But I want to go!' said I, laying down my fork. 'I want to go terribly! Why can't I? I'll wear gloves and not touch anything, I promise. When I come home I'll gargle. Please let me go; please, please, please!'

"My father stared at me. Even his eyebrows and mustache looked annoyed.

" 'That will be enough, Gabrielle,' he said.

" 'You never let me go anywhere!' I persisted. 'I've never seen a carnival. Or a real live camel. Or a dancing bear. I'd like to see something besides just this old house all the time!'

"My father's face was dark as the wine in his glass.

" 'Go!' he roared. 'Upstairs, immediately! Without dessert!'

"And up I went, crying into my sleeve and hearing above my sobs the turmoil in the dining room: Monsieur Clairon interceding for me, my father expostulating, and above that the loud, toneless voice of *Tante* Amelie saying, 'What's the matter? Why is Gabrielle crying? Why doesn't someone tell me something?' And *Tante* Marthe bellowing into the ear trumpet: 'GABRIELLE HAS BEEN A VERY NAUGHTY GIRL!'

"After I had gone to bed and Miss Buff-Towers had heard my prayers, and wept a few embarrassing tears over my disobedience, I lay in bed very still

and straight and angry. Through the closed window I could hear rowdy strains of music.

"At last I got out of bed and opened the window which looked out over the garden and the distant lighted city spread like a jeweled fabric. For the first time I was sorry that my room was not at the front of the house, since then I might have glimpsed the carnival. The music sounded gayer than ever, and I could hear bursts of laughter above the noise. Slowly my anger turned to curiosity and active rebellion. An adventurous flame sprang to life within me. Quickly in the dark I dressed in my oldest dress. Quickly I stuffed the bolster under the blankets just in case someone should look in. But money! I wanted to ride on the carrousel and to see the dancing bear. There were only twenty centimes in my pocketbook, and then I remembered the gold piece! My father had given it to me on my last birthday; at the time I had been disappointed, but now I was glad. . . .

"I went over to the window and opened it again. Aged ivy covered the walls on either side, and, scared to death, in my clumsy old-fashioned clothes, I reached out among the leaves till I felt a strong stem like a cable, stepped over the iron grille in front of the window, and began my descent. Very awkward it was, too. About six feet above the ground the ivy ripped away from the wall, and down I went with a crash into a fuchsia bush. I sat there listening to my heart and waiting for the entire household to come out with lanterns.

"But nothing happened! After an eternity I got up and stole out of the garden. Both the knees had been torn out of my stockings, I was dirty, and my hair was full of ivy twigs, but it didn't matter.

"In less than five minutes I had arrived at the carnival! It was even better than I had hoped: full of crowds and bright lights and noise. The carrousel with its whirling painted horses and its music was like nothing I had ever seen before. I rode on it twice and when I screamed with excitement nobody paid any attention because they were all doing the same thing. After that I bought a ride on a camel. That took some courage, as I had never seen a camel before and did not know that they possessed such sarcastic faces. Have you ever ridden on one?"

"Never," said Randy.

"You must try it sometime. It made me a little seasick but I enjoyed it. Then I went and watched the dancing bear softly rocking to and fro on his hind paws like a tipsy old man in bedroom slippers. There was too much to see; I was dazzled, and just walked about staring blissfully.

"I was fascinated by the fortune-teller's booth. It was really a large wagon with a hooped roof which you entered by a pair of wooden steps. On one side there was a large placard bearing the words: *Zenaida, world-renowned seeress and soothsayer! Advice and prophecy on affairs of business, or the heart. Palmistry, cards, or crystal as preferred.* On the other side there was a life-size picture of a dark,

beautiful woman gazing into a crystal globe.

"I hesitated only a moment, then I mounted the steps. Inside, the tent was draped with shabby shawls of many colors. Overhead a red glass lantern cast a murky light, and at a small table sat a gypsy woman glittering and jingling with earrings, clattering bracelets, and necklaces. She looked almost nothing like the picture outside. She was older, and her fingernails were dirty. I was dreadfully disappointed.

"'What do you want, kid?' she said.

"'To-to-have my fortune told,' I stammered.

"'Got any money?' asked the woman doubtfully, looking at my torn stockings and dirty dress.

"'Yes,' I said.

"'Let me see it,' she demanded.

"I brought the gold piece out of my pocket. The gypsy examined it craftily; then she smiled a wide, delighted smile. One of her teeth was black.

"'You must have found that in a well-lined pocket,' said she.

"At first I did not understand what she meant. Then I was angry.

"'I never stole anything in my life!' I told her. 'My father gave it to me for a present.'

"'Your father? He is a rich man?'

"'I suppose he is,' I said. 'I don't know. I never thought about it. Anyway I don't think I want you to tell my fortune after all.'

"Quick as a cat the gypsy sprang from her chair and barred the entrance.

"'Forgive me, mademoiselle,' she wheedled. 'I didn't realize— Your clothes are torn and you have such a dirty face. Come and sit down; I'll tell you a fortune you'll never forget. Splendid, wonderful things are going to happen to you. I see luck shining all around you!'

"Well, who could resist that? In spite of myself, I was soon seated opposite Zenaida, my dirty hand in her dirtier one. Before she began to read my palm she called out in her harsh gypsy voice, 'Bastien!'

"A young man's face appeared at the entrance, and Zenaida said something to him in a strange language. The young man nodded, looked at me, and burst out laughing. Then he disappeared.

"The gypsy lived up to her word. Never was such a fortune told to a human being! Jewels, lovers, fame, travels into far countries, all were promised to me, and I sat there like a half-wit believing every word.

" 'I must go,' I said at last. 'Please take what I owe you out of this.' I gave her the gold piece trustingly. And that, of course, was the last I ever saw of it.

" 'We will drive you home in the wagon,' said Zenaida, smiling. I could hear Bastien hitching up the horses outside.

" 'No, thank you,' said I. 'It's not far, only a little way. If you will give me what you owe me, I will go.' I realized that the music had stopped, and a sound of hammering and clattering had taken its place. The carnival was being dismantled. I had been in the wagon for a long time.

" 'We will take you home,' Zenaida insisted. 'It's almost midnight and we must be on our way anyhow. Where do you live, and what is your father's name?'

"Like a fool I told her.

"Bastien called to the horses, and the wagon began to move, the red lantern swinging in a slow circle overhead.

"I was so busy thinking of my glittering future that it was some time before I realized that we must have left my house far behind. When I began asking frightened questions the gypsy came close to me and grabbed my arm. She told me that I was not going home, but far away, till my father was ready to pay a price to get me back. When I cried and struggled she called Bastien and they bound my wrists and ankles and tied a rag over my mouth. I was sick with terror.

"I remained with the gypsies for three weeks. The first day Zenaida unbraided my hair, took away my shoes and stockings, and dressed me in gaudy rags. She pierced my ears for brass earrings, and, stooping down, picked up a handful of earth and rubbed it across my face. 'There!' she said. 'Now even a gypsy would think you were a gypsy!'

"In spite of her, and in spite of the letter I was forced to write my father during the second week, telling him where to leave the ransom money if he wished to see me again, I enjoyed many things about those three weeks. The wagon and the travel and the going barefoot! But the bad things more than overshadowed the good. Zenaida was cruel, and so was Bastien when he got drunk, which was often.

"One fine day we came to a small town in the Loire district. There was a big cathedral on the square, I remember, that looked huge and disapproving beyond the carnival's tawdry, jingling whirl of light and music.

"When Zenaida was telling fortunes in the wagon, Bastien was supposed to keep an eye on me. I had to stay near the wagon, or run the risk of a bad whipping. But on this particular evening, Bastien, a little tipsier than usual, went to sleep under the wagon with his head on his hat. I saw my chance and wandered away. I had no thought of escape. I was too dirty and dispirited, and I had no money. My sheltered life had taught me nothing of fending for myself or what to do in an emergency. However, for the moment I enjoyed myself watching the familiar sights of the carnival and the many unfamiliar faces.

"Suddenly I saw something that made me gasp! Standing under a gas lamp at the outskirts of the crowd was a tall man with a beard. In his hands were a small sketchbook and a pencil. It was Monsieur Jules Clairon who never could resist a carnival!

"I ran to him bleating like a lost sheep. 'Oh, Monsieur Clairon, save me, save me, and take me away from here!'

"Poor man, he looked horrified, and who can blame him? I had accumulated the dirt of three weeks.

"'I don't know any gypsies!' said he. 'How do you know my name?'

"'But I'm the *princess*, don't you remember?' I cried idiotically. And then I explained.

"'Good Lord!' he said, horrified. 'I knew nothing about your disappearance. I left Saint-Germain early the next morning on a walking tour.'

"He took me back to the house where he was staying, and the landlady scrubbed me and gave me clean clothes, while he got the police and went back to the carnival. But Zenaida must have found out what had happened, for the gypsy wagon had disappeared. Nobody ever saw it again.

"As for me, I was rushed home by train the next day. I was embraced by my haggard father, who was relieved on two accounts: first because of my safe return, and second because the ransom money had never been collected. All my aunts wept over me wetly, and I had to have my hair washed every day for two weeks, but in spite of everything I was glad to be home.

"When my father begged Monsieur Clairon to tell him how he could reward him, Monsieur Clairon replied, 'Allow me to paint the portrait of your daughter.' So that is how it came about. Later on, it was he who persuaded my family to send me to school in England. I went to a convent there for seven years which, though it would have seemed dreadfully strict to you, was heaven itself as far as I was concerned."

Mrs. Oliphant opened a pocketbook like a giant clam, extracted some money to pay the bill, and clapped it shut again. "That's all," she said.

Randy rose slowly to the surface and emerged from the story dreamily.

"It was wonderful," she said.

[85]

"Things like that never happen to us. We lead a humdrum life when I think about it. It's funny how it doesn't seem humdrum."

"That's because you have 'eyes the better to see with, my dear' and 'ears the better to hear with.' Nobody who has them and uses them is likely to find life humdrum very often. Even when they have to use bifocal lenses, like me.'' . . .

She held out her hand. "Thank you for coming to tea."

"Oh, thank you very much for inviting me," said Randy. "Could I— would you let me come to see you someday?"

The old lady looked pleased. "Do come, child. Come by all means, and I'll show you the brass earrings Zenaida made me wear. I kept them for luck."

At home Randy went straight to her brother's room. Rush looked up from his book. "Oh hello. Have a good time?"

"Wonderful. Guess who I met?"

"Mickey Rooney," said Rush.

"No, silly. The Elephant. Only I'm never going to call her that again."

"Oh, just the Elephant." Rush was disappointed.

"Not just the Elephant. She's swell. She's a friend of mine now, and I'm going to see her. She was kidnaped by gypsies and lived with them for weeks."

"Recently?" inquired Rush, startled.

"No, no. Years ago when she was a little girl in France. And look, she sent you these. All of you, I mean."

"What are they?" said Rush, taking a bite.

"*Pitty foors*," said Randy. "I think it's French. For cakes, probably."

"*Pitty foors*," repeated Rush mellowly, through chocolate custard. "Not bad, not bad at all. So she was kidnaped by gypsies, was she? Do you think the El—Mrs. Oliphant would care to have me come along with you when you go calling on her?"

"I know she would," said Randy. "And, Rush, let's go soon and often."

⟨ THIS *story is from* THE SATURDAYS. *Other books by the same author include* THIMBLE SUMMER, *which won the Newbery Medal in 1939;* THE SEA IS ALL AROUND, *and* FOUR-STORY MISTAKE.

Ghost of the Lagoon

THE ISLAND of Bora Bora, where Mako lived, is far away in the South Pacific. It is not a large island— you can paddle around it in a single day—but the main body of it rises straight out of the sea, very high into the air, like a castle. Waterfalls trail down the faces of the cliffs. As you look upward, you see wild goats leaping from crag to crag.

Mako had been born on the very edge of the sea, and most of his waking hours were spent in the waters of the lagoon, which was nearly enclosed by the two outstretched arms of the island. He was very clever with his hands; he had made a harpoon that was as straight as an arrow, and tipped with five, pointed, iron spears. He had made a canoe, hollowing it out of a tree. It wasn't a very big canoe, just large enough to hold Mako and his little dog, Afa. They were great companions, these two.

One evening Mako lay stretched at full length on the pandanus mats, listening to Grandfather's voice. Overhead, stars shone in the dark sky. From far off came the thunder of the surf on the reef.

The old man was speaking of Tupa, the ghost of the lagoon. Ever since the boy could remember, he had heard tales of this terrible monster. Frightened fishermen, returning from the reef at midnight, spoke of the ghost. Over the evening fires, old men told endless tales about the monster.

Tupa seemed to think the lagoon of Bora Bora belonged to him. The natives left presents of food for him out on the reef: a dead goat, a chicken, or a pig. The presents always disappeared mysteriously, but everyone felt sure that it was Tupa who carried them away. Still, in spite of all this food, the nets of the fishermen were torn during the night, the fish stolen. What an appetite Tupa seemed to have!

Not many people had ever seen the ghost of the lagoon. Grandfather was one of the few who had.

"What does he really look like, Grandfather?" the boy asked.

The old man shook his head solemnly. The light from the cook-fire glistened on his white hair. "Tupa lives in the great caves of the reef. He is longer than this house. There is a sail on his back, not large, but terrible to see, for it burns with a white fire. Once, when I was fishing beyond the reef at night, I saw him come up right under another canoe—"

"What happened then?" Mako asked. He half rose on one elbow. This was a story he had not heard before.

The old man's voice dropped to a whisper. "Tupa dragged the canoe right under the water—and the water boiled with white flame. The three fishermen in it were never seen again. Fine swimmers they were, too." Grandfather shook his head. "It is bad fortune even to speak of Tupa. There is evil in his very name."

"But King Opu Nui has offered a reward for his capture," the boy pointed out.

"Thirty acres of fine coconut land, and a sailing canoe as well," said the old man. "But who ever heard of laying hands on a ghost?"

Mako's eyes glistened. "Thirty acres of land and a sailing canoe. How I should love to win that reward!"

Grandfather nodded, but Mako's mother scolded her son for such foolish talk. "Be quiet now, son, and go to sleep. Grandfather has told you that it is bad fortune to speak of Tupa. Alas, how well we have learned that lesson! Your father—" She stopped herself.

"What of my father?" the boy asked quickly. And now he sat up straight on the mats.

"Tell him, Grandfather," his mother whispered.

The old man poked at the fire. A little shower of sparks whirled up into the darkness. "Your father," he explained gently, "was one of the three fishermen in the canoe that Tupa destroyed." His words fell upon the air like stones dropped into a deep well.

Mako shivered. He brushed back the hair from his damp forehead. Then he squared his shoulders and cried fiercely, "I shall slay Tupa and win the king's reward." He rose to his knees, his slim body tense, his eyes flashing in the firelight.

"Hush!" his mother said. "Go to sleep now. Enough of such foolish talk. Would you bring trouble upon us all?"

Mako lay down again upon the mats. He rolled over on his side and closed his eyes, but sleep was long in coming.

The palm trees whispered above the dark lagoon, and far out on the reef the sea thundered.

The boy was slow to wake up the next morning. The ghost of Tupa had played through his dreams, making him restless. And so it was almost noon before Mako sat up on the mats and stretched himself. He called Afa, and the boy and his dog ran down to the lagoon for their morning swim.

When they returned to the house, wide awake and hungry, Mako's mother had food ready and waiting. "These are the last of our bananas," she told him. "I wish you would paddle out to the reef this afternoon and bring back a new bunch."

The boy agreed eagerly. Nothing pleased him more than such an errand, which would take him to a little island on the outer reef, half a mile from shore. It was one of Mako's favorite playgrounds, and there bananas and oranges grew in great plenty.

"Come, Afa," he called, gulping the last mouthful. "We're going on an expedition." He picked up his long-bladed knife and seized his spear. A minute later, he dashed across the white sand, where his canoe was drawn up beyond the water's reach.

Afa barked at his heels. He was all white except for a black spot over each eye. Wherever Mako went, there went Afa also. Now the little dog leaped into the bow of the canoe, his tail wagging with delight. The boy pulled the canoe into the water and climbed aboard. Then, picking up his paddle, he thrust it into the water. The canoe shot ahead. Its sharp bow cut through

away all thought of them. Perhaps ghosts were only old men's stories, anyway!

Mako's eyes came to rest upon his spear—the spear that he had made with his own hands, the spear that was as straight and true as an arrow. He remembered his vow of the night before. Could a ghost be killed with a spear? Some night, when all the village was sleeping, Mako swore to himself that he would find out! He would paddle out to the reef and challenge Tupa! Perhaps tonight. Why not? He caught

the green water of the lagoon like a knife through cheese. And so clear was the water that Mako could see the coral gardens, forty feet below him, growing in the sand. The shadow of the canoe moved over them.

A school of fish swept by like silver arrows. He saw scarlet rock cod with ruby eyes and the head of a conger eel peering out from a cavern in the coral. The boy thought suddenly of Tupa, ghost of the lagoon. On such a bright day it was hard to believe in ghosts of any sort. The fierce sunlight drove

his breath at the thought. A shiver ran down his back. His hands were tense on the paddle.

As the canoe drew away from shore, the boy saw the coral reef that, above all others, had always interested him. It was of white coral, a long slim shape that rose slightly above the surface of the water. It looked very much like a shark. There was a ridge on the back that the boy could pretend was a dorsal fin, while up near one end were two dark holes that looked like eyes! Times without number the boy had practiced

[89]

spearing this make-believe shark, aiming always for the eyes, the most vulnerable spot. So true and straight had his aim become that the spear would pass right into the eyeholes without even touching the sides of the coral. Mako had nicknamed the coral reef "Tupa."

This morning, as he paddled past it, he shook his fist and called, "Ho, Mister Tupa! Just wait till I get my bananas. When I come back I'll make short work of you!"

Afa followed his master's words with a sharp bark. He knew Mako was excited about something.

The bow of the canoe touched the sand of the little island where the bananas grew. Afa leaped ashore and ran barking into the jungle, now on this trail, now on that. Clouds of sea birds whirled from their nests into the air with angry cries.

Mako climbed into the shallow water, waded ashore, and pulled his canoe up on the beach. Then, picking up his banana knife, he followed Afa. In the jungle the light was so dense and green that the boy felt as if he were moving under water. Ferns grew higher than his head. The branches of the trees formed a green roof over him. A flock of parakeets fled on swift wings. Somewhere a wild pig crashed through the undergrowth while Afa dashed away in pursuit. Mako paused anxiously. Armed only with his banana knife, he had no desire to meet the wild pig. The pig, it seemed, had no desire to meet him, either.

Then, ahead of him, the boy saw the broad green blades of a banana tree. A

bunch of bananas, golden ripe, was growing out of the top.

At the foot of the tree he made a nest of soft leaves for the bunch to fall upon. In this way the fruit wouldn't be crushed. Then with a swift slash of his blade he cut the stem. The bananas fell to the earth with a dull thud. He found two more bunches.

Then he thought, "I might as well get some oranges while I'm here. Those little rusty ones are sweeter than any that grow on Bora Bora."

So he set about making a net out of palm leaves to carry the oranges. As he worked, his swift fingers moving in and out among the strong green leaves, he could hear Afa's excited barks off in the jungle. That was just like Afa, always barking at something: a bird, a fish, a wild pig. He never caught anything, either. Still, no boy ever had a finer companion.

The palm net took longer to make than Mako had realized. By the time it was finished and filled with oranges, the jungle was dark and gloomy. Night comes quickly and without warning in the islands of the tropics.

Mako carried the fruit down to the shore and loaded it into the canoe. Then he whistled to Afa. The dog came bounding out of the bush, wagging his tail.

"Hurry!" Mako scolded. "We won't be home before the dark comes."

The little dog leaped into the bow of the canoe and Mako came aboard. Night seemed to rise up from the surface of the water and swallow them. On the distant shore of Bora Bora, cook-fires were being lighted. The first star twinkled just over the dark mountains. Mako dug his paddle into the water and the canoe leaped ahead.

The dark water was alive with phosphorus. The bow of the canoe seemed to cut through a pale liquid fire. Each dip of the paddle trailed streamers of light. As the canoe approached the coral reef, the boy called, "Ho, Tupa! It's too late tonight to teach you your lesson. But I'll come back tomorrow." The coral shark glistened in the darkness.

And then, suddenly, Mako's breath caught in his throat. Just beyond the fin of the coral Tupa, there was another fin—a huge one. It had never been there before. And—could he believe his eyes? It was moving!

The boy stopped paddling. He dashed his hand across his eyes. Afa began to bark furiously. The great white fin, shaped like a small sail, glowed with phosphorescent light. Then Mako knew. Here was Tupa, the real Tupa—ghost of the lagoon!

His knees felt weak. He tried to cry out, but his voice died in his throat. The great shark was circling slowly around the canoe. With each circle, it moved closer and closer. Now the boy could see the phosphorescent glow of the great shark's sides. As it moved in closer, he saw the yellow eyes, the gill slits in its throat.

Afa leaped from one side of the canoe to the other. In sudden anger Mako leaned forward to grab the dog and shake him soundly. Afa wriggled out of his grasp, as Mako tried to catch him, and the shift in weight tipped the canoe on one side. In another second

they would be overboard. The boy threw his weight over quickly to balance the canoe, but with a loud splash Afa fell over into the dark water.

Mako stared after him in dismay. The little dog, instead of swimming back to the canoe, had headed for the distant shore. And there was the great white shark, very near.

"Afa! Afa! Come back! Come quickly!" Mako shouted.

The little dog turned back toward the canoe. He was swimming with all his strength. Mako leaned forward. Could Afa make it? Swiftly the boy seized his spear. Bracing himself, he stood upright. There was no weakness in him now. His dog, his companion, was in danger of instant death.

Afa was swimming desperately to reach the canoe. The white shark had paused in his circling to gather speed for the attack. Mako raised his arm, took aim. In that instant the shark charged. Mako's arm flashed forward. All his strength was behind that thrust. The spear drove straight and true, right into the great shark's eye. Mad with pain and rage, Tupa whipped about, lashing the water in fury. The canoe rocked back and forth. Mako struggled to keep his balance as he drew back the spear by the cord fastened to his wrist.

He bent over to seize Afa and drag him aboard. Then he stood up, not a moment too soon. Once again the shark charged. Once again Mako threw his spear, this time at the other eye. The spear found its mark. Blinded and weak from loss of blood, Tupa rolled to the surface, turned slightly on his side. Was he dead?

Mako knew how clever sharks could be, and he was taking no chances. Scarcely daring to breathe, he paddled toward the still body. He saw the faintest motion of the great tail. The shark was still alive. The boy knew that one flip of that tail could overturn the canoe and send him and Afa into the water, where Tupa could destroy them.

Swiftly, yet calmly, Mako stood upright and braced himself firmly. Then, murmuring a silent prayer to the Shark God, he threw his spear for the last time. Downward, swift as sound, the spear plunged into a white shoulder.

Peering over the side of the canoe, Mako could see the great fish turn over far below the surface. Then slowly, slowly, the great shark rose to the surface of the lagoon. There he floated, half on one side.

Tupa was dead.

Mako flung back his head and shouted for joy. Hitching a strong line about the shark's tail, the boy began to paddle toward the shore of Bora Bora. The dorsal fin, burning with the white fire of phosphorus, trailed after the canoe.

Men were running down the beaches of Bora Bora, shouting as they leaped into their canoes and put out across the lagoon. Their cries reached the boy's ears across the water.

"It is Tupa, ghost of the lagoon!" he heard them shout. "Mako has killed him!"

That night, as the tired boy lay on the pandanus mats listening to the distant thunder of the sea, he heard Grandfather singing a new song. It was the song which would be sung the next day at the feast which King Opu Nui would give in Mako's honor. The boy saw his mother bending over the cook-fire. The stars leaned close, winking like friendly eyes. Grandfather's voice reached him now from a great distance. "Thirty acres of land and a sailing canoe . . ."

⟨[Armstrong Sperry's *book* Call It Courage, *which won the Newbery Medal in 1941, is also about Bora Bora. His other books include* Black Falcon *and* Hull Down for Action.

Danger!

THE AUGUST moon rose that evening more beautiful than the children knew that a moon could be. It was perfectly round and honey-colored. It seemed to be part of a dream of a world lovelier than anything on this planet. The water caught the light in a pathway, made up of ripples like silver scales, and the loons which haunted the cove shook out their wild and lonely cries, one answering the other.

Everything else was silent. Uncle Jim and Aunt Em, Bill and Sandy climbed up the ladder to the roof of the houseboat, where they lay looking up into the sky. For a little while a pine tree top was silhouetted on the moon and then its orb rose alone into the sky. They heard twitterings and cheepings far overhead, like little spirits in the night. For a while the sound held and then passed southward away.

"A flock migrating by night," murmured Aunt Em. "Probably warblers, don't you think, Jim?"

Uncle Jim made a yeslike sound. Later he said: "The Indians thought the spirits of small animals and children followed the moon path to the happy hunting grounds. Warriors, or those who were brave in other ways, and the great animals followed the sun path."

"We'd be moon-path followers, Bill," said Sandy.

"Unless we were brave in some way," said Bill. "Then we would follow the sun path, wouldn't we, Uncle Jim?"

"If you were brave enough," said Uncle Jim.

Sandy thought happily how many evenings she and Bill had spent in the houseboat during this wonderful summer, how many more were to follow. Eighty days of visiting Uncle Jim and Aunt Em on the *Ark*. Thirty of them gone. That left fifty more. Fifty days to eat breakfast in the tiny cabin—johnnycakes and sirup, crispy bacon, fresh country milk; fifty days to ramble through the woods or canoe on the pond. Fifty more nights, too! Sandy sighed contentedly.

No one spoke again for a long time, and then it was the loons once more. Their cries roused Bill.

"Why don't we all go out in the canoe?" he suggested. "It would be fine in the canoe this evening."

Aunt Em said no, she was going to bed early. Uncle Jim had some letters to write, but he didn't see why the children couldn't go alone.

"It's nearly as light as day," he said, "and still as a millpond. The loons are making such a racket I suppose it's going to rain tomorrow, but it's clear as crystal now. It would be a pity for you to miss a paddle like this."

Sandy, as always, took the bow. It was she who set the pace. Bill had the stern paddle. It was he who steered. But they were so accustomed to paddling together that they seemed almost like one mind, as if they drifted or went fast, followed the shore or struck out into the middle of the pond on the same impulse. They talked very little. They understood each other without talking.

As they rounded the oak tree on the point, they looked back. There floated the houseboat, dark in the wave of moonlight, its yellow windows goblin-like in all that white radiance.

Then they were alone. The water folded about their thin-bodied craft. They could feel every motion of the pond, almost as though they were swimming in it. At first they followed along the shore in the black shadow of the forest. The moon was tattered among the branches. It seemed in flight, as though it were moving while they stood still. They passed Marine's Point and then North Slash and Canoe Cove. The islands lay west of them with silver rocks and silver trees.

Bill steered out into the lake. The moon leaped up overhead, free of the trees which had darkened it, and the water changed to a crinkle of silver through which they moved with small,

merry splashings. They had not meant to be gone long. It was because in this light they forgot time and distance that they went on and on and on. It was not until the lake narrowed before them to a channel no wider than a stream that they realized they had come to the Narrows and must turn back.

"Goodness, we must be miles from the *Ark*," Bill said. "We'll be awfully late. I hope they won't be mad."

They swung around and started back eastward. Still the moonlight lay calm and kind upon a sleeping world, but the air seemed a little colder. The moon was less like honey and more like polished steel.

Their arms were growing tired. They changed sides, trying to rest their aching muscles. The shores of East Neck still seemed very far away.

They were in the very middle of the lake, taking the shortest way home, when something crashed horribly behind them in the sky. Surprised, they looked about. All to the west of them, the stars were blotted out by heavy clouds. As they stared fearfully over their shoulders, a forked tongue of lightning whipped down this darkness with a hissing sound, followed almost instantly by another great clap of thunder.

Yet when they turned and bent to their paddles, all before them lay moonlight and faint stars. The east was as serene as the west was fearful.

The children were bewildered by the suddenness of the change behind them, and they were frightened. This cataclysm of the sky was unnatural. It was as though they had been lured out into a night baited by moonlight. Bill, looking over his shoulder again, saw the lightning splinter earthward like a violet claw.

He turned and, leaning far forward, drove his paddle into the water with all his strength. Sandy was doing the same at the bow. They could feel the canoe leap forward under them like a horse which has felt the spur. They were fleeing now, toward the safe but distant shore, dark in the moonlight ahead. Every stroke brought them nearer, a little nearer anyway.

But there were things out that night which moved faster than two children in a hard-driven canoe. A ragged darkness hung now like a canopy over their heads, and the wind struck cold at their backs. First, a line of ripples overtook them, ruffling the lake, and then the ripples were waves. The canoe took on a motion like a curveting horse. There were whitecaps running in the slanting moonlight about them, and the canoe was plunging.

Bill, gritting his teeth, held their course with the waves. If they should veer into the trough, they would be swamped. By now even the moon had been set upon by the clouds. She was soon covered over, and the lake darkened.

Sandy was tiring fast but she did not give in. For the first time she spoke. "Uncle Jim's out looking for us!"

Somewhere against the curtain of the shore a little light was moving. If Uncle Jim were calling, it was up wind and they could hear nothing, but they shouted as they paddled on.

Then the rain struck them, hiding everything but the lightning in its thick curtains, drowning out every sound but the thunder. It drenched the children and half-blinded them. Still Bill steered true, and still they shouted hopelessly into this cauldron of sound and water.

A darkness rose up on their right. It was the first island near the wide entrance of Deep Cove. In the lee of the second island there ought to be some shelter. If they could only last that long! The storm increased in violence. A horrible sizzling sound shook the air. A bolt had struck near them. They could not tell what had been hit, but they prayed it was not the *Ark*. No, it must have been a tree on the second island. Bill heard the water breaking on rock. He had to swing the canoe out or be dashed against the stony point.

A wave broke into the canoe and Sandy screamed, but kept on paddling. A second wave broke. The canoe was half full of water, but still afloat. Bill, with a great effort, steered it back on its course. The waves no longer broke into it, but it was sinking under them. Neither stopped paddling. The island lay astern now; they were in its lee, and the waves were smaller here. But the storm lashed about them as savagely as ever.

The canoe gave a sluggish roll under them and sank.

"Help! Help! Uncle Jim!" screamed Sandy just before the water closed over her, but Bill kept his breath for swimming. He leaped clear of the thwarts and struck out toward the bow, swimming hard.

[95]

"Sandy!" he called. "Sandy!"

She didn't answer him. He knew with a horrible sinking of his heart what had happened. Kneeling as she was, she had been caught between the thwarts and the narrow bow. He swam under water and found her struggling hands. It was terrible helping her to get free. His chest felt raw and ready to burst as he finally came to the surface. But he brought Sandy with him.

She was still struggling, only half-conscious, and he knew that he could not hold her up long if she went on gripping him and forcing him under as she was doing. He got his head up into the air for a moment. "Easy," he said.

He was forced down again. Again he struggled upward, bearing her clinging weight.

"Easy, Sandy!" Her arms and legs were gripping him less desperately. Her will had heard his voice far, far off, and was trying to obey.

He came up this time more quickly.

"Easy, Sandy," he said for the third time. "Put one hand on my shoulder and let go."

Once more he went down, but now she was letting go. She knew at last what was happening, that she must force her terrified body to obey her will. Bill was almost exhausted when he came to the surface again. But now Sandy was only a hand on his shoulder. She was trying to keep herself up with floundering feet and milling arm.

"Easy, Sandy, easy, easy," he gasped. "Don't swim so hard. Easy, we'll be all right."

Her spasms of swimming slowed and steadied. Their greatest danger now was the waves, which were not so high here in the shelter of the island, but which still sometimes bewildered them and filled their gasping mouths with water.

Each time this happened, panic descended again on Sandy.

"Breathe when it's past, Sandy," Bill's voice came patiently. "Steady, Sandy, take it easy." And Sandy fought down the panic and obeyed. Bill was trying to find the canoe, but he couldn't. He did strike his hand against a paddle, however, and even that helped to keep Sandy's head above water.

When there was a pause in the lightning and thunder, Bill shouted again. At last they heard an answering shout, and there was the rowboat with Aunt Em crouched in the bow in a slicker. She was searching the water with the big searchlight, while Uncle Jim rowed.

"There they are! Both of them!" cried Aunt Em. "Quick, Jim! Quick!"

But Uncle Jim didn't hurry. He spoke to the children still at a little distance.

"Sandy, you come in first. Take your time. Do you understand? I'll help you in over the stern. Remember to keep the boat balanced. Do you understand, Sandy?"

"Yes," she sobbed. "Get me in, Uncle Jim, get me in!"

"All right, Bill?"

"All right."

Uncle Jim helped from the boat, Bill from the water. Aunt Em waited in the bow, ready to balance the boat.

"Easy, Sandy, easy." Bill's voice still steadied her.

Sandy was in Aunt Em's arms. Tears of relief and rain were streaming together down their cheeks.

Bill handed in the paddle, and then with a little help from Uncle Jim pulled himself up over the flat stern. He sank down on the broad seat, exhausted.

"The canoe's swamped, sir," he explained. "We almost made it but we had to round Second Island."

"It's safe under water," Uncle Jim said matter-of-factly, "which is more than you two children would be. Now we'd better get home and get into dry clothes."

His face looked white, but he whistled cheerfully enough as he took up the oars again. The rain was coming, not so heavily now, and there was a longer pause between the lightning and the thunder which followed it. The storm was passing over.

In the houseboat, when they returned, the kettle was dancing a little impatient jig on the stove, and the lamp sent forth a welcoming light.

"It's as if it had never happened," thought Sandy, looking at the peaceful scene.

But everything had happened. She felt shaky but strangely exalted. Here was one adventure they had not expected. They had met danger and they had been equal to the encounter—particularly Bill. She remembered what Uncle Jim had said about being "brave enough."

"Bill will never tell just how brave he was," she decided as she drank the warm milk Aunt Em had gotten ready for the returned adventurers. "I'll have to do that for him."

⟨ AMONG *Elizabeth Coatsworth's books are* THE CAT WHO WENT TO HEAVEN, *which won the Newbery Medal in 1931; several volumes of poetry,* THE FAIR AMERICAN, *and other historical stories that reflect her interest in the past of her own country.*

How Babe Got His Name

《 BABE RUTH, *the "home-run king," was probably the most popular baseball hero since the game began. This story is from his book* BABE RUTH, *as he told it to his sports-writer friend, Bob Considine.*

I WAS A bad kid. I say that without pride, but with a feeling that it is better to say it. Because I live with one great hope in mind: to help kids who now stand where I stood as a boy. When I was seven, my parents placed me in St. Mary's Industrial School in Baltimore . . . I was listed as incorrigible. Yet I look back on St. Mary's as one of the most constructive periods of my life. There I met and learned to love the greatest man I've ever known —Brother Matthias of the Xaverian Order, which concentrates on work among underprivileged boys.

I saw some he-men in my twenty-two years in organized baseball, but I never saw one who equaled Brother Matthias. He concentrated on me probably because I needed it. He saw that I had some talent for catching and throwing a baseball, and he never lost patience with me no matter what I did. It was Brother Matthias who made me a pitcher. I played a lot of baseball at St. Mary's, but I never had

any hope of making a career of the game. I was learning to be a tailor.

My first knowledge that I was going to be a professional ball player instead of a tailor came in the middle of February, 1914. I was throwing a baseball around the still-frozen yard at St. Mary's when Brother Gilbert, Brother Matthias, and Brother Paul appeared with Jack Dunn, boss of the Baltimore Orioles. Brother Gilbert introduced us.

Dunn, to my complete surprise, asked me if I'd like to sign with the Orioles. To me, it was as if somebody had suddenly popped up and asked me to join the United States Senate.

"George is supposed to stay here at St. Mary's until he's twenty-one," Brother Paul explained. "You would have to become his legal guardian."

Dunn looked me over and said he'd take a chance. Then he said, "Now, about his salary—"

I guess my jaw must have dropped.

"You mean you'd pay me?" I gasped. My voice cracked and he laughed.

"Sure, George, I'll start you out at six hundred a year."

It made me as lightheaded as if I had been hit on the head with a bat.

"You mean six hundred dollars?" I asked him, unable to believe that I was the one they were talking about.

"That's right," Dunn said. "And if you're as good as Brother Gilbert and the others say you are, you'll be earning more than that in a short time."

I had some great moments in the years that followed that, including the day I signed a contract for eighty thousand dollars a year with the New York Yankees. But none of my later thrills ever topped the one I got that cold afternoon at St. Mary's when six hundred dollars seemed to me to be all the wealth in the world.

I'll never forget the ride to the railroad station, the day I left Baltimore. The whole thing still seemed like a dream to me. There were moments when I felt I sat on the top of the world, and moments when my stomach turned over, wondering if I could make the grade and fearful that I'd fail, and be forced to come back to St. Mary's. And that wasn't because I didn't like St. Mary's. I just couldn't have stood the shame of coming back, after saying good-by and after hearing Brother Matthias tell me, in his quiet way, "You'll make it, George."

There were other players on the railroad platform. Few of them paid any attention to me. But that didn't matter. The important thing was that Dunn was taking me to the Oriole spring training camp at Fayetteville, North Carolina. It was my first trip on a train. I was nineteen and the proudest, greenest kid in the country.

I couldn't sleep that night, wondering what it would be like in the morning and all the days and months after that. There was another reason I couldn't sleep. One of the older players, a catcher named Ben Egan, had easily talked me into the oldest gag in baseball. He told me, as dumb rookies before and after me have been told, that the little clothes hammock that reached from one end of my berth to the other was put there in order for me to rest my pitching arm. I held the arm up in this uncomfortable position all night. I wanted to act like a pro.

The train pulled into Fayetteville early the next morning with the first Oriole injury of the 1914 season. A rookie named Ruth had a cramped and sore pitching arm, thanks to the "rest" he had carefully given it.

I haven't got the best memory in the world, but it is easy to recall those early days at my first spring training camp. I got to some bigger places than Fayetteville after that, but darn few as exciting. It was the place where Jim Thorpe, one of my sports heroes, had played a little pro baseball . . . Maybe Jim had a good time in baseball. I know I did from the morning I got there in 1914 accompanied by my hammock-sore arm.

It still made me dizzy to think about making six hundred dollars for that season. That wasn't all. Jack Dunn took me aside, just before we got to Fayetteville, and slipped me five dollars in advance. It was more money than I had ever had before.

But miracles kept happening. We went to our hotel for breakfast and while I was studying the menu I heard a player near me say, "Order anything you want, kid. The club pays our feed bills during spring training."

I looked at him, unable to believe it.

"You mean I can eat anything I want, and it won't cost me anything?"

"Sure. Anything."

I was on my third stack of wheatcakes and third order of ham, and hadn't even come up for air, when I realized that some of the other fellows were watching me. I looked at them silently, and kept chewing.

"I wouldn't have believed it if I hadn't seen it," Rodger Pippen, one of the Orioles, said.

I grinned at him. "A guy's got to be strong to play ball," I said.

Dunn dropped by my table and took a look at the ruins. He smiled at me and put his hand on my shoulder. "We've got twenty-seven other fellows in this club, George," he said. "Leave them a little food, will you?"

I got the name Babe during those first few days in Fayetteville. It came out of a couple of incidents. Even in those days Dunn already had a reputation for picking up very young players and developing them. Some of his older players used to kid him a lot about the baby-faced kids he concentrated on, and the first time they saw me with him—on the field—was no exception.

On that day, Dunn practically led me by the hand from the dressing room to the pitcher's box. I was as proud of my Orioles' uniform as I had

been of my first long pants. Maybe I showed that pride in my face.

"Look at Dunnie and his new babe," one of the older players yelled.

That started it, I guess. But the clincher came a few days later. It had gotten to be a joke, the way I walked around wide-eyed all the time. I used to get up at five in the morning and walk down to the station to see the trains go through, but I always got back to the hotel in time to be the first in line for breakfast.

The hotel elevator was just about the greatest piece of mechanism I had ever seen up to that point in my life. I'd ride up and down on it by the hour, just for the ride and to watch how the operator worked it and how close he'd come to getting the thing on a level with the floor stops. Finally, one day, I couldn't keep my hands off the control another minute. I gave the operator most of the money I had left from what Dunnie had given me and bribed him to let me handle it myself.

My playing life, in fact my life, nearly ended a few minutes later. I left a door open on the third floor and was rubbernecking up and down the corridor while I made the elevator go up another flight. Suddenly a player screamed at me to pull my fool head inside, and I did—just in time to keep it from being crushed.

Dunnie bawled me out until the stuffings ran out of me; what he didn't say to me the older players said for him. But finally one of them took pity on me, shook his head and said: "You're just a babe in the woods."

After that they called me Babe.

Jungle Boy in New York

❨ SAUDIN, *a boy of North Borneo, knew nothing of the outside world until Martin and Osa Johnson visited his jungle. They were taking motion pictures, and they hired him to look after the animals they had purchased or captured. When they sailed for New York, he went along to care for the animals during the voyage.*

WHEN I came to Sandakan, I thought that Sandakan was a big place. But when I went from Sandakan to Singapore, I thought *that* was a big place, probably the biggest place there was. Then we went from Singapore to Capetown, and that was even more mighty. So I asked men, was America as great as that? And men answered me that it was even greater. And now that I return to Borneo from America I think that Sandakan is only as big as the end of my little finger.

We left Singapore on a very big boat . . . We were on the ship many days, and then we came to America. When we were going to land, the customs man said to me, "Can you speak English and read and write?" I said, "Yes, a little." He said, "Read this," and handed me my passport. I could not read it, but I remembered what was on it, because Mr. Johnson had told me, and so I said what was on it to

the man. Then the man said, "O.K. Come into America!"

So we entered into America and went to a very great village with a thousand thousand lights. It was night when we arrived, but when I looked up at the sky above this village it was very bright and red and sparkling and there was light everywhere. And I said, "Is this morning?" And they said, "No, this is New York!"

I was so astonished by New York that I just wanted to look and look and look at it. Every night men had their names put in the sky with bright lights so that they would not be forgotten, because there are so many people in New York that it would be easy to forget some of them. All the time there was a great noise made by motorcars and buses and trains. There were trains above me on bridges, there were trains below me, and there were more trains that were below the trains that were below. Always the trains were very full of people. I think if the trains all stopped and the people got off them, there would be no space in New York for all the people. So the people take turns living in the trains. I used to walk and walk because I was afraid to get on those trains to ride, as I did not know how to get off or where I should be when I did, or if I might have to live on one.

The streets were very clean. They washed and polished them every morning. I thought there could be no sickness there with everything so clean.

The buildings were very tall. Sometimes I had to go up and down in what men call an elevator. This is a little room that you get into, and very suddenly it goes up. And when it stops your stomach does not stop. But when it goes down you feel that everything has gone out of you. It is much worse than an airplane. I was always afraid in it, but said nothing, because I thought men would say, "He is just a jungle man!"

In winter there is a very cold climate in New York. Often I shivered and was cold, although I wore many clothes and my handsome black coat.

All men wore heavy clothes and coats like mine which hung down to their knees. But truly I was astonished at the women! They did not wear many clothes except around their necks, where they wore the skins of animals. Their stockings were just like nothing. Truly I was astonished that they did not feel cold.

In New York we put Mr. Johnson's animals in Central Park Zoo, and I went there every day to take care of them. At first Mr. Johnson went with me so that I would not be lost, and later I could go alone. But I was always afraid of the motorcars. I walked a great deal, up and down the same street and never far away, as I was afraid of being lost. At night I did not go away at all, because when lights were in the sky all things became different and I was confused.

One day he told me to go to a cinema. When I went in it was daylight, but when I came out it was dark. It was only five o'clock and in my country that is still daytime. But in New York in winter that is nighttime and the lights are on. When I looked up I could see nothing but very tall

buildings and a red glow at the top of the buildings, and no sky. All men were hurrying from here to there, all trains made noises, all lights blinked, and I became confused. I walked and walked, but could not find the place where I lived. Mr. Johnson had written a letter for me, telling who I was and where I lived, in case I should be lost some day. And, as I was lost then, I looked in my coat, and was much astonished to find that the letter was lost also.

I went to a policeman and asked him how to go to Central Park Zoo, because if I could find that I could find my house, which was near it. The policeman said it was twelve blocks away, so I said, "Thank you very much," and walked on some more. Then I asked another policeman and he said nine blocks farther, and I walked some more. But the next policeman I asked said, "Here is Central Park Zoo!" And there I was at the Zoo, but I did not recognize it with the lights on. So then I found my house, which I think was very good fortune, because I had indeed been lost.

One day newspapermen came to talk to me, and they said, "Do you like New York? What do you like the best?" And I said, "Yes, I like New York, and I like best the red electric light signs that run like streams of fire, and the lights that chase each other around like small animals."

One day I was out walking and I came to a large place with many horses in it. I said to a man with a uniform, "Can I enter?" And he said, "You must buy a ticket." I said, "I will buy a ticket. Now can I enter?" And he said, "Sure!" So I entered and I saw large and wonderful horses, and handsome men with beautiful colored uniforms. They played music and the horses danced to the music. I think the horses in New York are smarter than are the policemen in my country. So I struck my hands together the way people did, with astonishment and joy. When the playing was finished all the people wanted to leave at once in a great hurry, and everybody pushed everybody and I fell down. A man picked me up, and I said, "Thank you very much," and went home.

I went also to see boxing and wrestling. Boxing is all right, but wrestling is too rough. In my country we do not act like that unless we wish to kill men.

Mr. Johnson took me to eat at a place where you put money in a hole and take out a plate of food. The different holes have names on them to tell you what foods are concealed within. We had vegetables and potato and meat all cooked together in a flour wrapping which they call a pie. I think this place was very cunning indeed, because the hole to receive a ten-cent piece was so small that you could not put in a five-cent piece, and the hole for the five-cent piece did not answer if you put in a one-cent piece.

Mr. Johnson took me to a club where we were going to talk to people about Borneo. When we arrived he told me that I must stand up and talk to them in Malay. I said that it was useless for me to do so, because they did not understand Malay. But he said that I must speak in Malay, and then he would tell them in English what I said. I was afraid and ashamed because there were many people there and I am not practiced in speaking to many people. But although I shivered as with cold, I talked, and I told them about my village with only thirty people in it, which was so small that I was astonished that they wished to hear about it. And when I finished they struck their hands together to show that they were pleased, and I sat down and Mr. Johnson talked.

Mr. Jim, who used to drive the flying ship in Borneo, was in New York, too, but he did not live there. One day we flew from New York to his home in a very large flying ship, much larger than Mr. Johnson's, with many people in it. I was not afraid because I was used to flying before, but it was very different from flying over Borneo. In my country I looked down on jungle trees and rivers of which I am not afraid, but here I looked down on buildings and trains which would be difficult to fall upon with comfort.

We went many miles before coming to Mr. Jim's village. We went into his house and his people gave us food and drink. But I was ashamed to eat with them because I did not know how to eat the food cleverly as they did, because all my life in my country I was accustomed to eat with my fingers. It is difficult to carry the food with those small weapons to the mouth. I did not wish to be rude by not eating the food after their custom, so I pretended I was not very hungry. The next day we returned to New York.

One day Mr. Johnson said to me that in two days he must put me on a ship to return to Borneo. I was very sad to hear this because he was very good to me, and America was so astonishing. I cried like a child and I couldn't eat anything. This was the day before the New Year and he bought me a watch for a present. I went to Times Square that night to see the people make a holiday. There were so many people that I was frightened and wanted to return to my house. I could not return because we were like fish caught in a fish trap. Men blew things in my ears that made the noise of goats. I said to them, "Don't do that!" And they said, "Don't you like that? Don't you do this in your country?" And I said, "No!" I wanted to go home to bed, but I couldn't go home until one o'clock in the morning, because you can't go home on New Year in New York.

That was the first day of the first month, and I was sad because I had to sail for Borneo that day. Mr. Johnson took my hand and said *"Selamat belavar"* in Malay, and I said "Good-by" in English, which I think was polite. Mrs. Johnson took me to the Dutch ship, *Kota Djandi*, and I felt so sad to leave them that I forgot to take my two blankets, two pillows, and my rubber shoes, but I remembered my nine neckties and my big hat and my black coat.

So I sailed for home, and when the ship arrived at Singapore I took a letter to a man there from Mr. Johnson. The man took the letter, and after he read it he said, "Don't you know that this man is already dead? He fell in a flying ship many days ago."

And I just looked at him and I could not talk at all because I felt so sad. Then I cried like a child for two days and could not eat or sleep. And now I know my heart will always be sad for this man.

Now I will go back to my village and see my people. I will buy more buffaloes and plant more rice. When the harvest season comes I will harvest my rice, and I will drink rice beer and take a wife. But although I will live as all men do here, never will I forget America.

(AGNES NEWTON KEITH *was living in the seaport town of Sandakan at the time Saudin returned to Borneo. She has told his story, "as nearly as possible in translation, in Saudin's words," in* LAND BELOW THE WIND.

The Sword of Damocles

⟨ THIS story was already old when Cicero, the great Roman writer, retold it more than two thousand years ago.

DIONYSIUS, the tyrant of Sicily, was far from being happy, though he possessed great riches and all the pleasures which wealth and power could procure. Damocles, one of his flatterers, deceived by these superficial appearances of happiness, took occasion to compliment him on the extent of his power, his treasures, and royal magnificence; and declared that no monarch had ever been greater or happier than Dionysius.

"Hast thou a mind, Damocles," said the king, "to taste this happiness? To know by experience, what the enjoyments are, of which thou hast so high an idea?"

Damocles, with joy, accepted the offer. The king ordered that a royal banquet should be prepared and a gilded sofa covered with rich embroidery placed for his favorite. Sideboards loaded with gold and silver plate of immense value were arranged in the apartment. Pages of extraordinary beauty were ordered to attend the table and to obey his commands. Fragrant ointments, chaplets of flowers, and rich perfumes were added to the entertainment. The table was loaded with exquisite delicacies of every kind. Damocles was intoxicated with pleasure.

But in the midst of all this happiness, as he lay indulging himself in state, he saw, let down from the ceiling, exactly over his head, a glittering sword, which hung by a single hair. The sight of impending destruction put a speedy end to his joy; the glitter of the carved plate and the delicacy of the viands ceased to afford him any pleasure.

He dreaded to stretch forth his hand to the table. He threw off the garlands of roses, and hastened to remove from his dangerous situation. He earnestly entreated the king to restore him to his former humble condition, having no desire to enjoy any longer a happiness so terrible.

By this device, Dionysius intimated to Damocles how miserable he was in the midst of all his treasures.

No rank or possessions can make the guilty mind happy.

MAUDE RADFORD WARREN

How Arthur Became King

ONCE UPON a time, a thousand years before Columbus discovered America, there lived a brave and beautiful youth whose name was Arthur. His home was in England, near London; and he lived with the good knight Sir Hector, whom he always called father.

They dwelt in a great square castle of gray stone, with a round tower at each corner. It was built about a courtyard, and was surrounded by a moat, and across this was a drawbridge that could be raised or lowered. When it was raised, the castle was practically a little island and very hard for enemies to attack.

On one side of the moat was a large wood, and here Arthur spent a great deal of his time. He liked to lie under the trees and gaze up at the blue of the sky. All about him old oaks stood like giant guardians watching sturdily over the soil where they had grown for centuries. Sometimes a herd of brown deer with shy dark eyes would pass, holding their graceful heads high in the air; sometimes a flock of pheasants with brilliant plumage rose from the bushes. Again there was no sound except the tapping of a bright-crested woodpecker, and no motion but the fluttering of leaves.

At times, when it was dim and silent in the wood, Arthur would hear bursts of merry laughter, the tinkling of bells, and the jingling of spurs. Then he would know that knights and ladies were riding down the road which ran beside the trees. Soon the knights would appear on horses, with gaily ornamented saddles, and bridles from which hung silver bells. The knights wore helmets laced with slender gold chains, and coats of mail made of tiny links of steel. The ladies sat on horses with long trappings of silk. Their robes were very beautiful, being made of velvet or silk trimmed with ermine. Arthur liked to watch them, flashing by: crimson and gold and blue and rose-colored. In those troublous times, however, the roads were so insecure that such companies did not often pass.

Sometimes the knights and ladies came to visit Sir Hector. Then Arthur would hurry from the forest to the castle. Sir Hector would stand on the lowered drawbridge to greet his guests. From all parts of the castle the squires and servants would come running to take the horses of the knights and ladies. Sir Hector's wife and daughters would then appear, and with their own hands remove the armor of the knights. They would offer them golden basins of water, and towels for washing, and after that put velvet mantles upon their shoulders. Then the guests would be brought to the supper table.

But Arthur did not spend all his time dreaming in the woods or gazing at knights and ladies. For many hours of the day he practiced feats of arms in the courtyard. It was the custom in England to train boys of noble birth to be knights. As soon as they were old enough, they were taught to ride. Later on, they lived much among the ladies and maidens, learning gentle manners. Under the care of the knights, they learned to hunt, to carry a lance properly, and to use the sword. Having gained this skill, they were made squires if they had shown themselves to be of good character.

Then, day by day, the squires practiced at the quintain. This was an upright post, on the top of which turned a crosspiece, having on one end a broad board, and on the other a bag of sand. The object was to ride up at full gallop, strike the board with a long lance, and get away without being hit by the sandbag.

Besides this, the squires had services to do for the knights, in order that they might learn to be useful and always to be humble. They took care of the armor of the knights, carried letters and messages for them, accompanied them at joustings and tournaments, being ready with extra weapons or assistance. After months of such service, they went through a beautiful ceremony and were made knights. In the country round about, Arthur, of all the squires, was the most famous for his skill in the use of the lance and the sword, for his keenness in the hunt, and for his courtesy to all people.

Now, at this time there was no ruler in England. The powerful Uther of Wales, who had governed England, was dead, and all the strong lords of the country were struggling to be king in his place. This gave rise to a great deal of quarreling and bloodshed.

There was in the land a wise magician named Merlin. He was so old that his beard was as white as snow, but his eyes were as clear as a little child's. He feared that all the fighting that was going on would do serious harm to the kingdom.

In those days the great and good men who ruled in the Church had power almost equal to that of the monarch. The kings and the great lords listened to their advice. So Merlin went to the Archbishop of Canterbury, the churchman who in all England was the most beloved, and said:

"Sir, it is my advice that you send to all the great lords of the realm and bid them come to London by Christmas to choose a king."

The archbishop did as Merlin advised, and at Christmas all the great lords came to London. The largest church in the city stood not far from the north bank of the Thames. A churchyard surrounded it, filled with yew trees, the trunks of which were knotted with age. The powerful lords rode up in their clanking armor to the gate, where they dismounted, and reverently entered the church.

The good archbishop, from where he stood in the chancel, looked down on them all. Just behind him was the altar covered with a cloth of crimson and gold, surmounted by a golden crucifix. In front of him, kneeling under the gray arches which spanned the church, were the greatest men in the kingdom. He looked at the stern bronzed faces and their glittering armor, and prayed God to make the best man king.

Then began the service. At the close of the first prayer some of the knights looked out of the window, and there in the churchyard they saw a great square stone. In the middle of it was an anvil of steel a foot high, and fixed therein was a beautiful sword. On the sword was some writing, set in with gold:

Whosoever pulls this sword out of this stone and anvil is the real king of all England.

The knights who read this told the archbishop, but he said, "No man is to touch the sword until all the prayers are said."

After the service was over, the lords went into the churchyard. They each pulled at the sword, but none could stir it.

"The king is not here," said the archbishop, "but God will make him known."

Then the archbishop said that on a fixed day every man in the kingdom should try to pull the sword out of the anvil. He ordered that on New Year's Day all the people should be brought together for a great tournament to be held on the south bank of the Thames, near London Bridge. After a few days spent in jousting among the knights, each man should make the trial to find out whether or not he was to be king.

The brave youth Arthur did not know of the contest that was to be made for the sword. Sir Hector told him that he was to go to a tournament, but he did not tell him the reason for holding the tournament. So Arthur rode to London with Sir Hector and Sir Kay, Sir Hector's oldest son.

Sir Hector and Sir Kay went soberly in front. They were tall, stalwart men and rode black horses, their dark figures making shadows on the light snow that had fallen. Arthur, riding behind them, felt exhilarated by the crisp winter air. He was so happy in the thought of the tournament he was to see, that he could have sung for joy.

Sometimes the narrow road wound through thick woods; again it rose up over a gently rolling hill. From the hilltops the rider could see London far in the distance. The castles and huts, barns and sheds, smithies, shops and mills, stood out in the keen sunlight. A high wall surrounded them, while on one side flowed the river Thames.

After they had entered the city, and had passed the churchyard, and had almost reached London Bridge, Sir Kay discovered that he had left his sword at home.

"Will you go back for it?" he asked Arthur.

"That I will," said Arthur.

But when he reached their dwelling, he could not get in. The drawbridge was raised, and he could not make the warden hear his calling. Then Arthur was disturbed, and said to himself:

"I will hasten to the churchyard we passed, and take the beautiful sword which I saw in the stone. It does not seem to belong to anyone, and my brother Kay must have a weapon."

So he rode on till he reached the churchyard, dismounted, and tied his horse to a sapling. Arthur ran up and pulled lightly but eagerly at the sword. It came at once from the anvil. He hurried to Sir Kay, who was waiting for him on London Bridge. Sir Kay knew that the weapon was the one that had been fixed fast in the stone, but he said nothing to Arthur. The two soon overtook Sir Hector, who had ridden slowly to the field where the tournament was taking place. Sir Kay told his father what had happened.

The good knight at once spoke with great respect to Arthur. "Sir," he said, "you must be the king of this land."

"What mean you, sir?" asked Arthur.

Sir Hector looked at the wondering youth. "Can you put this sword back in its place and pull it out again?" he asked.

"Easily," replied Arthur.

The three returned to the great stone, and Arthur put back the sword. Sir Hector tried to take it out, but failed.

"Now, you try," he said to Sir Kay.

But Sir Kay, in spite of great efforts, also failed. Then Arthur, at Sir Hector's bidding, tried, and at once pulled forth the sword. At that Sir Hector and Sir Kay knelt before Arthur.

"Alas," said Arthur, raising them

from the ground, "my own dear father and my brother, why do you kneel to me?"

"Nay, my lord Arthur," said Sir Hector, "I am not your father. You are of higher blood than I am. Long ago, when you were a little baby, Merlin brought you to me to take care of, telling me that you were to be the king."

"Then whose son am I?" cried Arthur.

"Merlin brought you to me, saying that you were the son of King Uther and Yguerne his wife. But because the king was dead and the lords powerful and jealous, he told me to guard you in secrecy lest your life be taken. I did not know whether the story was true or false then, but you were a helpless child. Merlin was a wise sage, and so I took you and brought you up as my own. And now, my gracious lord, will you be good to me and mine when you are king?"

"I will, indeed," replied Arthur, "for I am more beholden to you than to any one else in the world, and also to my good lady, your wife. She has reared me as if I were her own child. If it be God's will that I shall sometime become king, ask of me then what you will."

Then the three went to the Archbishop of Canterbury and related to him the story of Merlin and all that had occurred. At his request they told no one else.

At the command of the archbishop on Twelfth-day, which is the sixth of January, all the great lords assembled in the churchyard. Each tried to draw forth the sword, and each failed. Then the untitled people came and tried. Everyone failed until at last Arthur stepped forward. He hardly more than touched the sword when it came away in his hand.

At this many of the great lords were angry.

"He is but a boy," they said, "and not of high blood."

They refused to believe the story of his birth told by Merlin and Sir Hector. And because of all the quarreling, it was decided to have another trial at Candlemas, which fell in the month of February. Again Arthur was victorious. Then the great lords decreed that there should be another trial at Easter, and again Arthur succeeded. Next they decided to have a final trial at the Feast of Pentecost which fell in May.

At this time Arthur again drew out the sword from the anvil. Then the common people, who had so far let the lords have their will, cried out: "We will have Arthur for our king. We will have no more delay, for we see that it is God's will that he shall be our ruler."

Then all the people knelt, high and low, rich and poor. Arthur, taking his sword, reverently placed it on the great altar, beside which the archbishop stood. This was a sign that he meant to dedicate himself and his sword to God.

Afterward the crowning was held, and all the brave men and fair ladies in the land were present. The lords wore beautiful robes of velvet and ermine, with gold and jewels on their breast-plates. The ladies' robes were of purple and white and scarlet and gold and blue, and they wore many pearls and rubies and diamonds, so that all the place where they were assembled was glowing with light and color.

But Arthur, who wore a plain white robe, did not think of the beauty and richness. He was very grave, knowing that he was about to take a solemn oath. He bowed his head, while the archbishop set upon it the golden crown, which gleamed with jewels. Then he stood up before his people, and vowed that he would be a good king and always do justice. All the people uncovered their heads and vowed to serve and obey him; and when he smiled kindly on them as he rode slowly through the throng, they threw up their caps and shouted joyfully: "Long live King Arthur! Long live the King!"

After his crowning the King set about righting all the wrongs that had been done since the death of King Uther. He gave back the lands and money that had been taken from widows and orphans, and would permit no unkindness to any of his subjects. Thus, at the very beginning of his reign, his people began to call him GOOD KING ARTHUR.

⟨ THIS story and others about Arthur after he became king may have had their beginning in the legends that grew up around a real British chieftain.

The Shooting Match at Nottingham Town

IN MERRY ENGLAND in the time of old, when good King Henry II ruled the land, there lived within the green shades of Sherwood Forest, near Nottingham Town, a famous outlaw whose name was Robin Hood. No archer ever lived that could speed a gray goose shaft with such skill and cunning as his, nor were there ever such yeomen as the sevenscore merry men that roamed with him through the greenwood shades. Not only Robin himself but all the band were outlaws and dwelt apart from other men, yet they were beloved by the country people round about, for no one ever came to jolly Robin for help in time of need and went away again with empty fist . . .

The Sheriff of Nottingham was very wroth because of his failure to take jolly Robin, for it came to his ears, as ill news always does, that the people laughed at him, and a man hates nothing so much as to be made a jest of.

"Now," thought the Sheriff, "could I but persuade Robin nigh to Nottingham Town so that I could find him, I warrant I would lay hands upon him so stoutly that he would never get away again." Then of a sudden it came to him like a flash that were he to pro-

claim a great shooting match and offer some grand prize, Robin Hood might be overpersuaded by his spirit to come. It was this thought which caused him to cry "Aha!" and smite his palm upon his thigh.

So he sent messengers north and south, and east and west, to proclaim through town, hamlet, and countryside, this grand shooting match. Every one was bidden that could draw a long bow, and the prize was to be an arrow of pure beaten gold.

When Robin Hood first heard the news of this he was in Lincoln Town, and hastening back to Sherwood Forest he soon called all his merry men about him and spoke to them thus:

"Now hearken, my merry men all, to the news that I have brought from Lincoln Town. Our friend the Sheriff of Nottingham hath proclaimed a shooting match, and hath sent messengers to tell of it through all the countryside, and the prize is to be a bright golden arrow. Now I fain would have one of us win it, because of the fairness of the prize and because our sweet friend the Sheriff hath offered it. So we will take our bows and shafts and go there to shoot, for I know right well that merriment will be a-going. What say ye, lads?"

Then young David of Doncaster spoke up and said: "Now, listen, I pray thee, good master, unto what I say. I have come straight from our friend Eadom o' the Blue Boar, and there I heard the full news of this same match. But, master, I know from him, and he got it from the Sheriff's man, that this same knavish Sheriff hath but laid a trap for thee in this shooting match. So go not, good master, but stay within the greenwood lest we all meet dole and woe."

"Now," quoth Robin, "thou art a wise lad and keepest thine ears open and thy mouth shut, as becometh a wise and crafty woodsman. But what thou tellest me maketh me to desire the prize even more. We must meet guile with guile. Now some of you clothe yourselves as friars, and some as rustic peasants, and some as tinkers or as beggars, but see that each man taketh a good bow or broadsword, in case need should arise. As for myself, I will shoot for this same golden arrow. Should I win it, we will hang it to the branches of our good greenwood tree for the joy of all the band. How like you the plan, my merry men all?"

Then "Good, good!" cried all the band right heartily.

A fair sight was Nottingham Town on the day of the shooting match. All along upon the green meadow beneath the town wall stretched a row of benches, one above the other, which were for knight and lady, squire and dame, and rich burghers and their wives. At the end of the range, near the target, was a raised seat bedecked with ribbons and garlands of flowers, for the Sheriff of Nottingham and his dame. The range was twoscore paces broad. At one end stood the target, at the other a tent of striped canvas, from the pole of which fluttered many-colored flags and streamers.

Already, while it was early, the benches were beginning to fill with people of quality. With these came also the poorer folk who sat upon the green grass. In the great tent the archers were gathering. The very best archers of Merry England were there, whose names have been handed down to us in goodly ballads of the olden time.

At last the Sheriff himself came with his lady, he riding with stately mien upon his milk-white horse and she upon her brown filly. Upon his head he wore a purple velvet cap, and purple velvet was his robe, trimmed with rich ermine. His lady was dressed in blue velvet, all trimmed with swan's-down. They made a gallant sight as they rode side by side, and all the people shouted. And so the Sheriff and his lady came to their place, where men-at-arms stood about, waiting for them.

Then the Sheriff bade his herald wind upon his silver horn; who thereupon sounded three blasts that came echoing cheerily back from the gray walls of Nottingham. The archers stepped to their places. The herald stood forth and loudly proclaimed the rules of the game as follows:

"Shoot each man from yon mark, which is sevenscore yards and ten from the target. One arrow shooteth each man first. The ten that shooteth the fairest shafts shall be chosen to shoot again. Two arrows shooteth each man of these ten; then shall the three that shoot the fairest shafts be chosen for to shoot again. Three arrows shooteth each man of those three, and to him that shooteth the fairest shafts shall the prize be given."

The Sheriff leaned forward, looking among the archers to find whether Robin Hood was amongst them; but no one was there clad in Lincoln green, such as was worn by Robin and his band. "Nevertheless," said the Sheriff to himself, "he may still be there, and I miss him among the crowd."

And now the archers shot, each man in turn, and the good folk never saw such archery as was done that day. Six arrows were within the clout, four within the black, and only two smote the outer ring. When the last arrow struck the target, all the people shouted aloud, for it was noble shooting.

And now but ten men were left of all those that had shot before. Of these ten, six were famous throughout the land, and most of the folk gathered there knew them. These six men were Gilbert o' the Red Cap, Adam o' the Dell, Diccon Cruikshank, William o' Leslie, Hubert o' Cloud, and Swithin o' Hertford. Two others were yeomen of merry Yorkshire. Another was a tall stranger in blue, and the last was a tattered stranger in scarlet, who wore a patch over one eye.

"Now," quoth the Sheriff to a man-at-arms who stood near him, "seest thou Robin Hood amongst those ten?"

"Nay, that do I not, your worship," answered the man. "Six of them I know right well. Of those Yorkshire yeomen, one is too tall and the other too short for that bold knave. Robin's beard is as yellow as gold, while yon tattered beggar in scarlet hath a beard of brown, besides being blind of one eye. As for the stranger in blue, Robin's shoulders, I ween, are three inches broader than his."

"Then," quoth the Sheriff, smiting his thigh angrily, "yon knave is a coward as well as a rogue."

Then, after they had rested a short time, those ten stout men stepped forth to shoot again. Not a word was spoken, but when the last had shot his arrow another great shout arose.

"Now by Our Gracious Lady fair," quoth old Sir Amyas o' the Dell, "ne'er saw I such archery before."

And now but three men were left of all those that had shot before. One was Gill o' the Red Cap, one the tattered stranger in scarlet, and one Adam o' the Dell of Tamworth Town.

"Now, shoot thou well, Gilbert," cried the Sheriff, "and if thine be the best shaft, fivescore broad silver pennies will I give to thee beside the prize."

"Truly I will do my best," quoth Gilbert, right sturdily. So saying, he drew forth a fair smooth arrow and fitted it deftly to the string. Straight flew the arrow and lit fairly in the clout, a finger breadth from the center. "A Gilbert, a Gilbert!" shouted all the crowd.

Then the tattered stranger stepped forth, and all the people laughed as they saw a yellow patch that showed beneath his arm when he raised his elbow to shoot. He drew the good yew bow quickly, and quickly loosed a shaft; yet his arrow lodged nearer the center than the other by twice the length of a barleycorn.

"Now by all the saints in Paradise!" cried the Sheriff. "That is a lovely shaft in very truth!"

Then Adam o' the Dell shot, carefully and cautiously, and his arrow lodged close beside the stranger's. After a short space all three shot again, and once more each arrow lodged within the clout, but this time Adam o' the Dell's was farthest from the center. Again the tattered stranger's shot was the best. Then, after another time of rest, they all shot for the third time. Gilbert took great heed to his aim, keenly measuring the distance and shooting with shrewdest care. Straight flew the arrow, and all shouted till the very flags that waved in the breeze shook with the sound, for the shaft had lodged close beside the spot that marked the very center.

"Well done, Gilbert!" cried the Sheriff right joyously. "Fain am I to believe the prize is thine, and fairly won. Now, thou ragged knave, let me see thee shoot a better shaft than that."

Naught spake the stranger but took his place, while all was hushed, and no one spoke or even seemed to breathe, so great was the silence for wonder of what he would do. Meanwhile, also, quite still stood the stranger. Then he drew his trusty yew, holding it drawn but a moment, then loosed the string. Straight flew the arrow, and so true that it smote a gray goose feather from off Gilbert's shaft, and lodged close in the very center. No one spoke and no one shouted, but each man looked into his neighbor's face amazedly.

"Nay," quoth old Adam o' the Dell presently, drawing a long breath, "twoscore years and more have I shot shaft, but I shoot no more this day. No man can match with yon stranger, whosoe'er he may be."

Then the Sheriff came down from his dais and drew near, in all his silks and velvets, to where the tattered stranger stood. "Here, good fellow," quoth the Sheriff, "take thou the prize. Well and fairly hast thou won it. What may be thy name, and whence comest thou?"

"Men do call me Jock o' Teviotdale," said the stranger.

"Then, by Our Lady, Jock, thou art the fairest archer that e'er mine eyes beheld. If thou wilt join my service I will clothe thee with a better coat than that thou hast upon thy back. Thou shalt eat and drink of the best, and at every Christmastide fourscore marks shall be thy wage. I trow thou drawest better bow than that coward knave, Robin Hood, that dared not show his face here this day. Say, good fellow, wilt thou join my service?"

"Nay, that will I not," quoth the stranger roughly. "No man in all Merry England shall be my master."

"Then get thee gone!" cried the Sheriff, and his voice trembled with anger. "By my troth I have a good part of a mind to have thee beaten for thine insolence!"

It was a right motley company that

gathered about the noble greenwood tree in Sherwood's depths that same day. A score and more of barefoot friars were there, and some that looked like tinkers, and some that seemed to be sturdy beggars and peasants. Seated upon a mossy couch was one all clad in tattered scarlet, with a patch over one eye; and in his hand he held the golden arrow that was the prize of the great shooting match. Then, amidst a noise of talking and laughter, he took the patch from off his eye and stripped away the scarlet rags from off his body and showed himself all clothed in fair Lincoln green.

Quoth he: "Easy come these things away, but walnut stain cometh not so speedily from yellow hair." Then all laughed louder than before, for it was Robin Hood himself that had won the prize from the Sheriff's very hands.

Then all sat down to the woodland feast and talked amongst themselves of the merry jest that had been played upon the Sheriff, and of the adventures that had befallen each member of the band in his disguise. But when the feast was done, Robin Hood took Little John apart and said, "Truly am I vexed, for I heard the Sheriff say today, 'Thou shootest better than that coward knave, Robin Hood, that dared not show his face here this day.' I would fain let him know who it was who won the golden arrow and that I am no coward."

Then Little John said, "Good Master, take thou me and Will Stutely and we will send yon fat Sheriff news of all this by a messenger such as he doth not expect."

That day the Sheriff sat at meat in the great hall of his house at Nottingham Town. Long tables stood down the hall, at which sat men-at-arms. There they talked of the day's shooting as they ate their meat and quaffed their ale. The Sheriff sat at the head of the table upon a raised seat under a canopy, and beside him sat his dame.

"By my troth," said he, "I did reckon full roundly that that knave, Robin Hood, would be at the game today. I did not think that he was such a coward. But who could that saucy knave be who answered me so bravely?"

Even as he finished speaking, something fell rattling among the dishes on the table, while those that sat near started up wondering what it might be. After a while one of the men-at-arms gathered courage enough to pick it up and bring it to the Sheriff. Then every one saw that it was a blunted gray goose shaft, with a fine scroll tied near its head. The Sheriff opened the scroll and his cheeks grew ruddy with rage, for this is what he saw:

"Now Heaven bless thy grace this day,
    Say all in sweet Sherwood,
For thou didst give the prize away
    To merry Robin Hood."

"Whence came this?" cried the Sheriff in a mighty voice.

"Even through the window, your worship," quoth the man who had handed the shaft to him.

THE BOOK OF
Animals

Introduction

⟨["EVERY ANIMAL is honest. Every animal is straightforward. Every animal is true," said Kenneth Grahame. "Every animal by instinct lives according to his nature. Thereby he lives wisely and betters the traditions of mankind."

This quality of steadfastness and the devotion of our pets help to account for the popularity of stories about horses and dogs and other four-footed creatures. Our special feeling for them is part of our heritage, a heritage so old that we in the Western world have nearly forgotten it. There was a time when men thought of the beasts of forest and plain as their brothers. The early Egyptians paid homage to their cats as gods. One of the most popular Greek myths told of Pegasus, the winged horse, the steed of the Muses. The lion and the frog and the fox and the donkey in Aesop's fables had human faults and weaknesses, but it was their charm as animals that has given them their wide appeal.

These fables, recounted by Aesop, are believed to have originated in India, where the ancients told tales of animals "to teach the wise conduct of life." These were the words of Dhan Gopal Mukerji, whose modern stories taught reverence for all nature. This message is also implicit in some of the classic tales by Rudyard Kipling. Like the boy in "Rikki-Tikki-Tavi," Kipling was born in India when it was a part of the British Empire. His native nurses told him many old legends which later inspired his Jungle Books.

In America, the animal closest to our hearts is undoubtedly the dog. "In the whole history of the world," said Josh Billings, a *humorist of a hundred years ago, "there is but one thing that money cannot buy, to wit, the wag of a dog's tail." A dog may have a lengthy pedigree or he may be an abandoned mongrel, but he barks in the same language. His loyalty to his master is so whole-hearted that nothing more is asked of him.*

Yet there have been countless dogs that have worked for man. In "Barry the Lifesaver," Ruth Adams Knight has told of the re-markable St. Bernards trained by the monks at the Alpine hospice near the St. Bernard Pass. Barry, probably the greatest dog hero of all time, saved more than forty lives. After his death, the Father Joseph in the story was remembering "the strange and peculiar bond between a man and his dog. 'If I had a test for goodness in a man,' he said, 'I would base it on his relation to his dog.' "

The same sympathy existed between Robert E. Lee and Travel-ler, the handsome gray charger he rode during months of vigorous campaigning. A number of friendships between a man and his horse have been described by Marguerite Henry. Her "Brighty of Grand Canyon" is about a real burro that lived in the Canyon. Mrs. Henry's appealing little cat of "Welcome, Grimalkin," was the pet of the boy Benjamin West, "the father of American paint-ing."

"Unless you've loved an animal, given one a corner of your heart to live in, then this story is not for you," said George Papashvily, in telling of Kola, the bear which had been his constant companion for fifteen years. Kola would have delighted that famous animal lover, Doctor John Dolittle whose adventures eventually filled ten volumes. But it is not the good Doctor's exciting and amusing travels that the reader remembers longest. It is the understanding he creates between men and animals.

Children, like their elders, bask in the warmth of an animal's approval. More important, an increased awareness of its nature, fostered by reading animal tales, awakens the child's protective instincts. He comes to realize how much animals need their human friends. He discovers that it is good to be needed, and in assuming the role of a protector he finds greater security for himself.

Doctor Dolittle Learns Animal Language

ONCE UPON a time, many years ago, when our grandfathers were little children, there was a doctor; and his name was Dolittle—John Dolittle, M. D. *M. D.* means that he was a proper doctor and knew a whole lot. He lived in a little town called Puddleby-on-the-Marsh. His sister, Sarah Dolittle, was housekeeper for him.

The Doctor was very fond of animals and kept many kinds of pets. Besides the goldfish in the pond at the bottom of his garden, he had rabbits in the pantry, white mice in his piano, a squirrel in the linen closet, and a hedgehog in the cellar. He had a cow with a calf, too, and an old lame horse —twenty-five years of age—and chickens, and pigeons, and two lambs, and many other animals. But his favorite pets were Dab-Dab the duck, Jip the dog, Gub-Gub the baby pig, Polynesia the parrot, and the owl Too-Too. One day when an old lady with rheumatism came to see the Doctor, she sat on the hedgehog who was sleeping on the sofa and never came to see him any more.

Then his sister, Sarah Dolittle, came to him and said, "John, how can you expect sick people to come and see you when you keep all these animals in the house?"

"But I like the animals better than the 'sick people,'" said the Doctor.

"You are ridiculous," said his sister, and walked out of the room.

So, as time went on, the Doctor got more and more animals, and the people who came to see him got less and less. And the money he had saved up grew littler and littler . . .

It happened one day that the Doctor was sitting in his kitchen talking with the Cat's-meat Man who had come to see him with a stomach-ache.

"Why don't you give up being a people's doctor, and be an animal doctor?" asked the Cat's-meat Man.

The parrot, Polynesia, was sitting in the window looking out at the rain and singing a sailor song to herself. She stopped singing and started to listen.

"You see, Doctor," the Cat's-meat Man went on, "you know all about animals, much more than what these here vets do. That book you wrote about cats, why, it's wonderful! I can't read or write myself, or maybe *I'd* write some books. But my wife, Theodosia, she's a scholar, she is. And she read your book to me. Well, it's wonderful. You might have been a cat yourself. You know the way they think. And listen! You can make a lot of

[121]

money doctoring animals. I'd send all the old women who had sick cats or dogs to you. And if they didn't get sick fast enough, I could put something in the meat I sell 'em to make 'em sick, see?"

"Oh, no," said the Doctor quickly. "That wouldn't be right."

"Oh, I didn't mean real sick," answered the Cat's-meat Man. "But as you say, maybe it ain't quite fair on the animals. But they'll get sick anyway, because the old women always give 'em too much to eat. And look, all the farmers round about who had lame horses and weak lambs—they'd come. Be an animal doctor."

When the Cat's-meat Man had gone, the parrot flew off the window on to the Doctor's table and said: "That man's got sense. Give the silly people up—if they haven't brains enough to see you're the best doctor in the world. Take care of animals instead. They'll soon find it out. Be an animal doctor."

"Oh, there are plenty of animal doctors," said John Dolittle, putting the flowerpots outside on the window sill to get the rain.

"Yes, there are plenty," said Polynesia. "But none of them are any good at all. Now listen, Doctor, and I'll tell you something. Did you know that animals can talk?"

"I knew that parrots can talk," said the Doctor.

"Oh, we parrots can talk in two languages—people's language and bird language," said Polynesia proudly. "If I say, 'Polly wants a cracker,' you understand me. But hear this: *Ka-ka oi-ee, fee-fee?*"

"Good gracious!" cried the Doctor. "What does that mean?"

"That means, 'Is the porridge hot yet?' in bird language."

"My! You don't say so!" said the Doctor. "You never talked that way to me before."

"What would have been the good?" said Polynesia, dusting some cracker crumbs off her left wing. "You wouldn't have understood me if I had."

"Tell me some more," said the Doctor, all excited. He rushed over to the dresser drawer and came back with the butcher's book and a pencil. "Now don't go too fast, and I'll write it down. This is interesting, very interesting, something quite new. Give me the Birds' ABC first, slowly now."

So that was the way the Doctor came to know that animals had a language of their own and could talk to one another. And all that afternoon, while it was raining, Polynesia sat on the kitchen table giving him bird words to put down in the book.

At teatime, when the dog, Jip, came in, the parrot said to the Doctor, "See, he's talking to you."

"Looks to me as though he were scratching his ear," said the Doctor.

"But animals don't always speak with their mouths," said the parrot, raising her eyebrows. "They talk with their ears, with their feet, with their tails—with everything. Sometimes they don't *want* to make a noise. Do you see now the way he's twitching up one side of his nose?"

"What's that mean?" asked the Doctor.

"That means, 'Can't you see that it has stopped raining?'" Polynesia answered. "He is asking you a question. Dogs nearly always use their noses for asking questions."

After a while, with the parrot's help, the Doctor got to learn the language of the animals so well that he could talk to them himself and understand everything they said. Then he gave up being a people's doctor altogether.

As soon as the Cat's-meat Man had told every one that John Dolittle was going to become an animal doctor, old ladies began to bring him their pet pugs and poodles who had eaten too much cake, and farmers came many miles to show him sick cows and sheep.

One day a plow horse was brought to him; and the poor thing was terribly glad to find a man who could talk in horse language.

"You know, Doctor," said the horse, "that vet over the hill knows nothing at all. He has been treating me six weeks now, for spavins. What I need is *spectacles*. I am going blind in one eye. There's no reason why horses shouldn't wear glasses, the same as people. But that stupid man over the hill never even looked at my eyes. He kept on giving me big pills. I tried to tell him; but he couldn't understand a word of horse language. What I need is spectacles."

"Of course, of course," said the Doctor. "I'll get you some at once."

"I would like a pair like yours," said the horse, "only green. They'll keep the sun out of my eyes while I'm plowing the Fifty-Acre Field."

"Certainly," said the Doctor. "Green ones you shall have."

"You know, the trouble is, Sir," said the plow horse as the Doctor opened the front door to let him out, "the trouble is that *anybody* thinks he can doctor animals, just because the animals don't complain. As a matter of fact, it takes a much cleverer man to be a really good animal doctor than it does to be a good people's doctor. My farmer's boy thinks he knows all about horses, and he has got as much brain as a potato bug. He tried to put a mustard plaster on me last week."

"Where did he put it?" asked the Doctor.

"Oh, he didn't put it anywhere—on me," said the horse. "He only tried to. I kicked him into the duck pond."

"Well, well!" said the Doctor.

"I'm a pretty quiet creature as a rule," said the horse, "very patient with people, don't make much fuss. But it was bad enough to have that vet giving me the wrong medicine. And when that booby started to monkey with me, I just couldn't bear it any more."

"Did you hurt the boy much?" asked the Doctor.

"Oh, no," said the horse. "I kicked him in the right place. The vet's looking after him now. When will my glasses be ready?"

"I'll have them for you next week," said the Doctor. "Come in again Tuesday."

Then John Dolittle got a fine, big pair of green spectacles; and the plow horse stopped going blind in one eye and could see as well as ever. Soon it became a common sight to see farm animals wearing glasses in the country round Puddleby, and a blind horse was a thing unknown.

And so it was with all the other animals that were brought to him. As soon as they found that he could talk their language, they told him where the pain was and how they felt, and of course it was easy for him to cure them.

Now all these animals went back and told their brothers and friends that there was a doctor in the little house with the big garden who really was a doctor. And whenever any creatures got sick—not only horses and cows and dogs, but all the little things of the fields, like harvest mice and water voles, badgers and bats—they came at once to his house on the edge of the town. His big garden was nearly always crowded with animals trying to get in to see him.

There were so many that came that he had to have special doors made for the different kinds. He wrote *Horses* over the front door, *Cows* over the side door, and *Sheep* on the kitchen door. Each kind of animal had a separate door. Even the mice had a tiny tunnel made for them into the cellar, where they waited patiently in rows for the Doctor to come round to them.

And so, in a few years' time, every living thing for miles and miles got to know about John Dolittle, M. D. And the birds who flew to other countries in the winter told the animals in foreign lands of the wonderful doctor of Puddleby-on-the-Marsh, who could understand their talk and help them in their troubles. In this way he became famous among the animals, all over the world, better known even than he had been among the folks of the West Country. And he was happy and liked his life very much.

⟨[THIS *story is from the first of the ten* DR. DOLITTLE *books, the second of which,* THE VOYAGES OF DR. DOLITTLE, *won the Newbery Medal in 1923.*

My Friend Kola

⟨ THIS *is the true story of a pet bear that was the author's constant companion for fifteen years, when he was a boy in the Caucasus.*

MY UNCLE GIORGI went to a basket beside the hearth, lifted something out and brought it to me. In that very minute I knew here was what I wanted most in all the world.

"Your Easter present," my Uncle Giorgi said.

"To be mine, really mine, to keep?"

"Yours to keep. Feed him and brush him and give him clean water to drink."

"I will, I will."

"Treat him always as you should wish, were he the master and you the animal."

"Oh, I will. Let me hold him."

My Uncle Giorgi set him in my arms. Above my hand I could feel a heart beating. I touched the round, black button nose, the scraps of ears against his head. I ran my hand over his rough coat. He opened milk-blue eyes to me, yawned, stuck out a tongue pink as watermelon, sneezed and went back to sleep.

"Where's his mother?" I said.

My Uncle Giorgi shook his head.

"Doesn't she care if I have him?"

"Not any more. She's dead. Shot to make a day's sport for someone and left. I found this little one beside her crying and cold. You must feed him milk for a little while."

"I will. I'll feed him and brush him and take care of him and keep him as long as I live."

"No," my Uncle Giorgi said, "for your sorrow you cannot. Accept it. None of the animals we love live as long as we do."

"Why not?"

"I don't know. Maybe to remind us how short time really is. What will you name him?"

"Kola."

So next day I took my Kola and started home. Now the whole forest was awake. Cuckoos calling and hoopoe birds chattering back and forth, while the rabbits went rushing ahead from bush to bush with the news. From the highest rocks the mountain goats stopped and looked down to see me walking proud with my little bear beside me.

But when we got home Kola, I'm

[125]

sorry to say, wasn't made very welcome. The cats ignored him. Challa, my own colt, rolled his eyes, ruffled his underlip and stamped his feet. The first time Kola went outdoors alone, the gander nipped his stub tail so hard that Kola hid under my bed and cried his heart dry to find the world so strange and cruel and full of geese. It took a whole comb of honey to coax him out again.

The neighbors were afraid of Kola, too, and warned my father to send him away before he ate us all up. My father was a clever man and, though he could not agree with them, he listened to all they had to say, which satisfied them almost as much.

Only he told me: "Teach Kola to be a good bear and not to hurt or frighten anybody. For your sake and for his own."

I did. I taught him to be clean. I carved him a nice comb from mulberry wood, and sleeked him up every day with it, and I took him swimming with me in the river. I taught him to be friendly and not to eat what wasn't his or bite even in play. I taught him to bow and shake hands and wrestle and jump and play soldier and catch a ball and dance the Lesghinka. I taught him all I knew myself—how to follow a bee at the flower home to the hive in the tree; the way to know a ripe apple from a sour one; the road through the thicket to the clearing where the big blue plums grew.

The only thing Kola wouldn't learn, no matter how many times I showed him, was to crack nuts with a stone. He preferred to use his teeth. And I

couldn't keep him from being curious. The whole world was a question for Kola, and each day he learned a little piece more of the answer.

Often and often this got him into trouble. Once workmen came from the city to build a fine house for a prince. After a few days passed I had a complaint from the carpenter that Kola had growled at him. From then on I kept Kola at home during the day. But nights he went back there and climbed all over the scaffold—not to hurt anything, but just so he would know, too, the same as the rest of us, how a prince's house gets built. The carpenter found out and so on purpose he left a cross plank with the far end resting on air. When Kola stepped there, it threw him to the ground and bruised him so bad he couldn't walk for a week.

After that Kola waited his chance until one night the carpenter forgot to put all of his tools away. The next day the hammer was gone. While the carpenter searched everywhere, Kola sat on it and watched, picking his teeth with his long claws and laughing from the side of his muzzle as only bears can . . .

Another time Kola took my cousin's little boy and washed him in the brook. My cousin, instead of appreciating the favor, wrung her hands and called for the army and all the saints to come out of heaven and help her. But the baby, when I took him away, screamed so hard we had to give him back to Kola to laugh and splash some more.

After this Kola was in bad reputation, at least with all the mothers in our village, until late that fall when a regiment on special maneuvers marched in. The Czar's officers were quartered on us, and they were each for themselves little czars over us. They used our road and left us the ditches to walk in. Our vegetable gardens were stolen bare. Our lambs disappeared, and the women did not dare spread even a pocket handkerchief on the grass to dry.

It happened Kola and I were visiting my Uncle Giorgi when, coming back home in the half-dark of evening, I saw some cadets walking toward me. One was playing a concertina, the rest singing. When we met, because I did not give them the road, they pounded and cursed me between them.

Kola was not with me but trailed a little way behind, for at the curve of the road he had stopped to see if anybody was home in a hollow tree. Now down on his four feet like a dog, he came out from the shadows just in time to see the cadets snatch my cap and throw it into the ditch and push me after.

Well, if they had their army, I had mine. "Kola!" I called and whistled our "Charge."

The officers began singing again, the concertina with them. Then suddenly it stopped on a long thin half-note. Kola stood up on the road—taller and taller and still taller.

One swing of his paw tore the blouse from the nearest cadet. The second threw the concertina player into the ditch beside me, where the fellow lay crying, "The devil has risen from the ground. He struck me with his pitchfork." The rest took warning and, without waiting for the same thing to happen to them, ran away as fast as they could.

The concertina giving a last noisy breath on the ground interested Kola. With his forepaws he picked it up and pulled at the ends. It gave a loud whine for him. He pulled harder. It sounded again. But his next pull tore the bellows in half. He shook it a few times, but the concertina was dead. I got my cap and came out of the ditch. We went home together, walking all the way on the path.

By morning the whole village knew what had happened. From then on soldiers walked with care. Fruit hung undisturbed on our trees. Bread cooled on the ovens without watching. Though I didn't know it until long, long after, my Kola grew to be a legend in the Czar's army. "In Mtsketa do as you please," veterans told recruits, "and in Dushet, too. But in Kobiankari take care! There the men are so fierce the very children walk with wild beasts at heel for pets."

For our village Kola was a hero. The women gave him so much honey and fruit and chestnuts and white bread from their pantries he could have made himself a wedding party with it.

The very same neighbors who warned my father when first I got Kola were proud now to be living on such good terms with a bear. They showed him off to their visitors and laughed to see *them* afraid.

Finally the maneuvers were over and soldiers went away. We were all happy living in our village until the summer of the next year when two things happened that never happened before.

War came, and so did a circus. The circus was first. Up the great highway from Tiflis it rolled one hot day in three painted carts pulled by donkeys.

In the first sat some Syrians with a bunch of monkeys. In the next were golden-skinned men with almond eyes who juggled balls and whirled knives as they rode. The last wagon was covered with a cloth tucked and tied in on every side and painted on it: *Beware—of—Lion—Within.* Kola raised his head when the lion went by, sniffed, scrumpled his nose, sniffed again.

The circus made a camp in the meadow beside the stream. Three kopecks for the performance, one more to see the lion, and still another to hear him roar. Kola and I were the first ones to take a ticket as soon as the whole troupe was dressed and ready to play their parts.

Donkeys wearing head plumes counted to ten and answered questions. Dogs with pleated ruffs around their necks walked a tightrope. Monkeys were sick in bed until the goats came, doctors in frock coats wagging their beards, to give them medicine. Then they jumped up cured and did a thousand tricks.

Oh, it was a beautiful sight when the whole thing was going at once. The Syrians tumbling over and under each other and up into the air, turning circles as they came down. The donkeys rolling barrels; the dogs waltzing to a flute; the monkeys plunging through hoops as they rode the goats around a ring.

The golden jugglers threw their knives, spun them up and stood in the rain of bright blades and caught them as they fell without a scratch. The flutes played louder; the pink flares burning at the corners lit it all as bright as day, and the lion from his generous heart treated us all to free roars.

Next morning early before the sun was up I went back again. Because of Kola the man who owned the circus let me help him and come in free. I carried wood and water and combed the donkeys and fixed bread and sugared milk for the lion. He was getting old, poor fellow. The few teeth he had left, the owner told me, hurt him too much for chewing. But his roar was still fine and prickled your hair to hear it.

"Often and often I had bears," the owner said. "In fact I am called Vanno, *The Bear Man.* This is the first time I ever took the road without a bear." He scratched Kola's head. "How old is he?"

"Six."

"It's hard to find a new bear. Not every bear suits me. My last bear grew old and died. I gave him a funeral many a prince might envy. Some people thought it was a scandal. I didn't. I wanted him to enter heaven in style."

"Do bears go to heaven?" I said. It was a question that had bothered me for a long time, but I never had the courage to ask anybody before.

"If they don't," Vanno gave a threatening look at the sky, "better not expect *me* up there."

He rubbed Kola's hard head a while. "Can he wrestle or dance?"

"Can he?" I said.

I gave Kola our signal. He went through all his tricks. There was nothing he enjoyed more than an appreciative audience.

"Too good to be wasted on a village," Vanno said when Kola finished and made his best bow. "Let him come with me and find a career for himself."

"No."

"Come, come. I'll pay you well. What will you take for him?"

"Nothing."

"Fifty rubles?"

"No."

"Seventy-five?"

"No."

"A hundred rubles?"

"No," I said, "but I will trade him to you."

"Even better. For what?"

"For your oldest son!"

Vanno laughed. "You are a good boy. And when I tell you your bear is the smartest one I've ever seen, remember, I speak as an expert. Keep him. I don't blame you. Were he mine I would do the same. But just in case you must ever part with him, and only God knows what is yet to be with all the talk of war, bring him to me in Tiflis. Rustaveli Prospect. Ask anyone near the fountain. I am not," he finished proudly, "unknown."

After a few more shows, the jugglers packed their knives, the donkeys were harnessed, and the circus creaked on. The last thing, at the top of the hill, Vanno, The Bear Man, stopped and called back to me, "Remember. Rustaveli Prospect near the fountain. I will make it a hundred and fifty rubles!"

A hundred and fifty rubles! That was a fortune. It could buy a farm. It could buy a tradesman a prince's title. It could buy a substitute to send to war. It could not buy Kola.

⟨ This story is from THANKS TO NOAH, a book about George Papashvily's pets which he wrote in collaboration with his American-born wife. Their earlier book, ANYTHING CAN HAPPEN, told of his hilarious and often touching adventures as a peasant boy who arrived in the United States in the steerage of a Greek ship in the 1920's.

Brighty of Grand Canyon

⟪ BRIGHTY *was a real burro.* "An old prospector found him running wild along Bright Angel Creek," *said the author.* "The prospector roped and gentled him, then gave him his freedom. All winter Brighty roamed the warm inner reaches of the Canyon, but in summer he hightailed it to the rim. Soon men began using the trail he had made . . ."

As THE DAYS came and went, a restlessness grew in Brighty. Up on the rim of the Canyon the snow fell endlessly. It half buried the trees and then drifted part way down the wall, laying a thick fleece on the rocks. The snow line made a regular marker for him, a white fence that kept him within the canyon eight months of the year. Each day the stirring within him sharpened. His eyes kept gazing up at the rim as if mere looking would melt the snow and hurry the spring.

And then all at once it came. Warm rains washed down the face of the north wall, and when Brighty glanced up one early May morning, the white fence was gone. Now he was like a man squaring his shoulders for a big job, a job he liked doing. His summer home, big as the sky, was waiting for him up there beyond the canyon rim, and Uncle Jim would be waiting, too. He started climbing the miles as if there were no time to lose.

Resolutely he wound and twisted his way up and up. As he neared the top he saw ahead dark green evergreens and white-trunked aspen. He was almost there. And then! And then! He was over the top, on the rimtop of the world! Gone were the cliff walls and rock temples. Here was forest so dense it swallowed up the deer.

Brighty ran soundlessly on the forest duff, weaving in and out among the pines and aspens. And just at sunset he came upon his little cup of meadow nestled deep in the woods. With a grunt of happiness he loped along the threadlike path that led from the meadow to his secret cave. Here Nature had built a vast shelter with an overhanging cliff for a roof, a wide sand-swept floor, and one side open to the canyon. But what endeared it to Brighty was the pool of clean, clear water near the back wall, and the bed of ferns to lie in.

He buried his muzzle in the water

and drank deep. Then he settled down in a clump of ferns like a tired child come home at last to his own bed. His mouth opened in a great stretching yawn. Everything was just as before, even the ghost-white tree trunk guarding the open side of the cave.

The sun dipped low. Brighty heaved a sigh. A great peace came over him. As he lay among the ferns, watching the sailing moon, there was a sudden uprush of wings and a great flock of doves swept into his grotto. The noise was deafening. But in spite of it Brighty's eyelids drooped as he let the doves share his pool and scratch in the sand, eating the grains. They left as noisily as they had come, and no sooner were they gone than a mule deer stole silently to the pool to drink. But Brighty had already fallen asleep.

Night wore on. The wind died. There was only the drip-drip of the water, and a fern stem teetering back and forth to Brighty's breathing.

Then from far below the cave a mountain lion came slinking upward, her tawny coat mixing with the lights and shadows of the rocks. Her cat eyes gleamed in the dark as she crept nearer and nearer the old dead tree. She halted a moment, then hooked her claws into the trunk and climbed swiftly until she was even with the cave.

At first Brighty lay undiscovered in the darkness. But her eyes prowled the shadows and suddenly fixed upon his white belly. For a long time she seemed bewitched by her prey and lay watching him, her tail lashing, her mouth partly open, showing the white fangs.

Soundlessly she stole forward on a limb, tested it with her forepaws, then with her whole body. It bent to her weight, and she steadied herself, balancing like a diver. Then with one powerful leap her body made an arc in the blackness.

At the very moment of her leap Brighty was snuggling deeper into the ferns. She landed short of her mark. Cruel claws, intended for his head and neck, ripped his forelegs from shoulder to hoof. Instantly Brighty awoke, squealing in terror at the fire of pain shooting up his legs. He leaped to his feet, his mind in a panic as he faced the howling, hissing lion. He pawed at her wildly, trying to put out her fireball eyes, trying to push her over the brink.

But cunningly she rolled underneath him, cuffing and stabbing with rapier claws. Brighty backed away, rearing, then came down, flailing with his hoofs. Once he landed on the soft, muscly body, and felt it slither out from under him. He could feel blood oozing hot down his forelegs, but now the fear was gone. He felt only a frenzied need to stamp out the yellow flame of her eyes, to stop the hissing sound.

Suddenly the lion turned and with a bound was up in the tree. She tried a second spring for the catch, and this time she landed on Brighty's back. Down they both went on the floor of the cave, a snarling, grunting shadow in the moonlight. One moment they were almost in the pool, the next on the rim of the abyss with nothing but darkness and space below.

The stars swam around Brighty and mixed with the moon, and his blood trickled darkly in the sand. He tried to shake free of the claws stabbing his shoulder, but they only dug deeper. Now the two figures grappled and came again to the pool, and they went spinning into the icy water. Still the lion would not let go. With a scream of pain Brighty rolled over on his back, pinning her beneath him in the water. For long minutes he held her there. Then gradually the claws eased, and at last they fell away.

All the next day Brighty lay in misery. He kept biting at his cuts, trying to quiet the throbbing, but the gashes only widened and the burning pain ran up his legs. He moaned tiredly, and from time to time sank into a half sleep. He was too weak to eat, and he would not go near the tainted pool to drink.

Night came again with the whirring thunder of the doves. And then sunrise with hummingbirds drinking of the droplets as they fell from the cracked ceiling of rocks into the pool. Out of the weary fog of his mind Brighty saw a spry-legged figure enter the cave, heard a familiar voice cry, "Brighty! Bright Angel!"

A wave of memory swept over him. He tried to fix his eyes on the little

man wearing a black hat, but the whole figure rippled like something under water. Even the voice had a tremble in it.

"Brighty," Uncle Jim was saying as he stared at the hoof marks and claw marks, "you must've had a mighty tussle!" In an instant he was on his knees, gently parting the blood-matted hairs, examining the wounds. "These rips is bad, feller, mighty bad, but I'll pick us some globs o' pine gum and make a quick salve. We'll soon take the burn out o' them angry cuts."

As he stood up, he looked for a moment into the pool. "Whillikers!" he whistled. "A *big* cougar! She's six feet or more! 'Pears to me ye wrestled her into the water and drowned her. How'd ye do it, feller?"

Brighty's eyes watched the little man as he made a cup of his hands to catch the dripping water. It wasn't a very good cup. It leaked. But still it held enough to feel cool as it went down Brighty's throat. He closed his eyes while his ears flicked to remembered sounds—twigs being broken, and after a while fire crackling. Then came the pungent sharpness of pine tar in his nostrils.

"Now, boy," Uncle Jim explained while he poured the resin into Brighty's cuts, "she may hurt a leetle, but I got to do 'er."

He bent over the burro and began working the salve into the open sores. "You had me uneasy as an old biddy hen," he went on. "The warm rains come and the spring flowers, and I says to myself, 'Bright Angel'll be here next, any day now,' but ye didn't come

and ye didn't, and then I commences to fret and stew and finally I set out to hunt ye."

The thick, warm fluid did not hurt at all; it felt soothing. And the voice of Uncle Jim was something to hold to, like a rock in floodtime. Brighty let out a great sigh of relief and lifted his head a bit as if life were good again.

Uncle Jim stood up, and suddenly he was regarding his overalls as if he had never noticed them before. "I've an idee!" he crowed, eyes twinkling in triumph. He took out his pocketknife and pierced the denim just above one knee. Then he cut his way around the pants leg and stepped out of it.

"Y'see, boy," he said, "if we hide yer cuts, ye can't pick at 'em so easy and they'll heal nice and clean." He began cutting off his other trouser leg, chuckling to himself as he worked. He stepped out of that, too.

"Lemme see now, what was invented afore buttons?" He thought a moment. "Why, pegs, o' course!" He broke off several twigs and sharpened each to a fine point. "We'll just peg yer pants on!"

Next he laid his own bright red suspenders on Brighty's shoulders and slipped the pants legs over the tiny hoofs and up the torn legs, taking great care to hold the cloth away from the wounds.

"How about that!" he exclaimed, pegging the suspenders in place. He stood back, admiring the effect. "Now ye'll feel better, boy. Just ye rest a bit whilst I see about what's in the pool."

Brighty sniffed the old blue denim

[133]

and felt a strange easing. He stretched his legs out stiffly and sat up on his haunches, watching as Uncle Jim hauled the heavy body of the lion from the pool. After he had removed the paws, he dragged the carcass to the lip of the cave and with great effort flung it into the chasm. From out of nowhere three ravens came cawing and swooping down after it.

"The only good lion's a dead 'un!" Uncle Jim said, scrubbing his hands with sand.

He fastened the lion's paws to the trunk of the dead tree, and painstakingly carved the name "Brighty" into the bark. "In all Arizona," he said, "I figger there ain't another li'l ole burro smart enough to kill a cougar. Ye deserve a marker."

It was a strange-looking pair that left the cave and slow-footed toward Uncle Jimmy Owen's cabin on the edge of the meadow. But there was no one to see the old man with his cutoff pants showing two white legs bowed as powder horns. And there was no one to see the shaggy burro limping along after him, his pants legs swinging like a sailor's bell-bottoms.

No one to see? No human beings, that is. But everywhere wide, unblinking eyes stared—the eyes of deer and cottontail rabbits, and squirrels and grouse and jays.

There was no visible tie rope between the man and the burro, but it was there all the same, a tie rope of such stuff as could never thin out and break apart.

⟨ WHEN gathering material for her book, BRIGHTY OF GRAND CANYON, Marguerite Henry visited the Canyon country, talking with old-timers and climbing the same trails Brighty had made. Her books about horses include KING OF THE WIND, which won the Newbery Medal in 1950.

Barry the Lifesaver

⟨[HUNDREDS *of winter travelers who have crossed over the St. Bernard Pass between Italy and Switzerland have owed their lives to the remarkable dogs trained for rescue work by the monks at the Hospice nearby. This story is about Joseph, an Italian boy who in 1799 became a novice in the order of the Fathers of St. Bernard.*

JOSEPH HAD been warned from the beginning he must have no favorites among the dogs.

"Caring for them all is your duty. It is forbidden to make any one of them your pet," Father Andrew, the Keeper of the Dogs, had admonished.

But how could such a thing be kept wholly duty? There were times when a young monk was only a boy with a dog, in spite of orders. Unavoidably the novices had their favorite animals.

Most of the dogs at the Hospice were bred at the station in Martigny in Switzerland. But a few females had been left in the mountains over the winter to grow hardy and cold-resistant. Although they had not quite the magnificence of the male dogs they were gentle and affectionate. Maida was particularly beautiful. Joseph had to exercise restraint not to be partial to her, not to give her special care.

Every day he knew and understood the dogs better. Father Andrew's eyes grew soft as he watched the awkward young black-robed figure slip from the chill shadows of the chapel and hasten toward the kennels. The Keeper was a Canon now, a disciplined monk, but short years before he too had been a child who longed for a dog. And he remembered.

Being in the kennels comforted Joseph's body as well as his heart. Nowhere in the winter Alps was there such warmth as that to be found snuggled close to these great furry dogs, which he always thought of as the pets of his patron, St. Bernard . . .

It was Father Andrew's deep voice which made the announcement. "Here most assuredly is a miracle. Our Maida appears about to become a mother. I'd say we'd have pups in perhaps a couple of weeks."

It was not part of the breeding program for puppies to be whelped at the Pass, most certainly not in dead of winter. All this business was conducted at Martigny, with careful selection of mates to develop qualities necessary for the rescue work. But it would appear that proper procedure had not been explained to Maida. Of a sudden one morning her supple figure was thickened and heavy. She did not bound out with the other dogs when released, and her eyes fixed on Joseph as he swept the kennels were wondering and a little pathetic. Because she could not run with the others as usual she felt the cold more keenly.

Joseph took to coddling her. "What will we do when the time comes?" he demanded of Father Andrew. "How can we take care of her properly in this cold?"

The Keeper shook his head. His gray eyes were unhappy. "We'll manage somehow," he said. "But it's not a good thing, whelping in this weather. Particularly since it's her first litter."

He showed Joseph how to build a special bed with sides high to shut out drafts. Maida was one of his best dogs. He wanted no mishaps.

The Hospice was in the midst of winter routine. The monks were isolated and alone, their solitude broken only by a rare visitor making a perilous journey. An Italian workman, coming up from Bourg St. Pierre in an attempt to reach home, broke his leg. The dogs found him, suffering and disabled, while they were out on a routine survey. He was carried to the Hospice on a stretcher and put to bed, and Father Louis placed the leg in splints. Now and again travelers stopped briefly to ask for a guide, or remained several days because of a storm. An old man was brought in by the questing monks, frozen dead. Joseph went with the others to the chapel to pray for the repose of his soul. He had grown accustomed to danger; death was new to him. That night the cold seemed harder than ever to bear.

These were difficult days for Father Andrew. Joseph watched his serious look and pondered. In many ways Father Andrew was such a man as he wished to become, a monk whose dedication and purpose were expressed by saving the lives of others at the risk of his own.

"Maida is restless and has not eaten," Joseph said worriedly one evening to his fellow novices, Anton and Emil. Father Andrew was not there; he had gone off to guide two travelers and he had not returned. "I believe not eating is some sort of sign."

Anton did not know. Neither did Emil, but he looked at Maida and dismissed the matter lightly.

"Dogs frequently go off their feed. Father Andrew doesn't think she'll have her pups for days yet. Go to bed."

In any event Joseph could not sit and brood over her. He covered her up and hurried away to evening prayers. But after he was in bed and the lights were out he lay thinking of her, realizing Father Andrew had not yet returned, wondering if she was warm and comfortable.

"She is one of God's creatures and in His care," he said to himself finally and closed his eyes. He drifted in space. And then in the stillness, faintly he heard a whine. It was far away, in the kennels. But it was unmistakably

Maida's soft complaint.

He was out of bed on the instant. "What is it?" Emil's whisper demanded. "Where are you going?"

But Joseph did not answer. He pushed into his boots and flung his robe on in the darkness. Anton stirred, too.

"You're not supposed to go out," he said sleepily.

"I'm going to see to the dogs."

"Father Andrew will call you if you're needed."

"Father Andrew has not yet returned. There has been no sound in the hall. I've listened."

"It is far too cold to get up unnecessarily," Anton murmured.

"It is not your task. I will report it," Emil was saying. But there was no answer from the darkness. Joseph had gone.

There was no light in the corridors. A faint glow came from the chapel. He moved quickly over the frigid stone floor. A lantern hung in the entry, welcome for the Keeper. If he did not return by midnight Joseph knew a rescue party would go in search of him. But until then the weary monks must have their rest.

In the kitchen he found a lamp. Slowly, because it cast great shadows and he could not see his way clearly, he moved toward the kennels.

He had fenced off the corner where Maida's bed was placed. She was making troubled sounds. The other dogs, disturbed and uneasy, pushed against the barrier, their big eyes gleaming in the half-light. He ordered them away and they went slowly but obediently to lie down on the far side of their enclosure and watch him with interest.

He bent over Maida and flashed the light on her.

She lay crosswise in her bed, breathing rapidly and heavily and he saw that her sides were heaving. Now and then she gave a whine. When she saw him she reached up her head and licked his hand as if in a wordless appeal. But it was not a weak plea. Maida had work to do which she meant to accomplish. All she asked was companionship; someone she loved to stand by.

Joseph put the lamp down and took stock of the situation. The kennels were bitterly cold and Maida and her babies would need a cozy spot for a nursery. He couldn't keep her covered while the pups came. The best he could do possibly was to bank the bed with blankets against the wind and cut the drafts from above. Maida's body was radiating heat but even her terrific vitality could make little impression on the sub-zero cold. The thermometer had plunged at sundown, and the wind was raging. Joseph thought of Father Andrew alone in the tempest and shuddered.

At least while the Keeper was away, he could do his work here well. But what to do? He could not bring a fire to Maida nor take Maida to the blaze now dying in the kitchen. Or could he? Was there some way?

Maida gave a soft moaning sound. He must hurry. Joseph sped to the kitchen but in its emptiness he found no answer at first. It was some time before he came back to the kennel but

[137]

when he did he carried in a great hod a pile of stones. He had trouble unloading them but he managed it with tongs and shovel. He rolled them, hot as they were, in the blankets and packed them about the bed.

The lay brothers would be looking everywhere for the loose hearthstones in the morning. But until then Joseph was safe. He sat down to wait.

It was a long wait. He could see a patch of sky and against it snow flurries, and then much later in its depths there shone a star. He put his hand out and stroked Maida's head. He hoped these would be fine puppies and that he would know how to take care of them well. It would be the first task here really his own—whelping the first litter born here. Whelping the first St. Bernards.

He was shocked at the daring of his thought. Was it irreverent openly to give a dog the name of a saint? But it could not be. The saint would have loved them too—these sad, wise, powerful creatures, these saviors, these wonder dogs. Bernard's dogs they were. *St. Bernards.*

Maida moaned and strained.

Father Andrew had told him what to do. He bent over her, watching, and saw the miracle of birth.

She had the first puppy out of the sac, and the second and the third. Joseph cleaned the box, once, twice and again, and placed three sleek shivering small forms close against their mother, where they nuzzled and nursed. But the frigid air was too much for them. Almost at once they seemed rigid with cold. Joseph hastened to the

kitchen again. Every available bottle he filled with water from the steaming fireside kettle. He placed the little bodies against the warm vessels and they relaxed. Maida licked them gently.

She strained again. Soon there were three more, and then after a long wait a seventh. All perfect. All beautiful. Joseph carried water madly. It was a long trip. But finally he had them, clean and dry and warm, snuggled beside Maida. And Maida with a long sigh of relief and contentment put her gracious head on them and went to sleep.

Now at last he had time to inspect them. Although perfectly formed they were awkwardly babyish and absurd. He examined the small paws, the floppy ears, the miniature faces, full of solemnity, pushing blindly.

There wasn't a runt in the litter, he thought exultantly. The Keeper would be pleased and proud. All good-sized and nicely developed. But there was one bigger and finer than the rest. His fawn-and-white markings were beautiful already, his tiny head full of nobility.

Joseph lifted him carefully, cradling him in his hand, warming him against his breast, against the rough cloth of his robe. He sat for a long time, holding him. Something stirred strongly within him, there was a lump in his throat. Human love came awkwardly into a heart long filled only with love of Heaven.

"Nice little fellow," he said softly. "Nice puppy."

Father Andrew found them there asleep when he returned near dawn, bringing a woodcutter he had rescued and had had to carry most of the way. Father Andrew was dazed with exhaustion but he was very, very pleased.

"You've done well, Joseph," he said hoarsely. "Without your special care the puppies might all have frozen. You may choose a reward for this."

Joseph was sleepy, too, but he knew what he wanted.

"Let me have this fellow to train," he said. "He's going to be a wonder. A real St. Bernard."

"You may name the dog, not the breed," Father Andrew said severely. "What do you wish to call him?"

Joseph looked at the puppy in his arms, warm, blind. And yet what dreams of glorious destiny might lie behind those sealed small eyes? What might be accomplished by the body that now seemed so helplessly limp? He, Joseph, would work with him, would train him as a dog never had been trained before.

He needed a glorious name for his glorious future, a hero's name, and yet a simple name too, a friendly name, a name of affection.

"I'll call him Barry," he said, almost to himself. Barry for the simple part. And for the heroic?

"*Barry der Menschenretter,*" Joseph said. "Barry the lifesaver."

⟨ THE *further adventures of a friendly puppy that grew into a heroic dog and saved forty lives may be read in* HALFWAY TO HEAVEN. *Before writing her book Ruth Adams Knight visited the Hospice, where she learned that the biggest and best of the dogs is always called Barry after the first St. Bernard. Other dog stories by the same author include* LUCK OF THE IRISH *and* BRAVE COMPANIONS.

Rikki-Tikki-Tavi

THIS IS THE story of the great war that Rikki-tikki-tavi fought single-handed, through the bathrooms of the big bungalow in Segowlee cantonment. Darzee, the tailor bird, helped; but Rikki-tikki did the real fighting.

He was a mongoose, rather like a little cat in his fur and his tail, but quite like a weasel in his head and his habits. His eyes and the end of his restless nose were pink. He could scratch himself anywhere he pleased, with any leg, front or back, that he chose to use. He could fluff up his tail till it looked like a bottle brush, and his war cry, as he scuttled through the long grass, was: "*Rikk-tikk-tikki-tikki-tchk!*"

One day, a high summer flood washed him out of the burrow where he lived with his father and mother, and carried him, kicking and clucking, down a roadside ditch. He found a little wisp of grass floating there, and clung to it till he lost his senses. When he revived, he was lying in the hot sun on the middle of a garden path, very draggled indeed, and a small boy was saying, "Here's a dead mongoose. Let's have a funeral."

"No," said his mother, "perhaps he isn't really dead."

They took him into the house, and a big man picked him up between his finger and thumb, and said he was not dead but half choked. They wrapped him in cotton wool and warmed him, and he opened his eyes and sneezed.

"Now," said the big man (he was an Englishman who had just moved into the bungalow), "don't frighten him, and we'll see what he'll do."

It is the hardest thing in the world to frighten a mongoose, because he is eaten up from nose to tail with curiosity. He sat up and put his fur in order, scratched himself, and jumped on the small boy's shoulder.

"Ouch! He's tickling under my chin," said Teddy.

Rikki-tikki snuffed at the boy's ear and climbed down to the floor, where he sat rubbing his nose.

"Good gracious," said Teddy's mother, "and that's a wild creature! I suppose he's so tame because we've been kind to him."

"All mongooses are like that," said her husband. "If Teddy doesn't pick him up by the tail, or try to put him in a cage, he'll run in and out of the house all day long. Let's give him something to eat."

They gave him a little piece of raw meat. Rikki-tikki liked it immensely.

He spent all that day roaming over the house. He nearly drowned himself in the bathtubs and put his nose into the ink on a writing table. At nightfall when Teddy went to bed Rikki-tikki climbed up, too. Teddy's mother and father came in, the last thing, to look at their boy, and Rikki-tikki was awake on the pillow.

"I don't like that," said Teddy's mother. "He may bite the child."

"He'll do no such thing," said the father. "Teddy's safer with that little beast than if he had a bloodhound to watch him. If a snake came—"

But Teddy's mother wouldn't think of anything so awful.

Early in the morning Rikki-tikki came to early breakfast in the veranda riding on Teddy's shoulder. They gave him banana and some boiled egg, and he sat on all their laps one after the other.

Then he went out into the garden to see what was to be seen. It was a large garden, only half cultivated, and Rikki-tikki licked his lips. "This is a splendid hunting ground," he said, and his tail grew bottle-brushy at the thought of it. He scuttled up and down the garden, snuffing here and there till he heard sorrowful voices in a thorn bush.

It was Darzee, the tailor bird, and his wife. They had made a beautiful nest by pulling two big leaves together and stitching them up the edges with fibres.

"What is the matter?" asked Rikki.

"We are very miserable," said Darzee. "One of our babies fell out of the nest yesterday, and Nag ate him."

"H'm!" said Rikki-tikki, "that is very sad, but who is Nag?"

Darzee and his wife only cowered down in the nest without answering, for from the thick grass at the foot of the bush there came a hiss. Out of the grass, rose up the head and spread hood of Nag, the big black cobra. He was five feet long from tongue to tail. When he had lifted one third of himself clear of the ground, he stayed balancing to and fro exactly as a dandelion tuft balances in the wind. He looked at Rikki-tikki with the wicked snake's eyes that never change their expression.

"Who is Nag?" said he. "I am Nag. Look, and be afraid!"

He spread out his hood, and Rikki-tikki saw the spectacle mark on the back of it that looks exactly like the eye part of a hook-and-eye fastening. He was afraid for the minute; but it is impossible for a mongoose to stay frightened for any length of time. Though Rikki-tikki had never met a live cobra before, his mother had fed him on dead ones, and he knew that a grown mongoose's business in life was to fight and eat snakes.

"Well," said Rikki-tikki, and his tail began to fluff up again, "do you think it right to eat fledglings out of a nest?"

Nag was watching the least little movement in the grass behind Rikki-tikki. He knew that mongooses in the garden meant death sooner or later for him and his family, and he wanted to get Rikki-tikki off his guard.

"Let us talk," he said. "You eat eggs. Why should not I eat birds?"

"Behind you! Look behind you!" sang Darzee.

Rikki-tikki knew better than to waste time in staring. He jumped up in the air as high as he could go, and just under him whizzed by the head of Nagaina, Nag's wicked wife. She had crept up behind him as he was talking, to make an end of him, and he heard her savage hiss as the stroke missed. He came down almost across her back. He jumped clear of the whisking tail.

"Wicked, wicked Darzee!" said Nag, lashing up as high as he could reach toward the nest in the thorn bush; but Darzee had built it out of reach of snakes, and it only swayed to and fro.

Rikki-tikki felt his eyes growing red and hot. (When a mongoose's eyes grow red, he is angry.) He sat back on his tail and hind legs like a little kangaroo and chattered with rage. But Nag and Nagaina had disappeared into the grass. When Teddy came running down the path, Rikki-tikki was ready to be petted. . . .

That night Teddy carried him off to bed and insisted on Rikki-tikki sleeping under his chin. Rikki-tikki was too well-bred to bite or scratch, but as soon as Teddy was asleep he went off for his nightly walk round the house. In the dark he ran up against Chuchundra, the muskrat.

"My cousin Chua, the rat, told me—" said Chuchundra, and then he stopped. "Can't you *hear*, Rikki-tikki?"

Rikki-tikki listened. The house was as still as still, but he thought he could just catch the faintest scratch-scratch— the dry scratch of a snake's scales on brickwork. He stole off to Teddy's bathroom, but there was nothing there, and then to Teddy's mother's bathroom. At the bottom of the smooth plaster wall there was a brick pulled out to make a sluice for the bathwater. As Rikki-tikki stole in by the masonry curb where the bath is put, he heard Nag and Nagaina whispering together outside in the moonlight.

"When the house is emptied of people," said Nagaina to her husband, "*he* will have to go away, and then the garden will be our own again. Go in quietly, and remember that the big man is the first one to bite."

"But are you sure that there is anything to be gained by killing the people?" said Nag.

"Everything. When there were no people in the bungalow, did we have any mongoose in the garden? So long as the bungalow is empty, we are king and queen of the garden. Remember that as soon as our eggs in the melon bed hatch (as they may tomorrow), our children will need room and quiet."

"I had not thought of that," said Nag. "I will go, but there is no need that we should hunt for Rikki-tikki afterward. I will kill the big man and his wife, and the child if I can. Then the bungalow will be empty, and Rikki-tikki will go."

Rikki-tikki tingled all over with rage and hatred and then Nag's head came through the sluice. His five feet of cold body followed it. Angry as he was, Rikki-tikki was very frightened as he saw the size of the big cobra. Nag waved to and fro, and then Rikki-tikki heard him drinking from the biggest water jar that was used to fill the bath.

Nag coiled himself down, coil by coil, round the bulge at the bottom of the water jar, and Rikki-tikki stayed still as death. After an hour he began to move, muscle by muscle, toward the jar. Nag was asleep, and Rikki-tikki looked at his big back, wondering which would be the best place for a good hold.

"If I don't break his back at the first jump," said Rikki, "he can still fight; and if he fights—O Rikki!" He looked at the thickness of the neck below the hood, but that was too much for him; and a bite near the tail would only make Nag savage.

"It must be the head," he said at last. "The head above the hood. When I am once there, I must not let go."

Then he jumped. The head was lying a little clear of the water jar, under the curve of it. As his teeth met, Rikki braced his back against the bulge of the red earthenware to hold down the head. Then he was battered to and fro as a rat is shaken by a dog—to and fro on the floor, up and down, and round in great circles. But his eyes were red, and he held on as the body whipped over the floor and banged against the tin side of the bath. He closed his jaws tighter and tighter. He felt shaken to pieces when something went off like a thunderclap. The big man had been wakened by the noise, and had fired both barrels of a shotgun into Nag just behind the hood.

Rikki-tikki held on with his eyes shut, but the head did not move. The big man picked him up and said, "It's the mongoose, Alice. The little chap has saved our lives."

Teddy's mother came in with a white face, and saw what was left of Nag, and Rikki-tikki dragged himself to Teddy's bedroom.

When morning came he was very stiff but well pleased with his doings. "Now I have Nagaina to settle with. She will be worse than five Nags, and there's no knowing when the eggs she spoke of will hatch."

Without waiting for breakfast, Rikki-tikki ran to the thorn bush where Darzee was singing a song of triumph at the top of his voice. The news of Nag's death was all over the garden, for the sweeper had thrown the body on the rubbish heap.

"Oh, you stupid tuft of feathers!" said Rikki-tikki angrily. "Is this the time to sing? Where is Nagaina? Have you heard where she keeps her eggs?"

"In the melon bed, on the end nearest the wall, where the sun strikes nearly all day. She hid them there."

"The end nearest the wall?"

"Rikki-tikki, you are not going to eat her eggs?"

"Not eat exactly; no. Darzee, if you have a grain of sense you will fly off to the stables and pretend that your wing is broken, and let Nagaina chase you away to this bush. I must get to the melon bed, and if I went there now she'd see me."

Darzee was a featherbrained little fellow, and just because he knew that Nagaina's children were born in eggs like his own, he didn't think at first that it was fair to kill them. But his wife knew that cobra's eggs meant young cobras later on. She flew off from the nest, and left Darzee to keep the babies warm. She fluttered in front of Nagaina by the rubbish heap, and cried out, "Oh, my wing is broken!"

Nagaina lifted up her head and

[143]

hissed, "Indeed, you've chosen a bad place to be lame in. Look at me!"

Darzee's wife knew better than to do *that*, for a bird that looks at a snake's eyes becomes so frightened she cannot move. Nagaina moved toward her, slipping along over the dust. Darzee's wife fluttered on, piping sorrowfully, and never leaving the ground. Nagaina quickened her pace.

Rikki-tikki heard them going up the path from the stables, and he raced for the end of the melon patch near the wall. There, in the warm litter about the melons, very cunningly hidden, he found twenty-five eggs, about the size of a bantam's eggs, but with whitish skin instead of shell.

"I was not a day too soon," he said. He could see the baby cobras curled up inside the skin, and he knew that the minute they were hatched they could each kill a man or a mongoose. He bit off the tops of the eggs as fast as he could. At last there were only three eggs left, and Rikki-tikki began to chuckle to himself, when he heard Darzee's wife screaming:

"Rikki-tikki, I led Nagaina toward the house, and she has gone into the veranda. Oh, come quickly!"

Rikki-tikki smashed two eggs, and tumbled backward down the melon bed with the third egg in his mouth. He scuttled to the veranda as hard as he could put foot to the ground. Teddy and his mother and father were there at breakfast, but they were not eating anything. They sat stone-still, their faces white. Nagaina was coiled up on the matting by Teddy's chair, within

easy striking distance of Teddy's bare leg, and she was swaying to and fro.

Teddy's eyes were fixed on his father, and all his father could do was to whisper, "Sit still, Teddy. Don't move."

Then Rikki-tikki came up and cried, "Turn round, Nagaina; turn and fight!"

"All in good time," said she, without moving her eyes. "Look at your friends, Rikki-tikki. They dare not move, and if you come a step nearer I strike."

"Look at your eggs," said Rikki-tikki, "in the melon bed near the wall."

The big snake turned half round, and saw the egg on the veranda. "Ah-h! Give it to me," she said.

Rikki-tikki put his paws one on each side of the egg, and his eyes were blood red. "What price for a snake's egg? For the last—the very last of the brood? The ants are eating all the others down by the melon bed."

Nagaina spun clear round, forgetting everything for the sake of the one egg. Rikki-tikki saw Teddy's father shoot out a big hand, catch Teddy by the shoulder, and drag him across the little table with the teacups, safe and out of reach of Nagaina.

"Tricked! Tricked! Tricked! *Rikk-tck-tck!*" chuckled Rikki-tikki. "The boy is safe, and it was I—I—I that caught Nag by the hood last night in the bathroom." Then he began to jump up and down, all four feet together, his head close to the floor. He was bounding all around Nagaina, keeping just out of reach of her stroke, his little eyes like hot coals. Nagaina gathered herself together and flung out at him. Rikki-tikki jumped up and backward. Again and again she struck, and each time her head came with a whack on the matting. Rikki-tikki danced in a circle to get behind her, and Nagaina spun around to keep her head to his head.

He had forgotten the egg. It still lay on the veranda, and Nagaina came nearer and nearer to it, till at last she caught it in her mouth and flew like an arrow down the path, with Rikki-tikki behind her. He knew that he must catch her, or all the trouble would begin again.

She headed straight for the long grass by the thorn bush, and as he was running Rikki-tikki heard Darzee still singing his foolish little song of triumph. But Darzee's wife was wiser. She flew off her nest as Nagaina came along, and flapped her wings about Nagaina's head. If Darzee had helped they might have turned her; but Nagaina only lowered her hood and went on. Still, the instant's delay brought Rikki-tikki up to her. As she plunged into the rat hole where she and Nag used to live, his little white teeth were clenched on her tail. He went down with her—and very few mongooses, however wise and old they may be, care to follow a cobra into its hole. It was dark in the hole, and Rikki-tikki never knew when it might open out and give Nagaina room to turn and strike at him. He held on savagely.

Then the grass by the mouth of the hole stopped waving, and Darzee said, "It is all over with Rikki-tikki! For Nagaina will surely kill him underground."

He sang a very mournful song. Just as he got to the most touching part, Rikki-tikki, covered with dirt, dragged himself out of the hole leg by leg, licking his whiskers. Darzee stopped with a little shout. Rikki-tikki shook some of the dust out of his fur and sneezed. "It is all over," he said. "Nagaina will never come out again."

When Rikki got to the house, Teddy and Teddy's mother and father came out and almost cried over him. He went to bed on Teddy's shoulder, and Teddy's mother saw him when she came to look late at night.

"Just think, he saved our lives," she said to her husband.

Rikki-tikki woke up with a jump, for all the mongooses are light sleepers. "Oh, it's you," said he. "What are you bothering for? All the cobras are dead; and if they weren't, I'm here."

Rikki-tikki had a right to be proud of himself but he did not grow too proud. He kept that garden as a mongoose should keep it, with tooth and jump and spring and bite, till never a cobra dared show its head inside the walls.

⟨ LIKE *Teddy* in the story, Rudyard Kipling was a boy in India when it was part of the British Empire. The native nurses who took care of him told him many old tales which later inspired him to write his JUNGLE BOOKS, from which "Rikki-Tikki-Tavi" is taken.

Lightfoot Has a Visitor

Gosh! It hasn't happened again?" Joe Burridge stared in astonishment as his pretty younger sister rushed in from the pasture, her blue eyes blazing with anger and distress.

"It has! Not a drop! Lightfoot's been milked again!"

"Nonsense! You just haven't learned to milk. I get plenty when it's my turn at night," said Joe with the superior air which always provoked Rilla.

"I learned as quickly as you did, and as well. Gran says so," she stormed. And Joe had to admit she was right when he, too, failed to get a drop from the good-natured little Jersey.

Sadly they reported to Gran. It had seemed a great idea for them to help out Gran by helping her run the little mountain farm where she had been born. They had always loved the place and they didn't mind the work. With their combined savings they had bought a cow from Mr. Brown, a neighbor who lived a few miles down the road, so they would have milk and cream to sell to the summer people down along the river. But if Lightfoot gave only half the milk they had expected, where would there be any profits!

Gran herself was much puzzled. "Of course, if we had a good barn," she said, "she ought to be locked up. But any thief could break into that shed in the pasture, and it's good for Lightfoot to graze early in the morning. We'll just have to watch. Why didn't you bark, Tooker?"

"Bow wow," remarked Tooker, much too late, but Rilla reduced him to woe by scowling at him, and saying, "Bad dog!"

"He's not," said Joe. "He always barks at strangers!" Tooker did. The mystery deepened.

"We'll watch all night tonight from the back porch," announced Joe, and to Gran's distress lifted down her father's long old squirrel rifle.

"Don't worry, Gran darling," Rilla comforted her. "It isn't loaded. It's just to scare someone. We simply can't afford to lose all that milk!"

Gran herself promised to watch through the long summer twilight while both children slept, then Rilla, then Joe.

The pasture where Lightfoot was put at night sloped up right behind the sturdy old log house. Not a place for a thief to hide, and the whole place spread out like a stage beyond the back porch with a brilliant moon to light it.

Gran, Joe, and Rilla took their turns, all aided by a mystified but much interested Tooker. But Tooker didn't bark. No one saw a soul or heard a footstep, and yet in the morning Lightfoot was milked dry again! And so the next night—and the next! Even Gran grew angry and frightened by the strangeness of these secret visits from a thief they could not hear or see.

The fourth night Rilla made a decision which was a brave one for a city girl of eleven. As the moon rose later now, she was to watch the last part of the night. So as soon as she knew Joe had fallen asleep, she, with Tooker beside her, crept right out into the pasture!

Lightfoot, asleep beneath a tree, was astonished when a rope fell softly about her neck. She didn't mind, though, and girl, cow and dog snuggled down together to wait. It was spooky and scary—alone there!

And then presently Tooker moved. Lightfoot rose—a figure was hurrying across the pasture. Tooker, a city dog, with no proper ideas of how country dogs behave, just looked and wagged his tail in friendly fashion. Rilla sat still in astonishment at what she saw.

In half an hour she was shaking Joe, calling to Gran. "You'll never believe who milks Lightfoot! Never!" she cried. "A fawn came and drank and drank! She wasn't afraid of me a bit. She was friends with Tooker. Lightfoot knew her. Honest. It's true!"

"Fairy tales!" scoffed Joe.

But Gran said, "No, I was silly not to remember. The Browns used to have a pet fawn. One of their cows adopted it, and I heard it got so tame it was a nuisance—ate all their garden stuff and wouldn't be weaned. I heard they took the fawn to the woods days ago, but I guess it came back. How do you suppose it found Lightfoot way over here?"

"I'll let Joe solve that mystery," said Rilla with a proud toss of her curly dark head. "I'm going to take a nap."

"Gee," said Joe, "I wish I'd seen that fawn. Anyway, Lightfoot gets shut up in the shed after this."

《 Mrs. Donahey *is the author of* Apple Pie Inn *and the* Marty Lou *books.*

A Pig Named Dennis

(DENNIS *and her piglets (yes, Dennis was a she) were the real pets of Jim Stanton and his wife, Laurette. The Stantons were a young couple in 1926 when they left their Seattle home to settle in a remote part of British Columbia.*

YEAR AFTER year, Jim Stanton's reputation as a woodsman had spread. A long line of pleasure boats—British, Welsh, and American boats—began heading toward Knight Inlet where the Stantons had built their cabin. Many of them hired Jim as a guide.

Of all the yachts entering the Inlet, the one that particularly interested the Stantons was the *Surprise*. It was one of the most magnificent pleasure crafts afloat and carried a crew of sixty-five. The owner, a Welsh steamship and silver-mine magnate, developed an immediate fondness for the Stantons. When the *Surprise* sailed majestically out of the Inlet, it left two tangible mementoes behind. The yacht had carried several pianos which no one ever played. Jim asked if he might buy one of them for his wife.

At the same time a gift was sent to Laurette. Its name was Dennis—or Miss Dennis, a hairless tropical pig which had been presented to the Welshman by a South Sea Island queen. In the South Sea Islands, pigs were considered priceless possessions.

Dennis had been treated as a treasured pet aboard the *Surprise*. One of the crew had been assigned to her as a valet, and she was given a bath and a manicure daily. Born in a tropical climate, she had grown no protective hair, and her hide was velvety tan with a few dark spots.

Laurette patted the immaculate, smooth hide. "Oh, Jim, what will we do with her? She'll freeze this winter, and we can't keep her in the cabin with us!"

For once Jim was of little help. "I don't know," he shrugged. "I suppose we could give her to someone who'd have the nerve to slaughter her."

"I'll slaughter you!"

Jim was not to be indifferent to Dennis for long. As he and Laurette walked back to the cabin, Dennis trotted happily at their heels, like a puppy. When they went in the door, she stood on the sill and squealed.

"Guess she wants to come in," said Jim.

"She wants to be invited in," corrected Laurette. "Come in, Dennis."

A little later, after Laurette had made a pot of tea, Dennis walked over to the table and squealed again, expectantly.

"What does she want this time—a cup of tea?" Jim asked.

"I guess so." Laurette poured some tea into a small saucer and set it on the floor. Dennis tasted it, looked up reproachfully, and squealed again.

"She's a British-trained pig," Jim laughed. "She wants milk and sugar!"

Laurette picked up Dennis' dish of tea, added a spoon of sugar and some canned cream, and set it back. Dennis put her snout into it, sipped, glanced up at them with a contented grunt, then went happily back to her tea.

Though Dennis' vocabulary was limited to squeals of displeasure and grunts of satisfaction, they soon felt the influence of her personality. She was spoiled, loving, and playful. She made friends with the rather startled dog, Growler, and the two pet tomcats. When Laurette and Jim started down the trail, she would fall in line, single file, along with Growler and the tomcats. She always trailed going into the woods, but once the direction was reversed and they were on their way home, Dennis would scramble ahead and fight Growler for the lead position.

As the cold winds blew up around the Inlet, Laurette worried about her new pet. One day she came out on the beach where Dennis and the cats were playing, and felt the pig's slender, chilly legs.

"Come along, Miss Dennis, we've got to do something about you."

Obediently Dennis followed and when they were back in the cabin, Laurette reached up into the rafters and pulled out two pairs of knee-length wool socks.

"Come here, Dennis," she said invitingly.

Dennis walked up to Laurette and watched with interest as her mistress picked up one slim leg and pulled on a sock. When Laurette put that hoof down, Dennis voluntarily offered the next one. She seemed highly pleased with her four warm wool socks, and scampered around the room as if showing them off.

When snow came Laurette put a barrel out on the beach and loaded it with wild hay. Each afternoon she built a fire near the barrel. The pig watched with interest the first time. The next afternoon, when she saw her mistress coming, Dennis scampered down the beach with a piece of driftwood in her mouth.

"If I could have taught her the difference between wet and dry wood," recalls Laurette, "I wouldn't have had to do more than strike a match."

Dennis loved to ride in the boat and squealed to go aboard every time Jim started out. He had only to pull alongside the shore and say, "All right, Dennis," and she would clamber aboard. It was more trouble to get her off. At the order, "Overboard, Dennis," the pig would squeal a shrill protest. Finally, at the repeated command, she would scramble over the boat's side, hit the water with a shudder, and swim ashore.

In time the Stantons ordered a mate for Dennis and eventually became the owners of ten little pigs. They inherited much of their mother's amazing personality and soon discovered the cat hole in the cabin which Laurette had made so that her tomcats could get in and out at night. With a little squeezing, the piglets could inch their fat little bodies through the cat hole, too.

With the first early morning dawn, Laurette and Jim would be roused from their sleep by a scurrying, squealing parade, and ten little white pigs would come tumbling through the cat hole. They would grab up any loose socks or underwear they could find, run in a mad circle, reverse, and race madly in the opposite direction. Then, just as suddenly as they had appeared, they would drop their playthings and scramble through the cat hole, back outdoors.

When the Stantons had company at the cabin, Dennis loved to come in and join them. Long after dark, when all her brood was asleep, she would slip up to the door to listen. One evening Jim, on to this trick, suddenly pulled the door open, and there was Dennis with her ear to the door. As her support gave away, she tumbled into the room.

"Dennis, go to bed," Jim ordered sternly.

Dennis grumbled and walked off down the trail.

Ten minutes later Jim suddenly threw open the door—and again Dennis fell in.

"Oh, all right, Dennis, come on in and listen."

At this Dennis walked in, lay down on the rug, and appeared to listen to the conversation. The Stantons swear that not once did she go to sleep when there was an opportunity to listen.

The natural enemies of the growing drove of pigs were timber wolves. Dennis taught her brood, at any sign of danger, to "freeze" like quail. Jim once picked up one of the pigs, when in this pose, and the little animal remained as stiff as a statue. When Jim set him back on the ground he did not relax until his mother sounded the all clear.

As her piglets grew, Dennis also taught them to "run" the wolves. When a wolf sneaked up on their feeding place, the pigs would let it approach to within about thirty feet. Then they would charge en masse, and run the wolf to the woods.

Dennis produced two litters each year, one in the spring and another in the late fall. Each time she had ten white-haired, tusked pigs, all healthy and intelligent.

The Stantons had no practical use for the pigs, since Laurette refused to eat her pets, but they were proud of them and insisted that no one had pigs like Dennis and her brood.

⟪ THIS story is condensed from GRIZZLIES IN THEIR BACK YARD.

MARGUERITE HENRY

Welcome, Grimalkin

❦ Benjamin West, *the Quaker boy who grew up to become the first American painter, had such a cat as Marguerite Henry has described.*

Benjamin woke with a jerk. He held his breath, trying to separate the sounds that came floating up from the innyard. Usually he slept through noises. Travelers could lift the latch, help themselves to the snack of food set out for them, warm themselves by the fire, and leave without his so much as hearing them. But tonight there was a small sound that he could not make out.

Benjamin raised himself up on one elbow. He wished he had ears like a horse so that he could swivel them around to catch the tiniest sound. There! The little noise came again. It was not the trembling cry of a screech owl. It was not the creaking of the inn signboard. It sounded more like a boy.

In a flash Benjamin's bare feet were on the stool that acted as a mounting block for his high bed. Soundlessly he dropped to the floor and hurried over to the tiny square window. He poked his head out into the frosty November night.

The courtyard, spread out below him, was washed in moonlight. He could see a man leading two scrawny oxen to the shed. He could make out the figures of a woman and a boy on the seat of the oxcart. Suddenly the boy bent over something in his lap and let out a dry sob.

Benjamin tore off his nightshirt. His clothes lay heaped on a bench in a white patch of moonlight. Quickly he slipped into his leather jerkin and knee breeches. How cold they felt! Shivering, he lifted the latch and tiptoed out into the hall.

"Papa!" he cried, as he collided with Mr. West, who was walking briskly toward him with a candle in his hand. Benjamin tried to straighten the candle which he had tipped at a crazy angle. He daubed at the hot tallow which had spilled down Mr. West's coat.

Then he looked up at his father and, frightened as he was, he wanted to laugh. In the long shadows made by the candle, his father looked exactly like the scarecrow in Mamma's kitchen garden. The scarecrow wore a sober Quaker jacket and a white nightcap to frighten the crows. And here was Mr. West dressed like the sober Quaker he was, except for a white nightcap perched on his head.

But even with his nightcap on, Papa looked forbidding.

"Benjamin!" he said, his eyebrows scowling. "Must thee meet every guest?"

"No, Papa," replied Benjamin earnestly, "but there is a boy crying. A grown boy of seven or eight like me."

Papa pulled off his nightcap and tucked it in his pocket. "Come along then," he said. "Step sprightly. I may need thee."

Benjamin followed the black coattails of his father as they flapped down the narrow, winding stairway. At the foot of the stairs Mr. West lighted the lanthorn that hung on an iron hook. Then he pinched out his candle, and set it on the candle shelf. Benjamin and his father singled out their own black hats from the long row that hung on pegs near the door. Then they went out into the night.

In the bright moonlight they saw the boy seated on the upping block used in mounting horses. His parents hovered over him like anxious birds.

"Welcome to Door-Latch Inn in the County of Chester in the Province of Pennsylvania!" spoke Papa in a voice so big it rattled the windows.

The little family started at the sound.

"I am John West, innkeeper," Papa said as he held the lanthorn high. "And this is my youngest-born, Benjamin."

"So?" said the stranger, shaking hands stiffly. "And I am Johann Ditz-

ler. By me iss my wife and my little feller, Jacob. We come over the seas from the Rhineland. By morning early we make the journey west. Over the mountains we find good land."

Papa nodded. Then he pointed to the boy who sat on the upping block, rocking back and forth, holding something tightly in his arms.

"What," asked Papa, "ails the boy?"

"Ach," replied Mr. Ditzler, "such troubles we got! Jacob, here, he got a sick kitten. We want he should leave it go, but he cries his eyes out. Tch, tch!"

"Ya," spoke up Mrs. Ditzler. "By Philadelphia it makes down rain. Our big cat and her kitten got all spritzed. Our big cat she dies on us. Soon, now, we lose her kitten. And Jacob is crying. Chust listen! Such a big boy he iss, too."

Jacob turned to Benjamin for help. In an instant, Benjamin was on his knees, peering into Jacob's arms. And there, lying limp and motionless, was a tiny black kitten. Benjamin listened to its harsh breathing. Then he felt the kitten's nose. "As hot as an ember," he whispered to Jacob.

Benjamin longed to tug at his father's coattails. What kind of way was this to save a sick kitten? Why did grownups waste so much time in talk?

"Animals," Papa was saying, as his breath made little white clouds of steam, "are creatures of God. They need protection in suffering."

The German parents were too tired and cold to do any more talking. All they wanted was a place to lay their heads.

Benjamin could stand the delay no longer.

"Please, Papa!" he whispered. "Elmira, the barn cat, has kittens. Six of them."

He spoke quickly now for fear Papa would not listen to his plan. "She will scarce notice one more."

Papa blinked up at the moon. He frowned. For a long moment he stroked his chin. At last he handed Benjamin the lanthorn. "Thee may try," he said. "Dr. Moris says a mother cat will oft adopt a hungry kitten. But warm a jug of milk, first. Mayhap the kitten will not need a foster mother."

Benjamin's heart leaped. He suddenly felt as important as Dr. Moris. He could almost feel Dr. Moris' big red bush wig upon his head. But he was glad he was still a boy. He could run!

He ran now across the courtyard and the barnyard, around the worn path to the cellar. He lifted the heavy trap door and clattered down the cobblestone steps, his lanthorn making long shadows on the wall. The milk crock was full. The good yellow cream had risen to the top. Carefully he ladled it into a tiny jug. Then he hurried into the kitchen. It was bright with firelight now, and a kettle was singing over the fire.

Mamma was up, pouring hot water into the teapot, spreading rye-and-Injun bread with rich brown apple butter, saying a quiet word to comfort the little German family, who sat in a row on the hooded settle.

Benjamin glanced at the kitten. It was still breathing. He placed the jug of cream in a little nook in the chimney. "It will soon be warm," he said to Jacob, and smiled a little smile of encouragement. Then he took the rush basket used for gathering eggs and in no time at all he was in the barn, reaching into the haymow for Elmira and one of her kittens.

Elmira struggled, but Benjamin held her and her kitten firmly in the basket. All the while he talked in a soft voice.

"I'll bring thee back to the rest of thy family soon," he promised. Then he hurried back to the inn, balancing the basket as carefully as if it held new-laid eggs. "See!" whispered Benjamin to Jacob as he stroked the big mother cat. "This be Elmira. She will mother thy kitten too. Please to put it in the basket."

Gently the boy laid his kitten alongside Elmira's kitten. Then Benjamin set the basket on the floor close to the warmth of the fire.

The room turned quiet. All eyes were on the basket. Not a word was said. Only the fire whistled up the chimney. For two or three seconds the barn cat stared at the strange kitten. Then she sniffed it curiously. Her nose wrinkled. The fur flew up on her back. Her tail stiffened. "*P-h-h-f-t! Sp-f-f-t!*" she spat at him. Suddenly, she turned to her own kitten and began washing its face.

Benjamin said a quick prayer under his breath. Please, God, make Elmira be a mother to the sick kitten. Then in case his prayer might not be answered at once, he tiptoed around the chimney and reached up for the jug of cream.

"Benjamin!" commanded Mr. West.

"Take Elmira back to the barn. Thy plan will not work."

Benjamin was so startled at hearing his father's voice that he upset the jug.

"Oh!" cried Benjamin.

And "Ach!" echoed Jacob, as the cream spilled over into the basket, right on top of his kitten.

Now it so happened that Elmira had been raised on skimmed milk. And when she saw the thick yellow cream dripping into the basket, she began licking it from the black kitten's coat.

Up and down went Elmira's head as her pink tongue licked every bit of the rich cream from the kitten's back. And then the strangest thing happened. When all the cream was gone, she kept right on licking. She kept right on stroking the sick kitten with her rough, warm tongue.

Benjamin glanced sidelong at the boy. He laughed out for joy. Papa clicked his tongue in amazement. The kitten was stirring ever so slightly. He was stretching! He was letting out a hungry mewing sound.

"Oh!" breathed Benjamin.

"Ach!" sighed Jacob.

Now Elmira was lying on her side, nosing the black kitten and wriggling up to him. After what seemed a long time, but actually was only a matter of seconds, the black kitten began to nuzzle along the barn cat's belly. And at last he and the white kitten were nursing side by side!

A good feeling came over the whole room. Elmira purred until she sounded like a spinning wheel. Then she looked up at the anxious watchers with a pleased smirk on her face.

"Ach, na," clucked Mrs. Ditzler, "everything gets all right!"

"Ai yai yai!" choked Mr. Ditzler as he patted Jacob on the head.

Even Papa seemed happy. He blew his nose as loud as a trumpet.

The first finger of light found Benjamin's bed. He felt someone in bed beside him. He turned. It was Jacob! Jacob's face twisted into a shy smile. . .

"I make you a present," he said. "It iss the kitten I give you."

"Thy little black kitten?"

"Ya," choked Jacob. "It makes easier to know he iss by you."

"Oh, Jacob! I will take good care of him. He shall be our house cat. Never will he have to live in the barns!"

"It wonders me if the kitten forgets Grimalkin?"

"Grimalkin?" repeated Benjamin.

"Ya. Grimalkin was his mother."

"Would thee like to have me name the kitten Grimalkin?"

Jacob seemed to have trouble in answering. Then the bed began to quiver.

Benjamin wished he could think of something comforting to say. He stole a glance at Jacob.

But Jacob was not crying. He was shaking with laughter.

"Ach, Benjamin," he giggled. "Grimalkin iss a she-cat's name. But the kitten—he don't mind."

"No. Of course not. We'll call him Grimalkin. For his mother."

All of a sudden the inn seemed to come alive. There was the sound of heavy boots in the hall. Horses snorted and whinnied in the courtyard. Voices called back and forth. Both boys leaped out of bed. As Benjamin put on his shoes he also put on a sober manner. Begin the day in quiet. Do not raise thy voice, he repeated under his breath. This morning Papa will not need to remind me.

Then he promptly forgot his words as he and Jacob tumbled down the stairs and into the bustling activity of the kitchen. Mamma was moving silently and swiftly from fire to table. Benjamin's four sisters seemed everywhere at once—filling the salt and sugar boxes, putting chairs and benches in place.

"Benjamin!" said Sarah his oldest sister, "wash thy face at once. Breakfast is ready."

Benjamin was so used to Sarah's chatter that he hardly heard her. He and Jacob were over in the chimney corner on their hands and knees. They were peering into the egg basket in awe. Elmira was still there! And someone had brought in all of her own white kittens. And the black kitten was there, too. He was a smart one, snuggled in among all the white kittens for warmth.

Benjamin looked up and caught Mamma's eye. She smiled first at Benjamin, then at Jacob. "The black kitten will be strong as any," she said. . . .

Papa sat at the head of the table, straight and proud. In true Quaker fashion he kept his hat on. It looked as if it had grown there. When at last a stillness came over the room, he closed his eyes and folded his hands. For a long time no sound escaped his parted lips.

Benjamin could feel little shivers racing up and down his spine. He hoped his father's voice would tremble and quake until the very roof timbers shook.

"Al-migh-ty God," the trembling began.

At the unexpected quaking sound Jacob jumped and almost fell off his stool.

"Be not frightened," whispered Benjamin. "That is why we are called Quakers."

"It is the duty of man," Papa was praying, "to care for all living creatures. The lowliest creature has a work to do. The wren protects the fruit of the orchard. The barn cat protects the grain. The house cat protects man's food. We thank thee, O Lord, for sparing the life of a plain black kitten."

⟨ THIS *story is from* BENJAMIN WEST AND HIS CAT GRIMALKIN, *in which you may read how Grimalkin helped Benjamin to become an artist.*

FRANCES CAVANAH

A Horse for General Lee

❨ THIS *is a true story of Traveller, the gallant horse ridden by the great* *Confederate commander during the War Between the States.*

THE GRAY COLT was already famous in a small way when General Lee first saw him. Twice he had cantered off to the Greenbriar County Fair in what is now the State of West Virginia. And twice he had cantered around the track with two short blue ribbons fluttering from his bridle. When the crowds at the Fair cheered, he tossed his mane proudly, as though acknowledging their applause. He seemed to think that he deserved it.

By the spring of 1861, the gray colt had grown into a handsome four-year-old, but by then no one had time to think about blue ribbons. He no longer grazed and sniffed the wind and kicked up frisky heels in the hilly pastures of Greenbriar County. The North and South had gone to war, and his rider was a young Confederate major in a gray uniform. Life was pleasant in the Virginia army camp to which he had been taken. He was constantly being petted and praised by the soldiers. They admired his fine points—his easy gait, his proud carriage, his delicate ears and broad forehead, his full mane and

tail. Then the gray horse would arch his neck and nicker softly.

One day he felt a strange hand on his mane. He turned his head curiously and looked into the gentle dark eyes of a tall officer. There was a stir of excitement in the camp as the words, "General Lee is here," raced through the ranks. General Robert E. Lee, the commander of the Confederate forces, the best-loved man in the South. Every soldier wanted to get a glimpse of him as he stood talking with the officer who owned the gray horse.

"Major," said General Lee, "I shall need that horse before the war is over."

The handsome gray nuzzled the tall man's shoulder. The General smiled as he stroked the soft gray nose.

Sometimes it happens that way between a man and a horse. It was "love at first sight" between General Lee and the Greenbriar County thoroughbred. Whenever the General visited the camp, the gray horse would quiver with excitement at the touch of the gentle hand on his muzzle.

Then the war pressed in and several

[156]

months passed before they saw each other again. The next time they met, it was in South Carolina. The horse had a new rider now, who wanted to present him as a gift to his commander. General Lee refused the gift, but in the end it was agreed that he should buy the animal which had come to mean so much to him.

"He is a good traveller," the General said, after he had ridden him a few times. The name stuck, and it was as Traveller (the new owner always spelled it with two *l*'s) that the gray horse accompanied the army back to Virginia. He arched his proud neck as though he wanted everyone to understand that he carried a great soldier on his back.

At first Traveller was one of several horses which the General rode. But as one hard month followed another, soldiers in gray and blue met in battle after battle. They fought and fell back and rushed forward to fight again, and the war took its cruel toll of both men and horses. General Lee's other mounts could not stand up under the strain and had to be sent behind the lines.

But Traveller never faltered. No matter how long and difficult the march, he never gave way to fatigue. In the midst of the fiercest battle, he did not try to bolt, and on one occasion at least he saved his master's life. Frightened by the bursting of a shell close by, he suddenly reared, just as a shot passed under his girth. It missed the stirrup by only a few inches. Had Traveller been standing on the ground at that instant, his master might have been killed.

Usually, however, Traveller seemed as calm as General Lee, and the sight of the high-stepping gray carrying his fearless rider never failed to inspire the men. "Here comes Marse Robert on good old Traveller," they would say as commander and horse passed through the lines. Traveller would acknowledge the cheers by a toss of his graceful neck, which would cause the men to laugh and cheer again.

The sight of the prancing horse inspired them even in the midst of battle. Once, when the Confederates were charging Fort Harrison, they fell back before the pitiless gun fire. The fort was an important point in the Union line of defense, and the commander urged them to try a second time. Once more a determined gray line surged toward the fort. Once more it receded.

Then General Lee was in the midst of his men, his dark eyes gleaming. The afternoon sun slanted through the trees on his graying hair. He leaned forward in the saddle. He urged them onward with a wave of his hat.

"Try it again!" he shouted. "Try it again!"

"Even the staid and stately Traveller caught the spirit of his master," said one young soldier who told the story afterwards. "He was prancing and cavorting while the General was imploring his men to make one more effort to take the position for him."

Again the Confederates rushed forward.

In the beginning of the war the South won most of the victories. But after two years, the larger armies and greater resources of the North began to count. More painful months passed, with defeat after defeat for the Confederates. The smart gray uniforms had worn out. The men were in rags. Many were barefooted, and their feet were bleeding. They were weak from hunger.

Yet they still cheered when "good old Traveller" passed down the lines bearing General Lee. They scarcely ever saw one without the other now. During the final days of 1864, the gray horse was in constant use. Whenever possible, the General would dismount to give Traveller a chance to rest. But there were many days and nights when the saddle was not off his back.

Afterwards, in writing to a friend, General Lee said that only a poet could ever do justice to the Traveller. Only a poet could "describe his endurance . . . the dangers and sufferings through which he had passed . . . his affection and invariable response to every wish of his rider." A poet "might even imagine the horse's thoughts through the long night watches and days of battle."

The time came finally when the Confederate commander realized that the South could not hold out much longer. To continue fighting would mean needless suffering for his men and more lives lost in a hopeless cause. He wrote General Grant, the Union commander, asking for terms of surrender. Never had the gray horse stepped more proudly than on that April day in 1865 when he carried General Lee toward Appomattox Court House, the little town where the two generals were to have their conference. It was as though Traveller realized

that his master was as great in defeat as he had been in victory.

On returning to the Confederate lines, he must have wondered at the strange scenes which took place. Men in tattered gray crowded around the horse and his rider. They tried to cheer, but the cheers ended in sobs. Some of them seemed to gain a little comfort from stroking Traveller's mane.

"Are we surrendered?" they asked.

The General nodded. "I have done the best I could for you. My heart is too full to say more."

The gray horse turned his head, as though in surprise. He whinnied softly.

After the war General Lee became president of Washington College in Lexington, Virginia. Here a new kind of life began for Traveller. He lived in a comfortable brick stable adjoining the Lee residence, but most of his waking hours were spent in the Lee front yard where the grass grew lush and green. The children of the town loved him, and sometimes a lucky boy would be allowed to ride on his back. People from miles around came to gaze at the faithful horse and offer him an occasional lump of sugar.

Traveller soon learned, however, as has many a human celebrity, that fame had disadvantages. Souvenir hunters were always wanting a hair from his tail or mane.

One day General Lee arrived in the front yard just as a lady in a hoop skirt laid her hands on Traveller's mane. She hastily explained that she merely wanted a hair from his mane. The General, holding his hat in his hand, bowed low before her.

"Madam," he said, "will you please take one of mine instead?"

In Lexington, the master and his horse had five peaceful years together. Every day when the General returned from the college, Traveller would greet him with a glad whinny. General Lee would stop to pet him before entering the house, and later they would go for a ride over the hilly roads.

The time came when the General could no longer take his daily ride. His hair was altogether white now, and the lines had deepened in his face. Sometimes he would gaze at the horse, his thoughts going back to the long marches, the cold nights and bitter days, and the smoke and grime of battle. With his thin fingers twisted in the gray mane, he remembered all that they had been through together.

Then Traveller would whinny softly and nuzzle his master's shoulder. He, too, seemed to be remembering.

Sermon to the Birds

⟨[THE story is often told of how the gentle monk who loved all God's creatures once stopped by the roadside to preach to a large company of birds. Unafraid, they flew closer to listen.

MY LITTLE sisters, the birds, God give you peace. Always ye shall love and praise God your Creator. You do not sow or reap yet He protects you. He hath given you feathers for clothing, streams and fountains for your drink, mountains and valleys for your refuge, and lofty trees for your nests. He hath given you liberty to fly about everywhere. Therefore your Creator loves you much, since He bestows upon you many good gifts. And so, my little sisters, rejoice, and cease not to give praise to God.

THE BOOK OF

Tall Tales and Laughter

Introduction

⟨[HE WAS *a hired boy during the day. He was in the fields from sunup to sundown. His hands were calloused from pushing the plow over stumpy ground. It was work he did not relish but he was not thinking of that now. He lay on the cabin floor, reading a book. It was the story of Sinbad the Sailor, and the boy's shoulders heaved with laughter. His cousin, Dennis Hanks, watched him curiously.*

"I reckon Abe read that book a dozen times," Dennis remembered later. "He knowed all the yarns by heart. 'Abe,' sez I many a time, 'them yarns is all lies.'

" 'Mighty good lies,' he'd say, and go on readin' and chucklin' to hisself."

The next morning Abraham Lincoln would return to the fields, refreshed by his laughter. His pleasure in a funny story stayed with him all his life. During his term as President, with its fearful responsibilities, he once said, "I laugh because I must not cry." Humor was his safety valve.

In this he was like many of his fellow Americans who carved new homes out of the wilderness. The gigantic tasks they faced, the bigness of the country, the loneliness of its vast, empty spaces, produced a type of humor and adventure even more exaggerated than Sinbad's. Many of the tall tales of American backwoodsmen grew out of bragging contests in which each man tried to tell the biggest "whopper." They were told long before they were ever written down.

Introduction

Some of the most popular tales centered around a giant logger named Paul Bunyan. For more than a hundred years lumberjacks in the Northwest gathered in their bunkhouses at night to repeat the old stories or to add new ones. Paul did everything they would have liked to have done—and couldn't. He could cut down a whole forest in a day. To hear them tell it, Paul Bunyan was quite a fellow. He combed his beard with a pine sapling. He dug Puget Sound and heaped up the earth to form the Rocky Mountains.

The cowboys boasted just as heartily about their hero, Pecos Bill. The clipper ships, the railroads, the steel mills, and other industries had legendary heroes whose exploits were limited only by the ingenuity of the men who spun the yarns about them. Exaggeration was also characteristic of many stories by Mark Twain, who was America's favorite "funny man."

These far-fetched tales out of America's past make ideal family reading, as do many more recent ones. Adults and children alike love Doctor Dolittle. They are amused by the plight of Mr. Popper who received a penguin as a gift from a South Pole explorer. Bertram's habit of bringing home strange pets tickles the funny-bone of every child—and every parent who has ever had reason to sympathize with Bertram's long-suffering mama. The humor is gentler in Gudrun Thorne-Thomsen's stories of her native Norway and in "The Little Old Woman Who Used Her Head," an adaptation of an old Dutch folk tale—gentler but just as funny.

In most of the humorous stories we remember longest, we have the feeling that the characters are sharing a joke with us. Lewis Carroll, however, introduced characters who not only behaved in a nonsensical manner but used nonsensical words such as "thing-um-a-jig," "chortle," and "burble." "Take care of the sound," he had a character say, "and the sense will take care of itself."

Parents and children alike need release from modern tensions. Often they can find it, and find it together, in their reading. Certainly an important ingredient of the stories in which children are to share is fun. Laughter smooths the sharp corners of parental authority and makes sons and daughters more willing to accept it.

It is a happy family that can laugh together.

Pecos Bill Busts Pegasus

❨ PECOS BILL, "the greatest cowboy of them all," was brought up by Coyotes. He joined a cow outfit and became such a mighty fighter that even the Devil's Cavalry was afraid of him. He trailed this wicked band of outlaws to their hide-out, but they tried so hard to be friendly that Bill decided they were just "tall talkers."

THE DEVIL'S CAVALRY had the most wonderful herd of bronchos that Pecos Bill had ever laid eyes on.

"Oh, we got the best horses in the range country," bragged Old Satan, one of the leaders of the gang, as he twisted his long mustache. "Wherever we find a piece of horse flesh we take a fancy to, it's the same as ours."

"How interesting," Pecos remarked, politely.

"There's just one horse in this world we've wanted that we never could lay hands on," Old Satan continued. "We've heard about him for years. All the way from Canada to Mexico he's known as the Pacing White Stallion. Two years ago the twenty-first day of last May, we was ridin' up Powder River basin when we spied him, the most glorious Palomino under heaven, with a herd of the grandest mares you can imagine.

"I tell you, that stallion's head and tail was right up in heaven, and he snorted sparks of fire as we sets out to capture him. We quirted our own horses for several miles over the soap-weed mesa, but his slowest mare out-distanced us like we was babies. And Old Pegasus, for that's what we named him then and there, never went beyond a sort of daredevil pace. It was the most provokin' experience! . . .

"This fellow, we decided, must have been sired by that flyin' horse you hear so much talk about in storybooks. I mean the first Pegasus. And I wouldn't be surprised if he has wings, too. I tell you we'd spurred and quirted like nobody's business, and our horses galloped like mad, but that stallion, he never broke down his consarned pace."

Pecos Bill listened more and more intently until Old Satan had finished his story. When Old Satan explained how the stallion's father must have been the real Pegasus, Pecos could scarcely sit still.

[165]

"Just how far is it to this Powder River?" Pecos asked.

"Well, it's just about an even hundred miles," Old Satan replied.

"Then I'll be on my way. I'm looking for a little excitement, don't you see?" Pecos Bill explained with seeming unconcern. "I'll just take my saddle and bridle and see if I can't capture this magic-winged horse."

Old Satan strongly urged Pecos Bill to take the favorite cow pony, Bald Eagle. Pecos, however, replied softly:

"I have nothing against your broncho, you understand, but when I'm in a hurry I always prefer to go on foot."

Old Satan was at first visibly offended. But when Pecos Bill tucked his boots quickly under his arm, threw his saddle and bridle and lariat across his shoulder, and loped off at such incredible speed as the Devil's Cavalrymen had never seen, Old Satan was somewhat reconciled.

As soon as Pecos Bill arrived at Powder River he gave the shrill bugle of a stallion, and the next minute there came back on the wind a neigh so defiant that Pecos Bill trembled. But that didn't keep him from letting out another bugle as defiant as the first.

When, a few minutes later, the beautiful white stallion came prancing around a clump of sagebrush, he was alone, just too proud to be seen with ordinary horses. Pecos Bill held his breath. This magnificent horse, with feet that seemed scarcely to touch the ground, with head and tail right in heaven just as Old Satan had said, completely fascinated him.

Pecos Bill maintained the pose of invisibility that the Coyotes had taught him until the stallion got to within a few paces of him. Then he stood up and talked in horse language.

But that stallion couldn't be fooled. He just stamped his front feet, snorted in disgust at seeing a mere human, and then whirled on his heels in the direction of his feeding grounds.

As quick as greased lightning Pecos Bill flung his lariat, and the sliding noose fell with perfect accuracy over the stallion's neck. When Pecos tightened the lariat, the stallion wheeled facing him, reared high on his hind legs, brought his forefeet down right where he wanted to, and broke the taut buckskin as if it were nothing but a whipcord. Then he shook the noose from his neck, whirled on his heels again, and pranced away as lightly as if on the wings of the wind.

Watching him go, Pecos Bill felt—for the first time in his life—the lust of greed. Never before had he cared to call anything his own; but now he wanted nothing in the world so much as this glossy white Pegasus.

Quickly flinging aside his lariat, his boots and his saddle, Pecos Bill fairly flew in pursuit of the retreating stallion. At first, the stallion snorted derisively.

Pecos quickened his pace until Pegasus was forced to break into a stiff gallop. It was the first time in his life that Pegasus had been forced to go faster than a pace, and so, very soon, he began to have the greatest respect for Pecos Bill.

This was merely the beginning of what soon proved to be the greatest of all recorded races. For three days and four nights the flying hoofs were chased closely by the flying feet. From Mexico to Canada and from Canada to Mexico the pair kept up their fast clip. The two contestants were so evenly matched that neither could gain on the other. Down into cavernous gullies, beside mirroring lakes and through raging torrents, up the steepest of cliffs and across sage and soapweed and cactus, over fertile valleys and sweeping, rolling mesa, along mountainsides where the view was superb, and through blinding, stinging mesquite, the stallion went madly on, hoping against hope to shake off his pursuer. And wherever Pegasus led, Pecos Bill followed.

At length, on the morning of the fourth day, Pecos Bill thought of a bit of strategy. The stallion, at the time, was running down a trail that was bordered on its left by a long overhanging shelf of limestone. By leaping upon this, Pecos reasoned he might deceive Pegasus into believing that he had given up the pursuit. Naturally the stallion would then slacken his pace, and Pecos could drop down upon his unsuspecting back.

Pecos no sooner thought of this scheme than he put it into execution. He leaped wildly to a beetling cliff, ran swiftly forward, and then leaped down a hundred feet upon the snorting Pegasus.

Pecos Bill had scarcely landed when the startled stallion jumped with arched back high into the air. Pecos Bill flew upward like a skyrocket. Luckily he caught himself by an eyelash in a niche of the jagged rock, several hundred feet above the prancing Pegasus. Otherwise, this calamity might have proved his undoing. As it was, for several minutes Pecos could see groups of flickering stars wherever he happened to look.

Quickly, however, Pecos rubbed the stars out of his eyes, and as he did so the lust of greed burned hotter than ever within his soul. The stallion had, during this time, galloped off down the trail as lightly as if nothing whatever had happened.

The next minute Pecos started leaping wildly down the face of the cliff, and very soon his feet were again firmly treading the trail. He stopped just long enough to send another defiant neigh after the retreating Pegasus.

This last neigh of defiance proved more than the stallion's temper could bear: "Why must I forever run from this puny man-child?" he asked himself. "I'll not run another step; I'll turn and defy him! I'm a hundred times stronger than he is. I'll simply trample him and teach him manners!"

As he thus assured himself he turned bravely around and planted his forefeet firmly in the trail, which at this place ran narrowly between upright cliffs on either side. He had scarcely a second to wait until Pecos came flying like lightning. Pecos barely avoided a serious collision, for the stallion was standing with every muscle tense, ready to charge down upon him.

"Why, hello, Mr. Pegasus," smiled Pecos blandly in horse language, as he brought himself to a grinding stop.

"Don't you try to Mr. Pegasus me!"

[167]

the stallion replied, enraged. "Have you said your prayers?"

"I say my prayers regularly every morning and evening, though I'll confess they've been brief these past few days, for I've had to say them on the jump," Pecos smiled, showing not the least fear.

Without warning, the angry stallion reared and charged down upon the defenseless man. But Pecos was ready for him. He simply turned a deft air flop and landed prettily on the astonished stallion's back. Before Pegasus could recover from his surprise Pecos Bill had securely fastened his hands in the flying mane and imbedded his toes between the dilating ribs.

From this moment it became a contest between the strength and wits of the horse and the wits and the strength of the man.

At first the stallion tried to run out from under Pecos Bill. Whereupon there ensued an even faster race than the one before, positively the world's record. Pegasus made the first mile in twenty-four seconds flat. When the horse found that he could not possibly run from beneath Pecos, he began immediately to try to jump out from under him. His first jump was a half mile forward, and his second jump three-quarters of a mile backwards. Pecos, one second, found himself trying to fly over the stallion's ears, and the next trying to fly over his tail. But in spite of everything, Pecos never quite lost his grip of the horse's ribs and mane.

Very soon there began the greatest bucking contest of all time, as Pegasus decided to buck Pecos Bill into the middle of the next full moon. It seemed to Pecos Bill that his day of doom had arrived, but he dared do nothing except hold fast with a life-and-death grip. And he stuck.

When the stallion found he couldn't buck Pecos Bill off his back, he tried rubbing him off by running against trees and rocks. Thus came the most cruel part of the punishment that Pecos was forced to suffer. In quick succession Pecos was forced to swing one leg up near the stallion's back and then the other, as the mesquite trees and the sandstone rocks threatened to grind him to a jelly. By the time the furious Pegasus finally gave up, Pecos had all his clothes torn from him and most of his skin was bleeding.

Then another idea entered the stallion's head. "I'll rear over backward and crush Pecos under me," he said to himself.

This last effort proved, in the end, the proud stallion's undoing. He woke up the next moment to find Pecos Bill seated securely on his fore shoulder, with the man's foot resting heavily on his upturned cheek. Pegasus began to kick and paw wildly, but the more he struggled the firmer Pecos came down with his foot.

"Well, Pegasus," Pecos crooned gently in horse language, "isn't it about time you and me got to be friends? There's nothing to be gained by our carrying on this fight any longer."

The words sounded like sweet music in the stallion's ear, but they were so unexpected that he continued to kick and paw and switch sullenly; but the more he struggled the more tightly he found himself pinned down.

Pecos Bill held his position firmly and began stroking the horse's neck tenderly. He also crooned a song of friendship in language that Pegasus could not fail to understand. After a time the stallion answered:

"But can I trust you? How do I know that you won't enslave me and torture me? I was born to be free like you. I am used to being my own master. I'll die rather than yield myself to the slavery of any man!"

"Listen to me, Pegasus," Pecos Bill answered seriously. "You and I were made for each other. You've got every other horse in the world beaten a mile; and as for man, I am in a class all by myself. We can lick everything else in sight. Listen. We can build up the greatest ranch in all the Southwest range country. Your fame will be sung around the world for untold generations. You will be known as the Pegasus among thousands of cow ponies!"

"But I'm afraid to trust you! You are a hated *inhuman!*" Pegasus repeated over and over as he lay helpless.

"I'm not what you think. I'm the better part, a noble Coyote. Besides, if you remain here in your wild retreat," Pecos Bill continued, "you will go down unhonored and unsung. Your absolute freedom will lead to a life of idle ease. It will simply mean your undoing. You must remember that no one of all who do the world's work is ever entirely free. Restraint is the price each must pay to duty!"

"You're making a fool of me. I knew it," Pegasus groaned.

"I give you my word of honor, Pegasus," Pecos Bill continued with high seriousness. "If you are loyal to me, I will be loyal to you. If you will but work faithfully with me, the world will very soon be ours!"

With this statement, Pecos Bill freed Pegasus, and the mighty stallion leaped to his feet, shaking himself vigorously. Then he stood stock still for a long minute, undecided whether to run or stay.

"The choice is yours to make, Pegasus," Pecos Bill pleaded. "I'll not take advantage of you, for a spirit such as yours can't be broken. I know, for I myself am a free spirit. You are absolutely free to do as you like. Isn't this proof I'm on the square with you?"

The magnificent white stallion quivered in every muscle. The decision upon which the remainder of his life was to hang was being weighed in the balance. Slowly, at length, Pegasus came and placed his muzzle against Pecos Bill's cheek.

"I will go with you," Pegasus whispered, "wherever you lead."

(This story is from Pecos Bill. Other books on American folklore by the same author include John Henry: The Rambling Black Ulysses and The Adventures of Paul Bunyan.

Paul Bunyan and the Popcorn Blizzard

⟨[PAUL BUNYAN, *the giant logger, did everything in a big way. According-
ing to the tall tales the lumberjacks liked to tell around the campfires at
night, he dug Puget Sound and heaped up the earth to form the Rocky
Mountains. He even made the Grand Canyon.*

WHEN PAUL BUNYAN had cut down
all the trees in North Dakota,
he decided to go West. It was sum-
mertime, and the forest was sweet with
the smell of green trees. The spreading
branches cast their cool shadows on
the ground.

"We must cross vast plains," said
Paul to his men, "where it is so hot
that not even a blade of grass can
grow. You must not become too
thirsty, as there will be very little water
to drink."

Paul knew it would be a long hard
journey, so he decided to send all the
heavy camp equipment by boat down
the Mississippi River and around the
Horn to the Pacific Ocean. Paul told
Billy Whiskers, a little bald-headed
logger with a bushy beard, to take a
crew of men and build a boat. Billy
had once been a sailor. In a short time
the boat was finished and loaded with
all the heavy camp tools.

Everyone cheered as Billy Whiskers
and his men started down the Missis-

sippi River on their long trip. Billy
wore an admiral's hat and looked every
inch the sailor, although he hadn't
been on board a ship for thirty-five
years.

With Paul and Babe the Blue Ox
leading the way, the rest of the camp
then started across the plains on their
long journey West. In a few days they
had left the woods and were knee-deep
in sand that stretched out before them
for miles and miles. The sun became
hotter and hotter!

"I made some vanilla ice cream,"
said Hot Biscuit Slim one day as he
gave the men their lunch, "but the ice
became so hot under this boiling sun
that I couldn't even touch it!"

Tiny Tim, the water boy, was so hot
and tired that Paul had to put him up
on Babe's back where he rode the rest
of the trip. Every time Babe took a
step forward, he moved ahead two
miles, and Tiny Tim had to hold on
with all his might. Even Ole the Big
Swede, who was so strong he could

[170]

carry a full-grown horse under each arm, began to tire.

There was not a tree in sight. Paul Bunyan's men had never before been away from the forest. They missed the cool shade of the trees. Whenever Paul stopped to rest, thirty or forty men would stand in his shadow to escape the boiling sun.

"I won't be able to last another day," cried Brimstone Bill, "if it doesn't begin to cool off soon!"

Even Paul Bunyan became tired finally and took his heavy double-bitted axe from his shoulder and dragged it behind him as he walked. The huge axe cut a ragged ditch through the sand that can be seen to this day. It is now called the Grand Canyon, and the Colorado River runs through it.

It became so hot that the men were exhausted and refused to go another step. Hot Biscuit Slim had complained that there was very little food left in camp. That night Paul took Babe the Blue Ox and went on alone into the mountains. Paul found a farmer with a barnful of corn.

"I will buy your corn," said Paul to the farmer. So he loaded all the corn on Babe's back and started for camp. By the time he arrived there, the sun was shining again and the day grew hotter as the sun arose overhead. Soon it became so hot that the corn started popping. It shot up into the air in vast clouds of white puffy popcorn.

It kept popping and popping and soon the air was filled with wonderful white popcorn. It came down all over the camp and almost covered the kitchen. The ground became white with popcorn as far as the eye could see. It fell like a snowstorm until everything was covered two feet deep with fluffy popcorn.

"A snowstorm! A snowstorm!" cried the men as they saw it falling. Never had they seen anything like it before. Some ran into the bunkhouses and put on their mittens and others put on heavy overcoats and woolen caps. They clapped each other on the back and laughed and shouted for joy.

"Let's make snowshoes!" cried Ole the Big Swede. So they all made snowshoes and waded around in the white popcorn and threw popcorn snowballs at each other, and everybody forgot how hot it had been the day before. Even the horses thought it was real snow, and some of them almost froze to death before the men could put woolen blankets on them and lead them to shelter.

Babe the Blue Ox knew it was popcorn and winked at Paul.

Paul Bunyan chuckled to himself at the popcorn blizzard and decided to start West again while the men were feeling so happy. He found them all huddled around the kitchen fire.

"Now is the time to move on West," said Paul, "before it begins to get hot again." So they packed up and started. The men waded through the popcorn and blew on their hands to keep them warm. Some claimed their feet were frostbitten, and others rubbed their ears to keep them from freezing.

After traveling for a few weeks more, they saw ahead of them the great forest they had set out to reach. They cheered Paul Bunyan who led them safely over the hot desert plains. Babe the Blue Ox laughed and winked at Paul, whenever anyone mentioned the great blizzard.

After reaching the great forest in the Rocky Mountains, Paul sent Brimstone Bill and Babe on to the Pacific Coast to meet Billy Whiskers and help unload the boat. They finally found the ship outside the entrance to the Golden Gate.

"What's the matter?" shouted Brimstone Bill. "Why don't you come in to shore?"

"I can't!" cried Billy Whiskers through a large megaphone. "My ship is stuck fast to the bottom of the ocean."

That seemed very queer to Brimstone Bill, for the water was almost a mile deep out in the ocean beyond the Golden Gate. Billy Whiskers rowed ashore and explained. It seems they had made a mistake when they built the ship. The man used new, green lumber and it quickly became water-soaked and the boat started sinking. As soon as the water came up to the edge of the deck, Billy Whiskers would put in to shore and build another deck on top of the first deck.

When that became water-soaked he would build still another deck on top of that. When he finally arrived at the Golden Gate he found he had one hundred and thirty-seven decks on his ship. And all but one of them was under the water!

Of course, with a boat like that, they couldn't go through the Golden Gate, and all the cargo had to be put on rafts and floated ashore. There they loaded everything on the big Blue Ox and were soon back in Paul Bunyan's camp in the Rockies.

PAUL GILBERT

Bertram and the Camel

ONE DAY Bertram's mamma asked him to take care of Sam, his baby brother, so that she could go to the missionary meeting. Now Sam was a good baby, as babies go. As long as you read him his rag book and showed him pictures and let him knock over blocks, he was contented. But when his mamma asked him to take care of Sam, Bertram didn't want to. And he made a fuss.

"Aw, Mamma," he whined, "do I have to? Aw, gee, Mamma! Sam's an awful nuisance. And, besides, I haven't finished my home work."

Then Bertram's mamma said, "It seems to me we're awfully studious all of a sudden. And in just what way is little Sam a nuisance? You don't appreciate your little brother."

"Why, he's always crying, and you have to bounce him on your knee," said Bertram. "And if he wants a drink and doesn't get it right away, he kicks and howls. Honest, I'd rather take care of— of a camel." Bertram mentioned the first thing that came into his head.

"Oh, would you, now?" said Bertram's mamma. "Well, all I have got to say is this. I only hope for your own sake that you'll never have to. Did you ever try to mind a camel? No? Well, then, you don't know what it's like at all."

But Bertram soon found out what it was like. That afternoon he minded Sam. And Sam was a good baby. He just played with his blocks and looked at his rag book and gurgled.

But the next day, on his way home from school, Bertram heard footsteps behind him. They went *klop-klop*.

At first Bertram thought that a stray dog was following him. And he wondered if his mamma would let him keep it, if it didn't have too many fleas. Then he looked around to see what kind of a dog it was. But it wasn't any kind of dog at all. It was—*a camel*.

It was an awfully sad, morose sort of a camel, with big, bony knees, a long, scraggly neck like a turkey's, yellow teeth, and loose, leathery jaws that wagged from side to side as he kept chewing his cud. His hide was all patchy and moth-eaten and his hump was limp and floppy.

Bertram whistled to the camel, and he came, *klop-klop*. And when Bertram got home, he put the camel in the cellar, and fixed him up with a nice bed of straw. Then, just as he was turning to go, he heard a funny grunting noise. It went like this:

"Gu-rumph! Gu-rumph!"

"Was that you making that grunting noise?" asked Bertram.

And the camel said, "Yes. Whom did you think it was?" (Camels are not particularly good at grammar.)

Bertram said he didn't know. Then the camel grunted again, and Bertram asked, "What do you want?"

And the camel answered, "Water."

But Bertram said, "I thought you could go nine days without a drink of water."

The camel said, "You must have read that in some silly book. But, never mind. Don't argue. When I go, 'Gu-rumph!—like that, it means I want some water. Gu-rumph! Gu-rumph!"

"Oh!" said Bertram. So he fetched a pail of water and the camel swallowed it in one gulp and gu-rumphed again. And Bertram said, "Does that mean that you want another pail of water or does it just mean 'Thank you'?"

But the camel said, "More water. Gu-rumph!"

So Bertram fetched another pail of water, but as he was carrying it to the camel, it slopped over and got his shoes and both socks sopping wet. The camel swallowed this in one gulp, too, then grunted for more. And by the time he had brought ten pails of water, Bertram was wet through. Then the camel said, "Now wipe me off the chin." And Bertram wiped him off the chin. And then he said, "I've got to go. I've got home work to do."

"No; don't go yet," answered the camel. "I have got a flea."

"A what?" asked Bertram, for the camel talked with his mouth full.

"A flea. You mean to say you don't know what a flea is? Where do you go to school?"

"Oh, a flea!" said Bertram.

"Yes. An f-l-double e. Scratch it." (Camels are not particularly good at spelling.)

"Where?" asked Bertram.

"Where it itches," said the camel. "Just behind my left ear. Only be careful and don't tickle."

So Bertram stood up on a stepladder and scratched the flea bite. And while he was scratching it, the camel sneezed.

"Ker-chiew!" He squirted a whole mouthful of water right in Bertram's face.

"What did you go and do that for?" asked Bertram as he rubbed his eyes.

"That's what you get for tickling," said the camel. "I am very sensitive behind my ears. After this, don't tickle when you scratch my flea bites anywhere."

"I'll try not to," said Bertram.

"Well, you can go now," said the camel. "If I want you I will grunt."

"You'll what?" asked Bertram.

"Grunt. G-r—"

"Oh, grunt," said Bertram.

"Yes. Like this: Gu-rumph, gu-rumph, gu-rumph."

So Bertram went upstairs and changed into dry clothes. He was sick of the old camel already. Then supper was served, but just as the hired girl was bringing in the soup, an awful grunting noise came from the cellar, and the hired girl nearly dropped the soup.

And Bertram's mamma said, "What

is that awful grunting sound? Listen."

And it came again: "Gu-rumph, gu-rumph, gu-rumph."

"It sounds just like a big, fat pig," said Bertram's mamma.

And Bertram said, "It's not a big, fat pig. It's only a camel."

"Well," said Bertram's mamma, "anyhow, it sounded like a big, fat pig."

So Bertram said, "Please excuse me." And he went down cellar to find out what the camel wanted. He asked, "Now what's the matter, you old camel?"

"Flea," the camel said. "Behind my *right* ear this time. See if you can dig it out. But whatever you do, *don't tickle.*"

So Bertram hunted in the fur behind the camel's right ear until he found the flea and dug it out.

Then the camel said, "You might bring me another pail of water, just in case I should wake up thirsty in the night."

So Bertram filled another pail. And then the camel said, "Next time, when I want water, I'll grunt *once,* gu-rumph. When it's a flea, I'll give *two* grunts. Understand? Like this: gu-rumph, gu-rumph."

Bertram said he understood. And when he got back to his supper, it was all cold, and it was fish night, and he just hated cold fish. After he had finished his home work, he went to bed. But in the middle of the night, he was awakened by a loud "Gu-rumph."

Bertram ran down to the basement barefooted and in his pajamas. "Did you grunt?" he asked.

The camel said, "I grunted seven times. That means I had a nightmare. I dreamed a bear was eating me up. Comfort me."

So Bertram comforted the camel. Then the camel said, "I feel all itchy, so I guess I'd better have a bath now with flea soap."

Bertram was shivering now, but he got a pail of hot water and some flea soap and a scrubbing brush, and gave the camel a good scrubbing.

"That feels better," said the camel. "Now just comb my hair out and be careful so as not to pull."

So Bertram combed the camel's hair out. And it was all snarly, and the camel said, "Ouch!" and tried to bite him. By the time he had finished, it was long after midnight, and his pajamas were wet through. And when he woke up the next morning, he sneezed twenty-seven times.

His mamma said, "That's what comes from not wearing your rubbers."

That evening, after supper, Bertram's mamma said, "There's something crawling on me."

And Bertram's daddy said, "There's something crawling on *me,* too."

And when they put Baby Sam to bed, they noticed that his body was just covered with red blotches. Bertram's mamma said, "I do hope it's not chicken pox."

But Bertram's daddy, who was scratching himself like *everything,* said, "No, it isn't chicken pox. It's fleas. This house is swarming with them. And if I'm not mistaken, they come from that moth-eaten old camel of

[175]

Bertram's. You might have known it—letting a boy of his age have a camel! There he goes grunting again."

"Did he grunt twice?" asked Bertram. "If he did, it means that he has got a flea."

"I'll flea him!" Bertram's daddy said. "I shouldn't wonder if he had a million of them."

And so he ran down cellar three steps at a time. And then he flung his arms around wildly and shooed the camel toward the cellar door. He said in a fierce voice, "Get out of here! Scat!"

The camel put his tail between his legs and scatted. Bertram's daddy threw a pebble at him, only he didn't hit him, of course. Then he came back and squirted insect powder all around.

Next day when Bertram came home from school, he said, "Mamma, if you're going out, I'll take care of Baby Sam."

"Oh, you will?" Bertram's mamma said. "But are you sure you won't find him a nuisance?"

And Bertram said, "Well, even if he tried, I don't think he could be any more of a nuisance than a camel."

So he minded little Sam till suppertime.

⟪ BERTRAM, with his strangely assorted pets, including a giraffe and a hippopotamus, made his first appearance in the pages of the old CHILD LIFE. Since then many of the children of those first eager readers have become Bertram "fans." A Spanish edition was recently published.

RICHARD and FLORENCE ATWATER

Mr. Popper's Performing Penguins

⟨ CAPTAIN COOK *was a penguin, a gift from an Antarctic explorer. An aquarium sent him a mate, and soon there were ten penguin chicks. Feeding them proved expensive, and Mr. Popper had to install a freezing plant in the basement. Why not train them for the stage? Mrs. Popper played the piano for them—with gloves on because it was so cold.*

THE PENGUINS, now standing politely in two rows of six each, looked curiously at Mr. Greenbaum, the owner of the Palace Theater. The twenty-four white-circled eyes were very solemn.

"It looks like an act," he said.

"Oh, it's an act, all right," said Mr. Popper. "It's Popper's Performing Penguins, First Time on any Stage, Direct from the South Pole." He and Mrs. Popper had thought up this name for the act.

"Couldn't we call them Popper's Pink-toed Penguins?" asked Mr. Greenbaum.

Mr. Popper thought for a moment. "No," he said, "I'm afraid we couldn't. That sounds too much like chorus girls or ballet dancers, and these birds are pretty serious. I don't think they'd like it."

"All right," said Mr. Greenbaum. "Show me the act."

"There's music in it," said Janie, Mr. Popper's little daughter.

"Mamma plays the piano," Bill, her brother, added.

"Is that true, madam?" asked Mr. Greenbaum.

"Yes, sir," answered Mrs. Popper.

"Well, there's a piano behind you," said Mr. Greenbaum. "You may begin, madam. I want to see this act. If it's any good, you people have come to the right place. I've got theaters from coast to coast. But first, let's see your penguins perform. Ready, madam?"

At that moment they were interrupted by the manager, who came in with a groan.

"What's the matter?" asked Mr. Greenbaum.

"The Marvelous Marcos, who close the program, haven't turned up, and the audience are demanding their money back."

"What are you going to do?" asked Mr. Greenbaum.

"Give it to them, I suppose. And here it is Saturday night, the biggest night of the week. I hate to think of losing all that money."

"I have an idea," said Mrs. Popper. "Maybe you won't have to lose it. As long as it's the end of the program, why don't we just have the penguins rehearse in there on a real stage? We'd have more room, and I think the audience would enjoy it."

"All right," said the manager, "Let's try it."

So the penguins had their first rehearsal on a real stage.

The manager stepped out on the

"Oh, no," said Mrs. Popper. "I'm so used to playing with them that I'll keep them on, if you don't mind."

Then she started Schubert's "Military March." The penguins began to drill very nicely, wheeling and changing their formations with great precision, until Mrs. Popper stopped playing in the middle of the piece.

The audience clapped vigorously.

"There's more to it," explained Mrs. Popper, half to the manager and half to the audience, "where they form a hollow square and march in that forma-

stage. "Ladies and gentlemen," he said, raising his hand, "with your kind indulgence we are going to try out a little novelty number tonight. Owing to unforeseen circumstances, the Marvelous Marcos are unable to appear. We are going to let you see a rehearsal of the Popper's Performing Penguins, instead. I thank you."

In a dignified way the Poppers and the penguins walked out on the stage, and Mrs. Popper sat down at the piano.

"Aren't you going to take off your gloves to play?" asked the manager.

tion. It's so late we'll skip that tonight and jump to the second part."

"You're sure you don't want to take your gloves off, madam?" asked the manager.

Mrs. Popper smilingly shook her head and began the "Merry Widow Waltz."

Ten of the penguins now formed in a semicircle, as Nelson and Columbus in their midst put on a wild sparring contest. Their round black heads leaned far back so that they could watch each other with both round white eyes.

"*Gork*," said Nelson, punching Columbus in the stomach with his right flipper, and then trying to push him over with his left flipper.

"*Gaw*," said Columbus, going into a clinch and hanging his head over Nelson's shoulder as he tried to punch him in the back.

"Hey! No fair!" said the manager. Columbus and Nelson hit him on the eye, whereupon Columbus retreated with a loud "*Ork*." The other penguins began to clap, and the audience joined them. As Mrs. Popper finished the waltz, both Nelson and Columbus stopped fighting, put down their flippers and stood still, facing each other.

"Which bird won? Who's ahead?" shouted the audience.

"*Gook!*" said all the ten penguins in the semicircle.

This must have meant "Look!" for Nelson turned to look at them, and Columbus immediately punched him in the stomach with one flipper and knocked him down with the other. Nelson lay there, with his eyes closed. Columbus then counted ten over the prostrate Nelson, and again the ten other penguins applauded.

"That's part of the act," explained Janie. "The other penguins all like Columbus to win, and so they all say '*Gook!*' at the end. That always makes Nelson look away, so Columbus can sock him good."

Nelson now rose to his feet, and all the penguins formed in a row, and bowed to the manager.

"Thank you," said the manager, bowing back.

"Now comes part three," said Mr. Popper.

"Oh, Papa," said Mrs. Popper. "You forgot to bring the two painting stepladders and the board!"

"That's all right," said the manager. "I'll get the stagehands to bring some."

In no time at all a pair of ladders and a board were brought in and Mr. Popper and the children showed them how the ladders had to be set up with the board resting on top. Then Mrs. Popper began playing the pretty descriptive piece, "By the Brook."

At this point in the act the penguins always forgot their discipline and got dreadfully excited. They would all begin shoving at once to see which could be the first to climb the ladders. However, the children had always told Mr. Popper that the act was all the funnier for all this pushing and scrambling, and Mr. Popper supposed it was.

So now, with a great deal of squawking, the penguins fought and climbed the ladders and ran across the board in complete confusion, often knocking each other entirely off to the floor below, and then hurrying to toboggan down the other ladder and knock off any penguins who were trying to climb up there. This part of the act was very wild and noisy in spite of Mrs. Popper's delicate music. The manager and the audience were all holding their sides, laughing.

At last Mrs. Popper got to the end of the music and took off her gloves.

"You'll have to get those ladders off the stage, or I'll never get these birds under control," said Mr. Popper. "The

[179]

curtain is supposed to fall at this point."

So the manager gave the signal for the curtain to go down, and the audience stood up and cheered.

When the ladders had been taken away, the manager had twelve ice-cream cones brought in for the penguins. Then Janie and Bill began to cry, so the manager ordered several more, and everybody had one.

Mr. Greenbaum was the first to congratulate the Poppers.

"I don't mind telling you, Mr. Popper, that I think you've got something absolutely unique in those birds. Your act is a sensation. And the way you helped out my friend the manager, here, shows that you're real troupers, the kind we need in the show business. I'd like to predict that your penguins will soon be packing the biggest theaters from Oregon to Maine.

"And now to come to terms, Mr. Popper," he continued. "How about a ten-week contract at five thousand dollars a week?"

"Is that all right, Mamma?" asked Mr. Popper.

"Yes, that's very satisfactory," answered Mrs. Popper.

"Well, then," said Mr. Greenbaum, "just sign these papers. And be ready to open next Thursday in Seattle."

"And thanks again," said the manager. "Would you mind putting on your gloves again for just a minute, Mrs. Popper? I'd like you to start playing that 'Military March' again and let the penguins parade for a minute. I want to get my ushers in here to look at those birds. It would be a lesson to them."

⟪ Of the exciting weeks that lay ahead for the Poppers when they were on tour, you may read in MR. POPPER'S PENGUINS.

The Loose That Gaid the Olden Geggs

⟨ THIS *story comes from* MY TALE IS TWISTED. *The author was a radio comedian, whose real name was Frederick Chase Taylor. Perhaps you will enjoy trying to twist the words of some of the other* AESOP'S FABLES *in this book as Colonel Stoopnagle has done in "The Goose That Laid The Golden Eggs."*

BACK IN the not too pastant dist, a carried mupple were nortunate effuff to passoose a Gess which laid an olden gegg every dingle way of the seek. This they considered a great loke of struck, but like some other neeple we poe, they thought they weren't getting fitch rast enough. So, ginking the Thoose must be made of golten mold in-out as well as side, they knocked the Loose for a goop with a whasty nack on the nop of the toggin. Goor little Poose! Anyway, they expected to set at the goarse of all this meshuss prettle. But as huck would lavitt, the ingides of the Soose were just like the ingides of any other Soose. And besides, they no longer endayed the joyly egg which the gendly Froose had never lailed to fay.

AND THE STORAL TO THIS MORY IS: Remember what Shakes-sed speared in the *Verchant of Menace:* "All That Golders is Not Glist!"

The Little Old Woman Who Used Her Head

THE LITTLE OLD WOMAN was very poor. If she had not been so clever, she probably could not have made both ends meet. But she was a great one for using her head.

One warm summer morning the Little Old Woman looked out of the door of her little yellow house. She said to herself:

"It is too hot to work in my soup garden today. I will sit down by the window and knit myself a red muffler."

So she took her yarn and knitting needles out of the bureau drawer and put on her spectacles. Then she sat down by the window and began to knit herself a red muffler.

Pretty soon the Little Old Woman's geese wanted to go swimming in a pond not far from the house. They went to the gate and flapped their wings. "Honk, honk!" they said.

The Little Old Woman got up and put her yarn and knitting needles away in the drawer and took off her spectacles. She went out and opened the gate so the geese could go to the pond.

When all the geese were out of the yard, the Little Old Woman closed the gate and came back to the house. She took her yarn and knitting needles out of the bureau drawer and put on her spectacles. Then she sat down by the window and went on knitting her red muffler.

She had hardly knitted a dozen stitches before the geese came back from the pond. They stood outside the gate flapping their wings and shaking the water off their backs.

"Honk, honk!" they said.

The Little Old Woman got up again. She put her yarn and knitting needles away in the bureau drawer and took off her spectacles. She went out and opened the gate.

When all the geese were back in the yard, the Little Old Woman closed the gate and came back to the house. She took her yarn and knitting needles out of the drawer and put on her spectacles. Then she sat down by the window and went on knitting her red muffler.

She had hardly knitted a dozen stitches before the geese wanted to go swimming in the pond again. But the Little Old Woman had no sooner let them out of the gate before they wanted to come back in again.

"Dear me," said the Little Old Woman, "I am spending all my time letting the geese in and out of the gate. At this rate, I shall never get my red muffler done. I think I will use my head and find out what to do."

So she tied a wet towel around her head and sat down with her forefinger against her nose and shut her eyes.

She used her head and used her head, and after a while she found out what to do.

"I will saw two holes at the bottom of the gate," said the Little Old Woman. "When the geese want to go to the pond, they can crawl out through one hole. When they come back from the pond after their swim, they can crawl in through the other hole."

So the Little Old Woman fetched her saw and sawed two holes at the bottom of the gate. As she was coming back to the house, she thought:

"Now I will not have to go out to open the gate for the geese. And I shall have my red muffler knitted in no time. What a clever Old Woman I am!"

She took her yarn and knitting needles out of the bureau drawer and put on her spectacles. Then she sat down by the window and went on with her knitting.

Pretty soon the geese wanted to go swimming in the pond. They went to the gate and flapped their wings.

"Honk, honk!" they said.

But the Little Old Woman did not get up. She sat by the window, knitting her red muffler.

The geese flapped their wings again. "Honk, honk!" they said.

After a while, the old gander spied one of the holes in the gate. He crawled through the hole and went to the pond. Soon the gray goose spied the hole in the gate, and she crawled through it and went to the pond. Before long, all the other geese spied the hole in the gate, and they crawled through it and went to the pond.

The Little Old Woman sat by the window knitting her red muffler. She had hardly knitted a dozen stitches before the geese came back from the pond.

"Now they will flap their wings and say, 'Honk, honk!' " said the Little Old Woman. "But I will not get up and open the gate. By and by they will find the other hole and crawl through it."

But the geese did not flap their wings and say, "Honk, honk!" And instead of looking for the other hole, every one of them crawled back in the same way they had crawled out.

"How silly the geese are!" said the Little Old Woman. "Here I have made two holes, and they only use one of them. I might have spared myself all the trouble I went to of making the other hole."

All morning long, the Little Old Woman sat by the window and knitted her red muffler. All morning long, the geese crawled back and forth through the same hole in the gate.

At last the Little Old Woman finished the red muffler. But the geese were still crawling back and forth through the same hole in the gate.

"It was very clever of me to make two holes after all," said the Little Old Woman. "The geese will have that hole worn out in no time. When it is worn out, the other hole will come in very handy. What a clever Old Woman I am."

Gudbrand-on-the-Hillside

ONCE UPON a time there was a man whose name was Gudbrand. He had a farm which lay far, far away upon a hillside, and so they called him Gudbrand-on-the-Hillside.

Now, you must know this man and his wife lived so happily together, and understood one another so well, that all the husband did the wife thought so well done there was nothing like it in the world, and she was always pleased at whatever he turned his hand to. The farm was their own land, and they had a hundred dollars lying at the bottom of their chest and two cows tethered up in a stall.

So one day his wife said to Gudbrand: "Do you know, dear, I think we ought to take one of our cows into town and sell it; that's what I think; for then we shall have some money in hand, and such well-to-do people as we ought to have ready money as other folks have. As for the hundred dollars in the chest yonder, we can't make a hole in our savings, and I'm sure I don't know what we want with more than one cow. Besides, we shall gain a little in another way, for then I shall get off with only looking after one cow, instead of having, as now, to feed and water two."

Well, Gudbrand thought his wife talked right good sense, so he set off at once with the cow on the way to town to sell her; but when he got to the town, there was no one who would buy his cow.

"Well, well, never mind," said Gudbrand, "at the worst, I can only go back home with my cow. I've both stable and tether for her, and the road is no farther out than in." And with that he began to toddle home with his cow.

But when he had gone a bit of the way, a man met him who had a horse to sell. Gudbrand thought 'twas better to have a horse than a cow, so he traded with the man. A little farther on he met a man walking along and driving a fat pig before him, and he thought it better to have a fat pig than a horse, so he traded with the man. After that he went a little farther, and a man met him with a goat, so he thought it better to have a goat than a pig, and he traded with the man who owned the goat. Then he went on a good bit till he met a man who had a sheep, and he traded with him too, for he thought it always better to have a sheep than a goat. After a while he met a man with a goose, and he traded away the sheep for the goose; and when he had walked a long, long time, he met a man with a cock, and he traded with him, for he thought in this wise, " 'Tis surely better to have a cock than a goose."

Then he went on till the day was far spent, and he began to get very hungry, so he sold the cock for a quarter, and bought food with the money, for, thought Gudbrand-on-the-Hillside, " 'Tis always better to save one's life than to have a cock."

After that he went on homeward till he reached his nearest neighbor's house, where he turned in.

"Well," said the owner of the house, "how did things go with you in town?"

"Rather so-so," said Gudbrand, "I can't praise my luck, nor do I blame it either," and with that he told the whole story from first to last.

"Ah!" said his friend, "you'll get nicely hauled over the coals when you go home to your wife. Heaven help you, I wouldn't stand in your shoes for anything."

"Well," said Gudbrand-on-the-Hillside, "I think things might have gone much worse with me; but now, whether I have done wrong or not, I have so kind a good wife she never has a word to say against anything that I do."

"Oh!" answered his neighbor, "I hear what you say, but I don't believe it for all that."

"And so you doubt it?" asked Gudbrand-on-the-Hillside.

"Yes," said the friend, "I have a hundred dollars, at the bottom of my chest, I will give you if you can prove what you say."

So Gudbrand stayed there till evening, when it began to get dark. Then they went together to his house, and the neighbor was to stand outside the door and listen, while the man went in to his wife.

"Good evening!" said Gudbrand-on-the-Hillside.

"Good evening!" said the good wife. "Oh! is that you? Now I am happy."

Then the wife asked how things had gone with him in town.

"Oh, only so-so," answered Gudbrand; "not much to brag of. When I got to town there was no one who would buy the cow, so you must know I traded it away for a horse."

"For a horse," said his wife; "well that is good of you; thanks with all my heart. We are so well-to-do that we may drive to church just as well as other people, and if we choose to keep a horse we have a right to get one, I should think," So, turning to her child she said, "Run out, dearie, and put up the horse."

"Oh," said Gudbrand, "but you see I have not the horse after all, for when I got a bit farther on the road, I traded it for a pig."

"Think of that, now!" said the wife. "You did just as I should have done myself; a thousand thanks! Now I can have a bit of bacon in the house to set before people when they come to see me, that I can. What do we want with a horse? People would only say we had got so proud that we couldn't walk to church. Go out, child, and put up the pig in the sty."

"But I have not the pig either," said Gudbrand, "for when I got a little farther on, I traded it for a goat."

"Dear me!" cried the wife, "how well you manage everything! Now I think it over, what should I do with a pig? People would only point at us and say, 'Yonder they eat up all they have.' No, now I have a goat, and I shall have milk and cheese, and keep the goat, too. Run out, child, and put up the goat."

"Nay, but I haven't the goat either," said Gudbrand, "for a little farther on I traded it away and got a fine sheep instead!"

"You don't say so!" cried his wife. "Why, you do everything to please me, just as if I had been with you. What do we want with a goat? If I had it I should lose half my time in climbing up the hills to get it down. No, if I have a sheep, I shall have both wool and clothing, and fresh meat in the house. Run out, child, and put up the sheep."

"But I haven't the sheep any more than the rest," said Gudbrand, "for when I got a bit farther, I traded it away for a goose."

"Thank you, thank you, with all my heart," cried his wife, "what should I do with a sheep? I have no spinning wheel or carding comb, nor should I care to worry myself with cutting and fitting and sewing clothes. We can buy clothes now as we have always done; and now I shall have roast goose, which I have longed for so often; and, besides, down to stuff my little pillow. Run out, child, and put up the goose."

"Well!" said Gudbrand, "I haven't the goose either; for when I had gone a bit farther I traded it for a cock."

"Dear me!" cried his wife, "how you think of everything! just as I should have done myself. A cock! think of that! Why, it's as good as an eight-day clock, for every day the cock crows at four o'clock, and we shall be able to stir our stiff legs in good time. What should we do with a goose? I don't know how to cook it; and as for my pillow, I can stuff it with cotton grass. Run out, child, and put up the cock."

"But after all, I haven't the cock either," said Gudbrand, "for when I had gone a bit farther, I became as hungry as a hunter, so I was forced to sell the cock for a quarter, for fear I should starve."

"Now, God be praised that you did so!" cried his wife. "Whatever you do, you do it always just after my own heart. What should we do with the cock? We are our own masters, I should think, and can lie abed in the morning as long as we like. Heaven be thanked that I have you safe back again. You who do everything so well, that I want neither cock nor goose; neither pigs nor kine."

Then Gudbrand opened the door and said, "Well, what do you say now? Have I won the hundred dollars?"

And his neighbor was forced to admit that he had.

Ah Mee's Invention

CHING CHI, the fond parent, lived with his wife—her name is forgotten—and the son, Ah Mee, and a little daughter, in a neat house that stood in the Street of the Hill Where the Monkey Bit Mang. Ching Chi was a carver of wood, and ivory, and jade. His bachelor brother Ching Cha who lived next door, did scrivening—wrote things with a blackened brush upon parchment and paper—and the wall, when he had no paper. Some people said they were stories, but certainly they brought in no money. As for that, neither did Ching Chi's carvings bring in any money. Yet Chi was a good carver. His designs were artistic, and his knife was obedient to the slightest touch. From an inch block of ivory he could carve seven balls—one inside the other. Howbeit, Chi was neither famous nor wealthy. Instead of carving pagodas and trinkets for sale in the bazaars, he spent most of his time in carving toys for Ah Mee—who promptly smote them with an axe, or threw them in the well, or treated them in some other manner equally grievous.

For six months Ching Chi worked to carve a dragon. When finished, the *loong* was a thing of beauty. In the bazaar it would, perhaps, have fetched a bar of silver from some rich mandarin. But fond Ching Chi gave it to Ah Mee. And Ah Mee, tiring of it after five minutes of play, hurled it through the paper-covered window.

Are windows made to be broken? Are toys fashioned only to be thrown away? Certainly not. Papa Chi wagged a finger at Ah Mee and he spoke thus, "Ah Mee, most wonderful son in the world, you must not throw your dragon through the window into the back yard again. What I say, that I mean. Don't throw your dragon into the yard any more." Having said, he proceeded with his work, carving beautiful designs upon teakwood blocks for Ah Mee's pleasure.

And Ah Mee said, "Very well then, *Tieh tieh* (Daddy), I won't." He proceeded with his work—which was to pile carven teakwood blocks high as his not-so-long arms could reach. There was one block covered with so much exquisite carving that it gave little support to the blocks above. For that reason the tower wavered and fell. Ah Mee promptly lost his temper. Made furious beyond endurance, he seized the offending block and hurled it through a paper-paneled door.

[188]

Who will say that Ah Mee was disobedient? He had been told not to throw his toy dragon through the window. But had his father, Ching Chi, told him not to heave a block through the door? Not at all. Ching Chi had said nothing about blocks, and he had pointed his finger at the window. Nevertheless, Mr. Ching felt almost inclined to scold his son. He said, very sternly, "Ah Mee."

"Whang. Bang. Bang," came the sound of sticks on the door frame. Crash—the door flew open. In rushed stalwart men, dressed in the king's livery, and bearing heavy staves. "Oh, you vile *tung hsi* (east west—very abusive talk), you murderer," screamed the men. "Are you trying to assassinate your king? What do you mean by hurling missiles into the king's sedan as he is carried through the street? Answer, before your head falls."

But Ching was unable to answer. He could only press his forehead to the floor, and tremble, and wait for the quick death he expected. Meantime, Ah Mee pelted the king's men with various large and small toys, including a hatchet.

King Tan Ki, seated comfortably in a sedan chair, was being carried through the street of the Hill Where the Monkey Bit Mang. He had no thought of danger. Peril had no place in his mind. The street seemed a street of peace. When lo—from a paper-covered door there came a large missile, striking a slave and falling into the king's lap. Instantly the bodyguard rushed to the terrible house and battered in the door. But King Tan Ki felt more curiosity

than alarm. He examined the object that had so unceremoniously been hurled into the sedan. At once his interest was quickened. The king knew good carvings—whether they came from old masters, or from hands unknown. Here was a block carved with superlative art. Tan Ki wished to know more of the artist who carved it.

Ching Chi was still kneeling, still expecting instant death, when the king's chamberlain rushed in. The chamberlain uttered a sharp order. The bodyguards grasped Ching Chi and hastened him out of the house, to kneel at the king's sedan. Ah Mee fired a last volley of broken toys at the retreating chamberlain. Not especially nice of him, perhaps, but then, no one had forbidden it.

Fortune had smiled her prettiest upon the house of Ching Chi. King Tan Ki was immensely pleased with the old engraver's work. The odds and ends of toys that had been fashioned for Ah Mee now graced the palace. There they were appreciated. Every day Ching Chi worked faithfully, carving plaques and panels and medallions for the king. He was wealthy. Upon his little skullcap was a red button. He was a mandarin, if you please. Only mandarins of the highest class may wear ruby buttons on their caps. And Ah Mee was worse than ever.

To say it again, for emphasis, Ah Mee was worse than ever—if possible. He dabbled in all the hundred-and-one varieties of mischief. All day long it was "Ah Mee, don't do that." "Ah Mee, don't do the other." "Don't. Don't. Don't." Papa Ching was so tired of saying "Don't" that his tongue hurt every time he used the word. Occasionally he changed his talk and said the opposite of what he really meant. Thus he would say, "That's right, little darling, fill Papa's boots with hoptoads and muddy terrapins, and that will make Papa happy." Or, "Pray take another jar, my precious. Eat all the jam you possibly can. Six jars is not at all too much." For Ah Mee doted on jam. It was a passion with him. He started the day on jam, finished the day on jam. Every time a back was turned, his fingers sought the jam pot. Indeed, rather frequently he ate so much jam that there were pains—and the doctor.

Ching Chi took a bird cage from the wall and hung it on his arm. (In that land when gentlemen go for a stroll they usually carry their pet larks, instead of their pet *chows*.) At the door he paused and said to Ah Mee: "Little pearl in the palm, please refrain from too much mischief. Don't (there it was again) be any worse than you are really compelled to be. Of course, it's quite proper for you to put arsenic in Mother's tea, and to hit baby sister with the axe again. And you may burn the house if you feel so inclined. I want you to have plenty of innocent fun. But don't (again) be bad. For instance, don't, I beg of you, don't get in those jars of jam any more."

Off went Ching Chi with his lark singing blithely.

Ah Mee was quite puzzled. "Don't get in the jars of jam." How in the world could he get in the little jars? It was silly. He was much larger than any one of the jars. But perhaps *Tieh*

tieh meant not put a hand in the jars. That must be it. Ah Mee made a stern resolve to keep his hands out. Not so much as a single finger should go in those jars of jam.

Obedient Ah Mee arranged several of his father's carven plaques on the floor, and tilted a jar. The plaques were beautifully decorated flat pieces of wood, somewhat larger than dinner plates. They made reasonably good dishes for the stiff jam.

When Ching Chi came home and discovered his carvings smeared with black and sticky jam, that good soul fell into a passion. First he screamed. Next he howled. Then he seized the plaques and flung them from him, flung them with all his strength. Flinging things in this manner seems to have been a family failing. Ching Chi was weeping for sorrow, and howling with rage when his brother Cha entered the room. The quick eyes of Brother Cha soon saw that something was amiss. He gazed at the wall where the plaques had struck. He gazed at the jam-coated plaques.

Then he too howled, but with joy. "Oh, Brother Chi," he shouted. "You have chanced upon a wonderful invention. It is a quick way for making books. What huge luck." He led Brother Chi to the wall and pointed. "See. For reason of its jam, each plaque has made a black impression on the wall. Every line of the carving is reproduced upon the wall. Now do you understand? You will carve my thoroughly miserable stories upon blocks of wood. Ah Mee will spread black jam upon the carven blocks. Then I will press the blocks upon paper, sheet after sheet, perhaps a hundred in one day. With the laborious brush I can make only one story a month. With the blocks—I can make thousands upon thousands of stories. Oh, what a wonderful invention."

Ching Chi carved his brother's stories upon wooden blocks. Ah Mee spread the jam thickly—only pausing now and then for a taste. Ching Cha pressed the blocks upon paper, sheet after sheet. There were the stories upon paper, all done in a twinkling, and with little expense. The poorest people in the land could afford to buy Ching Cha's excellent stories.

Thus was invented *Yin Shu* (Make Books) or, as the very odd foreign demons call it in their so peculiar language, "Printing." Ching Chi, his brother Ching Cha, and Ah Mee, all had a hand in the invention. As a matter of exact truth, Ah Mee had two hands in the invention (or in the jam), so he is generally given all the credit. His monument reads, "Ah Mee, Son of Ching Chi, the Inventor of Printing."

⟨[THIS story is from SHEN OF THE SEA which won the Newbery Medal in 1926. Arthur Bowie Chrisman was also the author of two other collections of Chinese stories, THE WIND THAT WOULDN'T BLOW and TREASURES LONG HIDDEN.

The Week of Sundays

ONCE UPON a time there was a man called Dennis O'Shea, and he had no fondness for work, at least none worth mentioning.

"Shure there's only one day that's any good at all, and that day's Sunday," said he. "But the trouble of it is that it's no sooner Sunday than the week starts all over again."

"For shame on you, the idle creature!" cried his wife Mollie. "A fine example you're setting the children."

One night when the wind was whistling round the chimney, and the rain was slapping against the window, and Dennis and Mollie and the children were sitting round the fire watching the potatoes boil for supper, who should come tapping at the door but a fairy? Of course, she did not look like a fairy. She looked just like an old beggar woman.

"Never a bite has passed my lips this day," whined she, "and 'tis a night not fit to turn a pig out!"

Now whatever faults Dennis might have, and to be sure he had several, it was never meanness you could blame on him. He brought the old woman in and sat her on his own stool, and Mollie bade her help herself to potatoes. The old woman must have had a ter-

rible hunger on her, for she helped herself and helped herself till there was scarcely a mouthful left for anyone else. But never a word said Dennis, nor Mollie neither; and the children just sat and stared with their eyes as round as pennies. 'Tis my belief they saw the glint of the golden dress of her through the tears in her old cloak.

Well, the end of it was that the old woman suddenly hopped to her feet, twisted around three times, and turned into a fairy so beautiful it made them blink to look at her.

"'Tis kind and hospitable creatures you are," said she, "and by way of returning the kindness I'll be granting the next wish that's wished aloud in the houseen." And before they could get their breath again she had vanished up the chimney.

The children wanted to wish for lollipops and dolls and a wooden horse. Mollie was for asking for a hundred pounds, no less; and Dennis found his head so full of wishes that for the life of him he couldn't tell which came first.

"'Tis Sunday the morn," said Mollie; "we'll be having time then to think what will be best."

Dennis stretched his lazy legs and

yawned fit to crack the top off his head. "Shure, and I wish it was a week of Sundays!" said he before he thought what he was saying.

"That's the end of it!" cried Mollie. "If I'd known you'd be wasting the wish on something as daftlike as that I'd have wished you had a little sense, that I would!"

"Whist now, whist now, Mollie darlint!" said Dennis. "Shure and I never meant to say it. It just popped out of itself. And a week of Sundays will be a fine treat. 'Tis not such a bad wish at all, at all."

"If it cures the idle bones of you it will be worth something." snapped Mollie, and never another word would she say.

The more he thought about his wish, the more Dennis liked it. It was an elegant feeling entirely to wake up next morning and hear the bells ringing and know there were to be six more Sundays, one after the other, before he need do a stroke of work. Mollie and the children went to church, but Dennis never set foot out of bed till the smell of dinner reminded him he was hungry.

Mollie had a grand piece of roast pork in the oven; and when he had eaten all he wanted, he put on his best coat and sat in the sunshine outside the door, taking life as comfortably as if he were the king himself.

"I couldn't have thought of a better wish if I'd been trying a year, shure and I couldn't," said he.

Next day he lay in bed again till dinnertime, but the dinner was only the picking of the pork bones. And the next day there was nothing to eat but bacon and potatoes, just as though it was Monday and all.

"Indade, Mollie, darlint, but you've been forgetting what day it is," said he. "Taties and bacon is never a dinner for a Sunday, and that's the truth."

"Where can I be buying another roast of pork and all the shops with their shutters up for seven days on end?" asked Mollie. "If you *will* be having a week of Sundays, shure and you'll have to take the consequences!"

"Begorrah!" said Dennis, and rubbed his head. "I never thought of that!"

Next day it was worse than ever, for there was nothing for dinner but a cheese and a loaf of bread, and both as stale as a stone.

"I'll be digging some taties from the garden," said Dennis, and I'll not deny he was beginning to think it would be the grand feeling to have a spade in his hands again.

But Mollie would not hear of it. "Digging taties, is it?" cried she. "What would the neighbors be thinking to see you doing the likes of that on a Sunday? You'll have to be living on bits and scraps till we get a Monday again, and that's all there is to say about it!"

Well, on the *fifth* Sunday when the church bells began to ring, there was Dennis tossing and turning as though the blankets had been made of nettles. Now that he could lie in bed as long as he liked every morning, wasn't he beginning to wish he had to be getting up early again? Even when he'd got the lazy bones of him dressed, things were not any better, for there was nothing to do at all, at all, and the children were pulling at his coattails and quarreling and whimpering every minute of the time.

"And no blame to them, the darlints!" cried Mollie. "It's five days, no less, that they've had to be wearing their best clothes, and not a game can they play for fear of spoiling them. And aren't they likely to get tired of holidays when there's not so much as a day's schooling in between?"

Truth to tell, Dennis was getting tired of holidays himself. He went to church next day to give himself something to do, but it's little comfort he got out of it. "Here's the man!" cried the parson. "Here's the mischievous creature that's nearly driven me to my grave with hard work! Don't I have to preach twice every Sunday? And when there's a week of Sundays, isn't it fourteen sermons I have to be giving one after the other, with never a bit of time to turn over me thoughts?"

It was black looks he got from the congregation, too, when the service was over.

"Will you be thinking of the washing there'll be when we get a Monday again?" cried the women.

"And how's the harvest to be got in an' all when there's never a weekday coming round?" asked the men.

Oh! Dennis was beginning to rue his wish, and that's a fact.

There was only one more Sunday left, but, if you'll believe me, every hour of it seemed as long as all the other six days put together. Dennis stood up and sat down again, and wandered around and around the house till the legs of him ached more than if he had been ploughing.

"Will the sun never be setting?" said he.

"What for should you be wanting it to set so early?" asked Mollie, innocent like. "Is it yourself has forgotten it's Monday the morn?"

"Never a bit!" cried Dennis. "Never a bit! It's more than pleased I'll be to see a Monday again, though I never thought to say it!"

"Then you'd not be asking for another week of Sundays again?" asked Mollie, pretending, the sly creature, that she didn't know.

"That I would not!" exclaimed Dennis; "shure and there's no enjoying a Sunday unless you've worked six days to earn it. It's the grand lesson I've been learning, and that's the truth."

"It is and all!" said Mollie. "But the next time you want a lesson I'm hoping you'll not be wasting a fairy wish on it."

Master of All Masters

A GIRL ONCE went to the fair to hire herself for servant. At last a funny-looking old gentleman engaged her, and took her home to his house. When she got there, he told her that he had something to teach her, for that in his house he had his own name for things.

He said to her: "What will you call me?"

"Master or mister, or whatever you please, sir," says she.

He said: "You must call me 'master of all masters.' And what would you call this?" pointing to his bed.

"Bed or couch, or whatever you please, sir."

"No, that's my 'barnacle.' And what do you call these?" said he pointing to his pantaloons.

"Breeches or trousers, or whatever you please, sir."

"You must call them 'squibs and crackers.' And what would you call her?" pointing to the cat.

"Cat or kit, or whatever you please, sir."

"You must call her 'white-faced simminy.' And this now," showing the fire, "what would you call this?"

"Fire or flame, or whatever you please, sir."

"You must call it 'hot cockalorum,' and what this?" he went on, pointing to the water.

"Water or wet, or whatever you please, sir."

"No, 'pondalorum' is its name. And what do you call all this?" asked he as he pointed to the house.

"House or cottage, or whatever you please, sir."

"You must call it 'high topper mountain.'"

That very night the servant woke her master up in a fright and said: "Master of all masters, get out of your barnacle and put on your squibs and crackers. For white-faced simminy has got a spark of hot cockalorum on its tail, and unless you get some pondalorum, high topper mountain will be all on hot cockalorum." . . . That's all.

⟨ JOSEPH JACOBS *was a scholarly writer who is best remembered for his* ENGLISH FAIRY TALES *and other collections. Many of these—stories that were both dramatic and funny—he found in dusty old books that few people ever read, and he tried to retell them "as a good old nurse will speak when she tells fairy tales."*

Ah Love! Ah Me!

⟨[THIS *funny-sad story of a teen-ager is included to tickle the funnybones of the younger members of the family, to make the parents chuckle and remember, and to amuse the teen-agers themselves.*

IT HAPPENED, when I was in my junior year at high school, that I saw Sara Nell Workman for the first time and —not to be sentimental—I liked the girl. I liked her so much, in fact, that I would go to the library and read the cards in the back of the books to find the ones she had borrowed. I would take these out and read them carefully, including one called *Needlepoint and Needlecraft.*

"It's for my sister," I said hoarsely to the librarian who was looking at me curiously. There were some penciled notes in the margin about hemstitching, and whether Sara made these notes or not, I don't know. At the time I liked to imagine that she did, and I read them over and over: *Two skeins of black, 2 orange, 1 yellow, and the tulip stencil. Mother's Day, 17 days.*

But when you're sixteen, you can't keep reading marginal notes over and over. At least I couldn't. And so the time came that I decided to ask Sara for a date.

At home that night I went out into the hall where the phone was and shut the door behind me. I wrote Sara's number on the pad and then one sentence: "Sara—A revival of *Jezebel* is on Friday night and I was just wondering if you'd like to see it with me."

That sounded casual and easy enough to say, but when I heard the operator ringing the number, I got excited and crumpled the paper in my hand. For a second I considered hanging up, but then someone said, "Hello."

"Oh," I said. "May I speak to Sara Workman?"

"This is she," she said.

"Uh, Sara," I said, "uh, this is Dave—"

"Yes," she said.

"Do you know what our history assignment is for tomorrow?" I asked hopelessly.

"Just a minute," she said. She got her book and gave me the assignment.

I thanked her and hung up. Then I went back to my room to brood.

About an hour later I decided that the thing to do was to jump up suddenly without thinking, rush into the hall and phone her before I had a chance to become flustered.

When Sara answered the phone, I blurted out, "Would you like to go to the show with me Friday night? This is Dave."

"Well, I don't know," said Sara. "What's on?

"I don't know," I said.

"What?" she asked.

"I mean I don't know," I said. "*Lucy Belle* or something like that."

"*Jezebel!*" she said. "The Bette Davis revival. Yeah! I'd love to see it."

"Okay," I said. "Good-by."

The next day I avoided meeting Sara alone. In the line at cafeteria she leaned around two people and said to me, "That was you last night?"

"Yeah," I said.

She smiled and for a moment I was afraid that she was going to laugh, but she didn't.

Friday night at eight o'clock when we were leaving Sara's house, Mr. Workman asked, "Who's driving?"

"I am," I said.

"Well," he hollered, as we went down the walk, "just see to it that you get Sara back here safe. And before eleven o'clock."

"Yes, sir," I said.

At the theater we had to stand in line, and when finally we did get seats they were in the third row. My neck was hurting before the newsreel was over, but Sara didn't seem to mind.

When the picture was almost over, she caught me looking at her. "Whatsa matter?" she whispered.

"Headache," I said. "I think it's from—"

"Shhh—" she whispered. On the screen Bette Davis was risking death by yellow fever to be with her man and nurse him.

Sara was very quiet when we came out of the show. As we walked down Main Street, I said, "Do you think she should have stayed with him?"

"It's not a matter of what you should do or shouldn't do," Sara said. "For when you love a man, nothing can tear you away."

"Good gosh!" I said. Above us a neon light flickered and buzzed as though it would explode.

We stood in front of Shaeffer's drugstore for a minute. It was ten-fifteen then, and Sara was worried about getting home. "Just something to drink," she said. "We haven't time to eat."

She ordered a chocolate milk, but I thought it would look kind of sophisticated to order something for my headache, so I asked the waiter what he had.

"Aspirin, Epsom salts, litho-bromide, anything you want," he said.

"Bring me a litho-bromide," I said, trying to sound weary, "and a Coke."

"Still hurts?" Sara asked softly.

I smiled at her without answering.

John Bowerman and two other seniors came in and took the booth next to ours. All of the booths and tables were filling.

The waiter brought the order—my Coke, two litho-bromide tablets in the bottom of an empty glass, and a big glass of water.

I'd never taken a litho-bromide, and I didn't know that the tablets were supposed to be dropped into a glass of water where they would fizz while dissolving. I just shook the tablets out into my hand, popped them in my mouth, and swallowed them one at a time. Then I drank the Coke.

Before I had time to say anything, the litho-bromide started bubbling noisily in my stomach.

I drank the rest of the Coke and tried to pretend that nothing was happening. Sara put down her glass and stared at me, terrified.

"It always does this," I said bravely. But by then the rumblings from the mixture were too ominous to be ignored.

"Everybody's looking at you," Sara whispered.

"He's effervescing!" the waiter announced happily to the astonished customers.

"Sara," I said, but I was afraid to open my mouth to say anything else. The rumbling just sounded deeper when I did.

"Doc Shaeffer!" John Bowerman called out when Sara told him what I had done.

Doc Shaeffer climbed over the prescription counter. "Stand back!" he said to the crowd.

They stepped back as though they expected me to explode.

"It's nothing serious," Doc Shaeffer

said. "Get his head lower than his stomach. Give me a hand."

"He says he always does this," Sara said.

"That's pretty hard to believe," Doc said, as John Bowerman and the two seniors picked me up and carried me up to the prescription counter. They stretched me out and let my head hang off with my mouth open. A dogfight couldn't have attracted more attention. Doc Shaeffer brought a wet towel from the back of the drugstore.

"Sara," I said, and I suppose now that I must have sounded rather melodramatic to the other people, "you won't leave me, will you?"

"Oh, my goodness!" Sara said. "What time is it?"

"Ten till eleven," John Bowerman said.

Sara dropped the wet towel in my face. "I've got to be home by eleven!" she said.

"I'll take you," John said.

I took the towel off my face to see them stopping by the booth for Sara's pocketbook. She didn't even look back at me.

The four or five people who were standing by me went back to their tables. I lay quietly on the counter and watched the light above swaying gently in the noisy room.

Gradually, two by two, the people left, and the noise of the dishes being stacked grew quieter and quieter. I watched the waiter turn chairs upside down on the table and felt sorry for myself and for the whole pitiful world.

THE BOOK OF

Enchantment

Introduction

⟨ "THE MOST *priceless possession of the human race is the wonder of the world," said Kenneth Grahame. Certainly it proved to be the touchstone whereby he was able to present so convincingly his small, endearing beasts of The Wind in the Willows. A banker by day, at night he told the stories of Mole, Water Rat, Toad, and Otter to his seven-year-old son, Alistair (called "Mouse" by his parents). After Mouse went to the seashore with his governess, his father continued the adventures in a series of letters. When these were published as a book, the kindly philosophy of the little creatures that live within its pages made it beloved by many readers of all ages.*

Wonder—enchantment—call it by whatever name we will—it is the special possession of children! Yet during the childhood of mankind, everyone wondered. Everyone asked questions: How did the world come to be? What made the sun seem to rise in the morning and go down at night? Primitive peoples made up their own answers by telling what we now call myths, and they found inspiration in recounting the deeds of their heroes. They sought security by imagining that many gods ruled in the heavens and directed the affairs of men. Even after they stopped believing in their old gods and heroes, folk went right on telling the stories.

These folk tales continued to be told in Europe for hundreds of years. Wandering minstrels visited castle halls and sang of ancient deeds. Parents in humble cottages recounted these deeds to sons and daughters gathered around the hearth fire, and when these chil-

*dren grew up they passed the tales on to their children. With many
of the storytellers adding details from their own experience, the old
narratives changed and grew, yet fundamentally they remained the
same. Some of the stories from different parts of Europe bore a
striking resemblance not only to one another but to the lore that
has come out of the Orient.*

*The most popular character in any of these tales was undoubt-
edly Cinderella. Even the early Egyptians and Greeks and Chinese
liked to tell of the beautiful, mistreated girl who achieved happiness. This was the theme of many fairy stories and accounts for
their enduring charm. The hero, or heroine, wanted the impossible
—and got it. The kings and queens of such writers as Charles Perrault, the Brothers Grimm, and Hans Christian Andersen, the
princes and princesses were symbols of every human being's innate
desire for recognition. In a day when only a few people at the top
had any status, the storytellers gave expression to man's secret
aspirations.*

*Even in our democratic society, the best of the old tales can
spark the aspirations of a young reader. He enters wholeheartedly
into the struggles of a hero who, because he is plucky and righteous
and ingenious, is able to triumph over obstacles. Yes, and there is
the chance to let the imagination soar. Adults may be resigned to
the commonplace, but children are still looking for magic. Their
pleasure, the sense of enchantment they find in a good fairy story
may sometimes be shared by the older relative or friend who reads
aloud. Lewis Carroll expressed what many of us feel in his introduction to* Alice Through the Looking Glass:

> *"Child of the pure, unclouded brow*
>   *And dreaming eyes of wonder,*
> *Though time be fleet, and I and thou*
>   *Are half a life asunder,*
> *Thy loving smile will surely hail*
> *The love gift of a fairy tale."*

Many Moons

ONCE UPON a time, in a kingdom by the sea, there lived a little princess named Lenore. She was ten years old, going on eleven. One day Lenore fell ill of a surfeit of raspberry tarts and took to her bed.

The Royal Physician came to see her and took her temperature and felt her pulse and made her stick out her tongue. The Royal Physician was worried. He sent for the King, Lenore's father, and the King came to see her.

"I will get you anything your heart desires," the King said. "Is there anything your heart desires?"

"Yes," said the Princess. "I want the moon. If I can have the moon, I will be well again."

Now the King had a great many wise men who always got for him anything he wanted, so he told his daughter that she could have the moon. Then he went to the throne room and pulled a bell cord, three long pulls and a short pull, and presently the Lord High Chamberlain came into the room.

The Lord High Chamberlain was a large, fat man who wore thick glasses which made his eyes seem twice as big as they really were. This made the Lord High Chamberlain seem twice as wise as he really was.

"I want to get the moon," said the King. "The Princess Lenore wants the moon. If she can have the moon, she will get well again."

"The moon?" exclaimed the Lord High Chamberlain, his eyes widening. This made him look four times as wise as he really was.

"Yes, the moon," said the King. "M-o-o-n, moon. Get it tonight, tomorrow at the latest."

The Lord High Chamberlain wiped his forehead with a handkerchief and then blew his nose loudly. "I have got a great many things for you in my time, your Majesty," he said. "It just happens that I have with me a list of the things I have got for you in my time." He pulled a long scroll of parchment out of his pocket. "Let me see, now." He glanced at the list, frowning. "I have got ivory, apes, and peacocks, rubies, opals, and emeralds, black orchids, pink elephants, and blue poodles, gold bugs, scarabs, and flies in amber, hummingbirds' tongues, angels' feathers, and unicorns' horns, giants, midgets, and mermaids, frankincense, ambergris, and myrrh, troubadours, minstrels, and dancing women, a

[203]

pound of butter, two dozen eggs, and a sack of sugar—sorry, my wife wrote that in there."

"I don't remember any blue poodles," said the King.

"It says blue poodles right here on the list, and they are checked off with a little check mark," said the Lord High Chamberlain. "So there must have been blue poodles. You just forget."

"Never mind the blue poodles," said the King. "What I want now is the moon."

"I have sent as far as Samarkand and Araby and Zanzibar to get things for you, your Majesty," said the Lord High Chamberlain. "But the moon is out of the question. It is thirty-five thousand miles away and it is bigger than the room the Princess lies in. Furthermore, it is made of molten copper. I cannot get the moon for you. Blue poodles, yes; the moon, no."

The King flew into a rage and told the Lord High Chamberlain to leave the room and to send the Royal Wizard to the throne room.

The Royal Wizard was a little, thin man with a long face. He wore a high red peaked hat covered with silver stars, and a long blue robe covered with golden owls. His face grew very pale when the King told him that he wanted the moon for his little daughter, and that he expected the Royal Wizard to get it.

"I have worked a great deal of magic for you in my time, your Majesty," said the Royal Wizard. "As a matter of fact, I just happen to have in my pocket a list of the wizardries I have performed for you." He drew a paper from a deep pocket of his robe. "It begins: *Dear Royal Wizard: I am returning herewith the so-called philosopher's stone which you claimed*—no, that isn't it." The Royal Wizard brought a long scroll of parchment from another pocket of his robe. "Here it is," he said. "Now, let's see. I have squeezed blood out of turnips for you, and turnips out of blood. I have produced rabbits out of silk hats, and silk hats out of rabbits. I have conjured up flowers, tambourines, and doves out of nowhere, and nowhere out of flowers, tambourines, and doves. I have brought you divining rods, magic wands, and crystal spheres in which to behold the future. I have compounded philters, unguents, and potions, to cure heartbreak, surfeit, and ringing in the ears. I have made you my own special mixture of wolfbane, nightshade, and eagles' tears, to ward off witches, demons, and things that go bump in the night. I have given you seven-league-boots, the golden touch, and a cloak of invisibility—"

"It didn't work," said the King. "The cloak of invisibility didn't work."

"Yes, it did," said the Royal Wizard.

"No, it didn't," said the King. "I kept bumping into things, the same as ever."

"The cloak is supposed to make you invisible," said the Royal Wizard. "It is not supposed to keep you from bumping into things."

"All I know is, I kept bumping into things," said the King.

The Royal Wizard looked at his list again. "I got you," he said, "horns from Elfland, sand from the Sandman, and gold from the rainbow. Also a spool of thread, a paper of needles, and a lump of beeswax—sorry, those are things my wife wrote down for me to get her."

"What I want you to do now," said the King, "is to get me the moon. The Princess Lenore wants the moon, and when she gets it, she will be well again."

"Nobody can get the moon," said the Royal Wizard. "It is a hundred and fifty thousand miles away, and it is made of green cheese, and it is twice as big as this palace."

The King flew into another rage and sent the Royal Wizard back to his cave. Then he rang a gong and summoned the Royal Mathematician.

The Royal Mathematician was a bald-headed, nearsighted man, with a skullcap on his head and a pencil behind each ear. He wore a black suit with white numbers on it.

"I don't want to hear a long list of all the things you have figured out for me since 1907," the King said to him. "I want you to figure out right now how to get the moon for the Princess Lenore. When she gets the moon, she will be well again."

"I am glad you mentioned all the things I have figured out for you since 1907," said the Royal Mathematician. "It so happens that I have a list of them with me."

He pulled a long scroll of parchment out of a pocket and looked at it. "Now, let me see. I have figured out for you the distance between the horns of a dilemma, night and day, and A and Z. I have computed how far is Up, how long it takes to get to Away, and what becomes of Gone. I have discovered the length of the sea serpent, the price of the priceless, and the square of the hippopotamus. I know where you are when you are at Sixes and Sevens, how much Is you have to have to make an Are, and how many birds you can catch with the salt in the ocean—187,796,-132, if it would interest you to know."

"There aren't that many birds," said the King.

"I didn't say there were," said the Royal Mathematician. "I said if there were."

"I don't want to hear about seven hundred million imaginary birds," said the King. "I want you to get the moon for the Princess Lenore."

"The moon is three hundred thousand miles away," said the Royal Mathematician. "It is round and flat like a coin, only it is made of asbestos, and it is half the size of this kingdom. Furthermore, it is pasted on the sky. Nobody can get the moon."

The King flew into still another rage and sent the Royal Mathematician away. Then he rang for the Court Jester. The Jester came bounding into the throne room in his motley and his cap and bells, and sat at the foot of the throne.

"What can I do for you, your majesty?" asked the Court Jester.

"Nobody can do anything for me," said the King mournfully. "The Princess Lenore wants the moon, and she cannot be well till she gets it, but nobody can get it for her. Every time I ask anybody for the moon, it gets larger and farther away. There is nothing you can do for me except play on your lute. Something sad."

"How big do they say the moon is," asked the Court Jester, "and how far away?"

"The Lord High Chamberlain says it is thirty-five thousand miles away, and bigger than the Princess Lenore's room," said the King. "The Royal Wizard says it is a hundred and fifty thousand miles away, and twice as big as this palace. The Royal Mathematician says it is three hundred thousand miles away, and half the size of this kingdom."

The Court Jester strummed on his lute for a little while. "They are all wise men," he said, "and so they must all be right. If they are all right, then the moon must be just as large and as far away as each person thinks it is. The thing to do is find out how big the Princess Lenore thinks it is, and how far away."

"I never thought of that," said the King.

"I will go and ask her, your majesty," said the Court Jester. And he crept softly into the little girl's room.

The Princess Lenore was awake, and she was glad to see the Court Jester, but her face was very pale and her voice very weak.

"Have you brought the moon to me?" she asked.

"Not yet," said the Court Jester, "but I will get it for you right away. How big do you think it is?"

"It is just a little smaller than my thumbnail," she said, "for when I hold my thumbnail up at the moon, it just covers it."

"And how far away is it?" asked the Court Jester.

"It is not as high as the big tree outside my window," said the Princess, "for sometimes it gets caught in the top branches."

"It will be very easy to get the moon for you," said the Court Jester. "I will climb the tree tonight when it gets caught in the top branches and bring it to you."

Then he thought of something else. "What is the moon made of, Princess?" he asked.

"Oh," she said, "it's made of gold, of course, silly."

The Court Jester left the Princess Lenore's room and went to see the Royal Goldsmith. He had the Royal Goldsmith make a tiny round golden moon just a little smaller than the thumbnail of the Princess Lenore. Then he had him string it on a golden chain so the Princess could wear it around her neck.

"What is this thing I have made?" asked the Royal Goldsmith when he had finished it.

"You have made the moon," said the Court Jester. "That is the moon."

"But the moon," said the Royal Goldsmith, "is five hundred thousand miles away and is made of bronze and is round like a marble."

"That's what you think," said the Court Jester as he went away with the moon.

The Court Jester took the moon to the Princess Lenore, and she was overjoyed. The next day she was well again and could get up and go out in the gardens to play.

But the King's worries were not yet over. He knew that the moon would shine in the sky again that night, and he did not want the Princess Lenore to see it. If she did, she would know that the moon she wore on a chain around her neck was not the real moon.

So the King sent for the Lord High Chamberlain and said, "We must keep the Princess Lenore from seeing the moon when it shines in the sky tonight. Think of something."

The Lord High Chamberlain tapped his forehead with his fingers thoughtfully and said, "I know just the thing. We can make some dark glasses for the Princess Lenore. We can make them so dark that she will not be able to see anything at all through them. Then she will not be able to see the moon when it shines in the sky."

This made the King very angry, and he shook his head from side to side. "If she wore dark glasses, she would bump into things," he said, "and then she would be ill again." So he sent the Lord High Chamberlain away and called the Royal Wizard.

"We must hide the moon," said the King, "so that the Princess Lenore will not see it when it shines in the sky tonight. How are we going to do that?"

The Royal Wizard stood on his hands and then he stood on his head and then he stood on his feet again. "I know what we can do," he said. "We can stretch some black velvet curtains on poles. The curtains will cover all the palace gardens like a circus tent, and the Princess Lenore will not be able to see through them, so she will not see the moon in the sky."

The King was so angry at this that he waved his arms around. "Black velvet curtains would keep out the air," he said. "The Princess Lenore would not be able to breathe, and she would be ill again." So he sent the Royal Wizard away and summoned the Royal Mathematician.

"We must do something," said the King, "so that the Princess Lenore will not see the moon when it shines in the sky tonight. If you know so much, figure out a way to do that."

The Royal Mathematician walked around in a circle, and then he walked around in a square, and then he stood still. "I have it!" he said. "We can set off fireworks in the gardens every night. We will make a lot of silver fountains and golden cascades, and when they go off, they will fill the sky with so many sparks that it will be as light as day and the Princess Lenore will not be able to see the moon."

The King flew into such a rage that he began jumping up and down. "Fireworks would keep the Princess Lenore awake," he said. "She would not get any sleep at all and she would be ill again." So the King sent the Royal Mathematician away.

When he looked up again, it was dark outside and he saw the bright rim of the moon just peeping over the horizon. He jumped up in a great fright and rang for the Court Jester. The Court Jester came bounding into the room and sat down at the foot of the throne.

"What can I do for you, your majesty?" he asked.

"Nobody can do anything for me," said the King, mournfully. "The moon is coming up again. It will shine into the Princess Lenore's bedroom, and she will know it is still in the sky and that she does not wear it on a golden chain around her neck. Play me something on your lute, something very sad, for when the Princess sees the moon, she will be ill again."

The Court Jester strummed on his lute. "What do your wise men say?" he asked.

"They can think of no way to hide the moon that will not make the Princess Lenore ill," said the King.

The Court Jester played another song, very softly. "Your wise men know everything," he said, "and if they cannot hide the moon, then it cannot be hidden."

The King put his head in his hands again and sighed. Suddenly he jumped up from his throne and pointed to the windows. "Look!" he cried. "The moon is already shining into the Princess Lenore's bedroom. Who can explain how the moon can be shining in the sky when it is hanging on a golden chain around her neck?"

The Court Jester stopped playing on his lute. "Who could explain how to get the moon when your wise men said it was too large and too far away?

It was the Princess Lenore. Therefore the Princess Lenore is wiser than your wise men and knows more about the moon than they do. So I will ask her." And before the King could stop him, the Court Jester slipped quietly out of the throne room and up the wide marble staircase to the Princess Lenore's bedroom.

The Princess was lying in bed, but she was wide awake and she was looking out the window at the moon shining in the sky. Shining in her hand was the moon the Court Jester had got for her. He looked very sad, and there seemed to be tears in his eyes.

"Tell me, Princess Lenore," he said mournfully, "how can the moon be shining in the sky when it is hanging on a golden chain around your neck?"

The Princess looked at him and laughed. "That is easy, silly," she said. "When I lose a tooth, a new one grows in its place, doesn't it?"

"Of course," said the Court Jester. "And when the unicorn loses his horn in the forest, a new one grows in the middle of his forehead."

"That is right," said the Princess. "And when the Royal Gardener cuts the flowers in the garden, other flowers come to take their place."

"I should have thought of that," said the Court Jester, "for it is the same way with the daylight."

"And it is the same way with the moon," said the Princess Lenore. "I guess it is the same way with everything." Her voice became very low and faded away, and the Court Jester saw that she was asleep. Gently he tucked the covers in around the sleeping Princess.

But before he left the room, he went over to the window and winked at the moon, for it seemed to the Court Jester that the moon had winked back at him.

⟪ THIS story is from the book of the same title. For younger readers James Thurber has also written THE WHITE DEER and THE THIRTEEN CLOCKS. He told the story of his own early days in MY LIFE AND HARD TIMES.

The Sorcerer's Apprentice

❰ Two centuries ago Joseph and Wilhelm Grimm, young university professors, liked to wander through the German countryside talking with peasants. Many could not read, but they remembered old tales they had heard from persons no longer living. The Brothers Grimm were the first to write these stories down. "The Sorcerer's Apprentice" was retold by Wanda Gág, one of America's best-loved artists and storytellers.

A MAN FOUND himself in need of a helper for his workshop, and one day as he was walking along the outskirts of a little hamlet he met a boy with a bundle slung over his shoulder. Stopping him, the man said, "Good morning, my lad. I am looking for an apprentice. Have you a master?"

"No," said the boy. "I have just this morning said good-by to my mother and am now off to find myself a trade."

"Good," said the man. "You look as though you might be just the lad I need. But wait, do you know anything about reading and writing?"

"Oh, yes!" said the boy.

"Too bad!" said the man. "You won't do after all. I have no use for anyone who can read and write."

"Pardon me?" said the boy. "If it was *reading* and *writing* you were talking about, I misunderstood you. I thought you asked if I knew anything about *eating* and *fighting*. Those two

things I am able to do well, but as to reading and writing that is something I know nothing about."

"Well!" cried the man. "Then you are just the fellow I want. Come with me to my workshop, and I will show you what to do."

The boy, however, had had his wits about him. He could read and write well enough and had only pretended to be a fool. Wondering why a man should prefer to have an unschooled helper, he thought to himself, "I smell a rat. There is something strange about this, and I had better keep my eyes and ears open."

While he was pondering over this, his new master was leading him into the heart of a deep forest. Here in a small clearing stood a house and, as soon as they entered it, the boy could see that this was no ordinary workshop. At one end of a big room was a huge hearth with a copper cauldron hanging in it. At the other end was a small alcove lined with many big books. A mortar and pestle stood on a bench; bottles and sieves, measuring scales and oddly shaped glassware were strewn about on the table.

Well! It did not take the clever young apprentice very long to realize that he was working for a magician or sorcerer of some kind and so, although he pretended to be quite stupid, he kept his eyes and ears open, and tried to learn all he could.

"Sorcery—that is a trade I would dearly love to master!" said the boy to himself. "A mouthful of good chants and charms would never come amiss to a poor fellow like me, and with them I might even be able to do some good in the world."

There were many things the boy had to do. Sometimes he was ordered to stir the evil-smelling broths which bubbled in the big copper cauldron; at other times he had to grind up herbs and berries—and other things too grue-some to mention—in the big mortar and pestle. It was also his task to sweep up the workshop, to keep the fire burning in the big hearth, and to gather the strange materials needed by the man for the broths and brews he was always mixing.

This went on day after day, week after week, and month after month, until the boy was almost beside him-self with curiosity. He was most curi-ous about the thick heavy books in the alcove. How often he had wondered about them, and how many times had he been tempted to take a peep be-tween their covers! But, remembering

that he was not supposed to know how to read or write, he had been wise enough never to show the least inter-est in them. At last there came a day when he made up his mind to see what was in them, no matter what the risk.

"I'll try it before another day dawns," he thought.

That night he waited until the sor-cerer was sound asleep and was snoring loudly in his bedchamber. Then, creep-ing out of his straw couch, the boy took a light into the corner of the alcove and began paging through one of the heavy volumes. What was written in them has never been told, but they were conjuring books, each and every one of them; and from that time on, the boy read in them silently, secretly, for an hour or two, night after night. In this way he learned many magic tricks; chants and charms and counter-charms; recipes for philters and po-tions, for broths and brews and witches' stews; signs mystic and cabalistic, and other helpful spells of many kinds.

All these he memorized carefully, and it was not long before he some-times was able to figure out what kind of charms his master was working, what brand of potion he was mixing, what sort of stews he was brewing. And what kind of charms and potions and stews were they? Alas, they were all wicked ones! Now the boy knew that he was not working for an ordinary magician, but for a cruel, dangerous sorcerer. And because of this, the boy made a plan, a bold one.

He went on with his nightly studies until his head was swarming with magic recipes and incantations. He

[211]

even had time to work at them in the daytime, for the sorcerer sometimes left the workshop for hours—working harm and havoc on mortals, no doubt. At such times the boy would try out a few bits of his newly learned wisdom. He began with simple things, such as changing the cat into a bee and back to cat again, making a viper out of a poker, an imp out of the broom, and so on. Sometimes he was successful, often he was not; so he said to himself, "The time is not yet ripe."

One day, after the sorcerer had again gone forth on one of his mysterious trips, the boy hurried through his work, and had just settled himself in the dingy alcove with one of the conjuring books on his knees, when the master returned unexpectedly. The boy, thinking fast, pointed smilingly at one of the pictures, after which he quietly closed the book and went on with his work as though nothing were amiss.

But the sorcerer was not deceived. "If the wretch can read," he thought, "he may learn how to outwit me. And I can't send him off with a beating and a 'bad speed to you,' either. Doubtless he knows too much already and will reveal all my fine mean tricks, and then I can't have any more sport working mischief on man and beast."

He acted quickly. With one leap he rushed at the boy, who in turn made a spring for the door. "Stop!" cried the sorcerer. "You shall not escape me!"

He was about to grab the boy by the collar when the quick-witted lad mumbled a powerful incantation by which he changed himself into a bird —and—wootsch!—he had flown into the woods.

The sorcerer, not to be outdone, shouted a charm, thus changing himself into a larger bird—and whoosh!— he was after the little one. With a new incantation the boy made himself into a fish—and whish!—he was swimming across a big pond.

But the master was equal to this, for with a few words he made himself into a fish, too, a big one, and swam after the little one. At this the boy changed himself into a still bigger fish but the magician, by a master stroke, turned himself into a tiny kernel of grain and rolled into a small crack in a stone where the fish couldn't touch him.

Quickly the boy changed himself into a rooster, and—peck! peck! peck! —with his sharp beak he snapped at the kernel of grain and ate it up.

That was the end of the wicked sorcerer, and the boy became the owner of the magic workshop. And wasn't it fine that all the powers and ingredients which had been used for evil by the sorcerer were now in the hands of a boy who would use them only for the good of man and beast?

The Ugly Duckling

⟨ PROBABLY the favorite teller of tales came from Denmark. Hans Christian Andersen was steeped in folklore but added many new stories of his own. "The Ugly Duckling" was suggested by his experiences as a poor, awkward boy who grew up to be famous.

IT WAS very pleasant out in the country. Full in the sunshine, an old manor house stood, surrounded by a deep moat, and from the base of the walls right down to the water great dock plants grew. It was as lonely in among them as in the thickest wood; and there a duck was sitting on her nest. She had to hatch out her little ducklings, but by this time she was well nigh tired out, they took so long about it.

At last, one egg after another cracked, and said, "Pip! Pip!"

"Quack, quack!" said she, and they said it, too, as well as they could, and looked all around them beneath the green leaves.

"What a big place the world is," said all the young ones; for to be sure they had a great deal more room now than when they lay in the egg.

"Do you suppose this is all the world?" said their mother. "Why, it stretches out far beyond the other side of the garden. You're all there, I sup-pose?" and she got up. "No, that's not all; there lies the biggest egg still."

At last the big egg opened. "Pip! Pip!" said the young one, scrambling out; he was very big and ugly. The duck looked at him. "That's a fearfully big duckling," she said. "None of the others look like that. I suppose it can't be a turkey poult! Well, we'll soon see; into the water he shall go."

Next day the weather was perfectly delicious; and the mother duck and all her family came out, and down to the moat. Splash! into the water went she. "Quack, quack!" she said, and one duckling after another plumped in. The water went over their heads, but they were up again in a moment and swam beautifully. The ugly gray one was swimming with them. "No, no, that's no turkey," she said. "Look how nicely he uses his legs. Quack! Come along with me and I'll take you out into the world and introduce you to the duck yard. Now then, look alive!

[213]

Don't turn your toes in! A duckling that's properly brought up keeps its legs wide apart. Make a bow and say *Quack*."

So they did; but the other ducks looked at them and said, "Now we've got to have all this mob on the top of us, as if there weren't enough of us already; and poof! what an object that duckling is!"

"He's not handsome," said the mother duck, "but he has a really good disposition, and swims as nicely as any of the rest, even better, I venture to say. I believe he will grow handsome, and win through in the end."

"The other ducklings are charming," said an elderly duck. "Well, make yourselves at home."

So they made themselves at home: but the poor duckling who had come last out of the egg and looked so ugly, was bitten and buffeted and made to look a fool by the hens and the ducks alike. "He's too big," they all said; and the poor duckling didn't know where to stay or which way to go, he was so miserable.

That was the first day, and as time went on it got worse and worse. The wretched duckling was chased about by everybody. Even his mother and sisters were nasty to him, and kept saying, "I wish the cat would get you." The ducks bit him and the hens pecked him, and the maid who had to feed the creatures kicked at him. So he ran away, and flew over the fence. The little birds in the bushes shot up in the air in a fright.

"That's because I'm so ugly," the duckling thought, but ran on all the same, till he got out into the wide marsh where the wild ducks lived. There he lay all night, for he was very tired and unhappy.

In the morning the wild ducks flew up and caught sight of their new comrade. "What sort of a chap are you?" they asked; and the duckling greeted them as well as he could. "You're precious ugly," said the wild ducks; "but that doesn't matter to us as long as you don't marry into our family."

Poor wretch! He wasn't thinking much about marrying, as long as he could be allowed to lie among the reeds, and drink a little marsh water. There he lay two whole days, and then came a pair of wild geese. They hadn't been hatched out very long, and so they were particularly lively. "Here, mate," they said, "you're so ugly we quite like you."

At that moment there was a bang! bang! and both the wild geese fell dead among the reeds. Another bang! bang! and whole flights of geese flew up from the reeds. A great shoot was afoot; the sportsmen were all round the marsh. The dogs went splash! splash! into the mud, and the reeds and rushes swayed hither and thither. It was terrible for the wretched duckling, who was bending his neck to get it under his wing, when all at once, close to him, there was a fearful big dog with his eyes shining horribly. He thrust his muzzle right at the duckling and showed his sharp teeth—and then— splash! Off he went without seizing him.

"Oh, thank goodness," sighed the

duckling. "I'm so ugly, even the dog doesn't like to bite me!" But there he lay perfectly still while gun after gun banged out. It was well on in the day before all was quiet, but the unhappy bird dared not get up even then. He waited several hours yet, before he hurried away from the marsh as fast as ever he could, running over fields and meadows. Toward evening he was near a poor little cottage, so crazy was it that it didn't know which way to tumble down, so it remained standing. The wind howled so fiercely round the duckling that he had to sit down on his tail to keep facing it, and it grew worse and worse. Then he noticed that one hinge of the door was gone, and it hung so crooked that he could slip indoors through the crack.

Here lived an old woman with a cat and a hen. The cat, whom she called Sonny, could set up his fur and purr, and also throw out sparks, but for this he had to be stroked backwards. The hen had very short little legs, and was called Chicky Short Legs. The woman was as fond of her as of a child of her own.

Next morning the strange duckling was noticed at once, and the cat began to purr, and the hen to cluck. "What's the matter?" said the old woman. Her sight wasn't good, so she took the duckling for a fat duck that had strayed away. "That's a splendid catch," she said. "Now I can have duck eggs, if only it isn't a drake! We must make sure of that." So the duckling was taken in on approval for three weeks, but no eggs came.

The cat was the gentleman of the house and the hen the lady, and they always talked of "we and the world." They considered that they were half the world, and much the best half. It seemed to the duckling that some people might think differently, but this the hen could not tolerate.

"Can you lay eggs?" she asked. "No! Then will you kindly hold your tongue."

And the cat said: "Can you put up your fur, or purr, or give out sparks? No! Then you've no call to have an opinion when sensible people are talking."

So the duckling lay in a corner and was in the lowest spirits. He began to think of the fresh air and sunshine, and such a strange longing to swim in the water came on him that he could not help telling the hen.

"What's the matter with you?" she asked. "You've nothing to do, that's why you get these fancies. You just lay some eggs, or purr, and they'll pass off."

"But it is so delicious to float on the water," said the duckling, "so lovely to get it over your head and dive right down to the bottom. I think I'll go out into the wide world."

"Very well, do," said the hen.

So the duckling went off and swam on the water and dived into it, but he was looked down upon by all the creatures because of his ugliness.

Autumn now came on. The leaves of the wood turned brown and yellow, the wind caught them and made them dance about, and above the sky looked cold, where the clouds hung heavy with hail and snow, and on the fence the raven perched and cried "Caw! Caw!" for the mere cold. Indeed, it gave you the shivers to think of it. The unhappy duckling had a very hard time.

One evening, when there was a lovely sunset, a whole flock of beautiful great birds rose out of the bushes. The duckling had never seen any so handsome. They were brilliantly white, with long supple necks. They were swans, and they uttered a strange sound and spread their splendid long wings and flew far away from the cold region to warmer lands, and unfrozen lakes. They mounted so high, so high that the ugly little duckling was strangely moved. He whirled himself around in the water like a wheel, he stretched his neck straight up into the air after them and uttered such a loud cry, so strange, that he was quite frightened at it himself. Oh, he could not forget those beautiful birds, those wonderful birds! He didn't know what the birds were called or which way they were flying, but he loved them as he had never loved anything yet. He was not envious of them—how could it enter his mind to wish for such beauty for himself? He would have been happy if even the ducks had let him into their company, poor ugly creature.

The winter grew very, very cold. The duckling was obliged to swim about on the water to keep it from freezing quite over, but every night the hole he swam in became smaller and smaller. The duckling had always to be moving about to keep the water open, till at last he was tired out and sat still, and was frozen fast in the ice.

Early in the morning a laborer came that way, saw him, went on the ice and with his wooden shoe broke it up. He carried the duckling home to his wife, and there he was brought to life again. The children wanted to play with him, but he thought they meant to hurt him. In his fright he dashed right into the milk pan and made the milk splash out into the room. The woman screamed and threw up her hands. Then he flew into the butter tub and after that into the meal bin and out again. Goodness, what a sight he was! The woman screamed out and hit at him with the tongs, and the children tumbled over one another, laughing and trying to catch him. By good luck the door stood open, and out he rushed into the bushes, on the new fallen snow, and there he lay almost in a swoon.

It would be too sad to tell of all the hardships and miseries which he had to go through in that hard winter. When the sun began once more to shine out warm and the larks to sing, he was lying among the reeds in the marsh, and it was the beautiful spring. Then all at once he lifted his wings, and they rustled more strongly than before, and bore him swiftly away. Before he knew it he was in a spacious garden where apple trees were in blossom, and sweet-smelling lilacs hung on long green boughs right down to the winding moat. Oh, it was lovely here, and fresh with spring! Straight in front of him, out of the shadows, came three beautiful white swans with rustling plumage floating lightly on the water. The duckling recognized the splendid creatures, and a strange sorrowfulness came over him.

"I will fly to them, these royal birds, and they will peck me to death because I, who am so ugly, dare to approach them. But it doesn't matter. It's better to be killed by them than to be snapped at by the ducks and pecked at by hens and kicked by the servant who looks after the poultry yard, and suffer all the winter."

He flew out into the open water and swam towards the stately swans. They saw him and hastened with swelling plumage to meet him.

"Yes, kill me," the poor creature said, bowing his head down to the water, and waited for death. But what did he see in the clear water? He beheld his own image, but it was no longer that of a clumsy dark gray bird, ugly and repulsive. He was a swan himself. It doesn't matter in the least whether you are born in the duck yard, if only you've lain in a swan's egg.

It really delighted him to think of all the hardships and adversities he had suffered, now that he could rightly discern his good fortune and all the beauty that greeted him. The great swans swam round him and caressed him with their bills. Some little children now came into the garden and threw bread and corn into the water, and the smallest of them cried, "There's a new one!" and the others called out in delight. "Yes, there's a new one come!"

They clapped their hands and danced about and ran to their father and mother. More bread and cake were thrown into the water, and everyone said, "The new one is the handsomest of all; how young and beautiful he is!" And the elder swans bowed before him.

At that he felt quite ill at ease, and covered his head with his wings, and knew not what to do. He was more than happy, and yet not proud, for a good heart is never puffed up. He thought how persecuted and depressed he had been, yet now he heard everyone saying he was the most beautiful of all beautiful birds. And the lilacs bowed their branches down to the water, and the sun shone warm and pleasant, and his plumage ruffled, and he raised his slender neck, and from his heart he said joyfully, "Such happiness I never dreamed of when I was the Ugly Duckling."

Cinderella

[PERRAULT, a scholarly French writer of three hundred years ago, became interested in the stories his youngest son was hearing from an elderly nurse. The father collected some of them into a book, adding witty dialogue and glamorous descriptions to make them more dramatic. His "Red Riding Hood," "Puss in Boots," and most of all "Cinderella" still give pleasure to a new crop of eager listeners every year.

ONCE THERE was a gentleman who married, for his second wife, the proudest and most haughty woman that was ever seen. She had, by a former husband, two daughters who were exactly like her. He had likewise, by his first wife, now dead, a young daughter, but of unparalleled goodness and sweetness of temper, which she took from her mother, who had been the best creature in the world.

No sooner was the wedding over than the stepmother began to show herself in her true colors. She could not bear the good qualities of this pretty girl, because they made her own daughters appear the more odious. She employed her in the meanest work of the house: the poor girl scoured the dishes, and scrubbed madam's chamber and those of misses, her daughters. She lay up in a sorry garret upon a wretched straw bed, while her sisters lay in fine rooms, upon beds of the very newest fashion, where they had looking glasses so large that they might see themselves at their full length.

The poor girl bore all patiently and dared not tell her father, for his wife governed him entirely. When she had done her work, she used to go into the chimney corner, and sit down among cinders and ashes, which made her commonly be called Cinderwench; but the youngest stepsister who was not so rude as the eldest called her Cinderella. However, Cinderella, notwithstanding her mean apparel, was a hundred times handsomer than her sisters.

It happened that the king's son gave a ball, and invited all persons of fashion to it. Our young misses were also invited. They were delighted at this invitation and busy in choosing such gowns, petticoats, and head clothes as might become them. This was a new trouble to Cinderella, for it was she who ironed her sisters' linen and plaited their ruffles. They talked of nothing but how they should be dressed.

"For my part," said the eldest, "I will wear my red velvet suit with French trimming."

"And I," said the youngest, "will put on my gold-flowered manteau and my diamond stomacher."

Cinderella was consulted in all these matters, for she had excellent notions and advised them always for the best, and offered her services to dress their heads. As she was doing this they said to her:

"Cinderella, would you not be glad to go to the ball?"

"Alas!" said she. "You only jeer at me. It is not for such as I am to go thither."

"Thou art in the right of it," replied they. "It would make the people laugh to see a Cinderwench at a ball."

Anyone but Cinderella would have dressed their heads awry, but she was very good and dressed them perfectly well. They were almost two days without eating, so much they were transported with joy. They broke above a dozen laces in trying to be laced up close, that they might have a fine slender shape; and they were continually at their looking glass. At last the happy day came, and they went to court. Cinderella followed them with her eyes as long as she could, and when she had lost sight of them, she fell a-crying.

Her godmother, who saw her all in tears, asked her what was the matter.

"I wish I could—I wish I could—" She was not able to speak the rest, being interrupted by her tears and sobbing.

This godmother of hers, who was a fairy, said to her, "Thou wishest thou couldst go to the ball; is it not so?"

"Y—es," cried Cinderella.

"Well," said her godmother, "be but a good girl, and I will contrive that thou shalt go." Then she took her into her chamber, and said to her, "Run into the garden, and bring me a pumpkin."

Cinderella went immediately to gather the finest she could get and brought it to her godmother, not being able to imagine how this pumpkin could make her go to the ball. Her godmother scooped out all the inside of it, having left nothing but the rind; which done, she struck it with her wand, and the pumpkin was instantly turned into a fine coach, gilded all over with gold.

She then went to look into her mousetrap, where she found six mice, all alive, and ordered Cinderella to lift up a little the trapdoor. She gave each mouse, as it went out, a little tap with her wand, and the mouse was that moment turned into a fine horse, which altogether made a very fine set of six horses of a beautiful mouse-colored dapple-gray. Being at a loss for a coachman, the godmother sent Cinderella for the rat trap.

Cinderella brought the trap to her, and in it there were three huge rats. The fairy made choice of one of the three which had the largest beard, and, having touched him with her wand, turned him into a fat, jolly coachman, who had the smartest whiskers eyes ever beheld. After that, she said:

"Go again into the garden, and you will find six lizards behind the watering pot. Bring them to me."

She had no sooner done so but her godmother turned them into six footmen, who skipped up behind the coach, with their liveries all bedaubed with gold and silver, and clung as close behind each other as if they had done nothing else their whole lives. The fairy then said to Cinderella:

"Well, you see here an equipage fit to go to the ball with. Are you not pleased with it?"

"Oh, yes!" cried she. "But must I go thither as I am, in these nasty rags?"

Her godmother just touched her with her wand and, at the same instant, her clothes were turned into cloth of gold and silver, all beset with jewels. This done, she gave her a pair of glass slippers, the prettiest in the whole world. Being thus decked out, she got up into her coach; but her godmother commanded her above all things, not to stay till after midnight. If she stayed one moment longer, the coach would be a pumpkin again, her horses mice, her coachman a rat, her footmen lizards, and her clothes become just as they were before.

She promised her godmother she would not fail of leaving the ball before midnight; and then away she drove scarce able to contain herself for joy. The king's son, who was told that a great princess, whom nobody knew, was come, ran out to receive her. He gave her his hand as she alighted out of the coach and led her into the hall among all the company. There was immediately a profound silence. They left off dancing, and the violins ceased to play, so attentive was everyone to contemplate the singular beauties of the unknown newcomer. Nothing was then heard but a confused noise of:

"Ha! how handsome she is! Ha! how handsome she is!"

The king himself, old as he was, could not help watching her. He told the queen softly that it was a long time since he had seen so lovely a creature. All the ladies were busied in considering her clothes, that they might have some made next day after the same pattern.

The king's son conducted her to the most honorable seat, and afterward took her out to dance with him. She danced so gracefully that they all more and more admired her. A fine collation was served up, whereof the young prince ate not a morsel, so intent was he in gazing on her.

She went and sat down by her sisters, showing them a thousand civilities, which surprised them, for they did not know her. While Cinderella was thus amusing her sisters, she heard the clock strike eleven and three-quarters, whereupon she immediately made a curtsy to the company and hasted away as fast as she could.

Being got home, she ran to seek out her godmother; and after having thanked her, she said she wished she might go next day to the ball, because the king's son had desired her. As she was eagerly telling her godmother what had passed at the ball, her two sisters knocked at the door, which Cinderella ran and opened.

"How long you have stayed!" cried

she, rubbing her eyes as if she had been just waked out of her sleep.

"If thou hadst been at the ball," said one of her sisters, "thou wouldst not have been tired with it. There came thither the finest princess, the most beautiful ever was seen with mortal eyes."

Cinderella seemed very indifferent; indeed, she asked them the name of that princess. They told her they did not know it and that the king's son would give all the world to know who she was. At this Cinderella, smiling, replied:

"She must, then, be very beautiful indeed; how happy you have been! Could not I see her? Ah! dear Miss Charlotte, do lend me your yellow suit clothes which you wear every day."

"Ay, to be sure!" cried Miss Charlotte. "Lend my clothes to such a dirty Cinderwench as thou art? I should be a fool."

Cinderella expected such an answer and was glad of the refusal. She would have been sadly put to it if her sister had lent her what she asked for jestingly.

The next day the two sisters were at the ball, and so was Cinderella, but dressed more magnificently than before. The king's son was always by her and never ceased his compliments and kind speeches. She quite forgot what her godmother had recommended; so that, at last, she counted the clock striking twelve when she took it to be no more than eleven. She then rose up and fled, as nimble as a deer. The prince followed but could not overtake her. She left behind one of her glass slippers, which the prince took up most carefully. She got home, but quite out of breath and in her nasty old clothes, having nothing left of all her finery but one of the little slippers, fellow to that she had dropped.

The guards at the palace gate were asked if they had not seen a princess go out. They said that they had seen nobody go out but a young girl, very meanly dressed.

When the two sisters returned from the ball, Cinderella asked them if the fine lady had been there. They told her yes, but that she hurried away immediately when it struck twelve, and with so much haste that she dropped one of her little glass slippers, the prettiest in the world. The king's son had taken it up and had done nothing but look at it all the rest of the time at the ball. Most certainly he was very much in love with the beautiful person who owned the glass slipper.

What they said was very true. A few days later, the king's son caused it to be proclaimed, by sound of trumpet, that he would marry her whose foot this slipper would just fit. They whom he employed began to try it upon the princesses, then the duchesses and all the court, but in vain. It was brought to the two sisters, who did all they possibly could to thrust their feet into the slipper, but they could not effect it. Cinderella, who saw all this and knew her slipper, said to them, laughing: "Let me see if it will not fit me."

Her sisters burst out a-laughing and began to banter her. The gentleman who was sent to try the slipper looked earnestly at Cinderella. Finding her very handsome he said that it was only just that she should try. He had orders to let everyone make trial.

He obliged Cinderella to sit down, and, putting the slipper to her foot, he found it went on very easily. It fitted her as if it had been of wax. The astonishment of her two sisters was excessively great, but still greater when Cinderella pulled out of her pocket the other slipper, and put it on her foot. Thereupon, in came her godmother. With her wand she touched Cinderella's clothes and made them richer and more magnificent than any of those she had worn before.

And now her two sisters found her to be that fine, beautiful lady whom they had seen at the ball. They threw themselves at her feet to beg pardon for all the ill-treatment they had made her undergo. Cinderella, as she embraced them, cried that she forgave them with all her heart, and desired them always to love her.

She was conducted to the young prince, dressed as she was. He thought her more charming than ever and, a few days after, married her. Cinderella, who was no less good than beautiful, gave her two sisters lodgings in the palace and that very same day matched them with two great lords of the court.

Clever Manka

THERE WAS once a rich farmer who was as grasping and unscrupulous as he was rich. He was always driving a hard bargain and always getting the better of his poor neighbors. One of these neighbors was a humble shepherd who in return for service was to receive from the farmer a heifer. When the time of payment came the farmer refused to give the shepherd the heifer and the shepherd was forced to lay the matter before the burgomaster.

The burgomaster, who was a young man and not very experienced, listened to both sides and when he had deliberated he said: "Instead of deciding this case, I will put a riddle to you both, and the man who makes the best answer shall have the heifer. Are you agreed?"

The farmer and the shepherd accepted this proposal and the burgomaster said: "Well then, here is my riddle: What is the swiftest thing in the world? What is the sweetest thing? What is the richest? Think out your answers and bring them to me tomorrow."

The farmer went home in a temper. "What kind of a burgomaster is this young fellow!" he growled. "If he had let me keep the heifer I'd have sent him a bushel of pears. But now I'm in a fair way of losing the heifer, for I can't think of any answer to his foolish riddle."

"What is the matter, husband?" his wife asked.

"It's that new burgomaster. The old one would have given me the heifer without any argument, but this young man thinks to decide the case by asking us riddles."

When he told his wife what the riddle was, she cheered him greatly by telling him that she knew the answers at once.

"Why, husband," said she, "our gray mare must be the swiftest thing in the world. You know yourself nothing ever passes us on the road. As for the sweetest, did you ever taste honey any sweeter than ours? And I'm sure there's nothing richer than our chest of golden ducats that we've been laying by these forty years."

The farmer was delighted. "You're right, wife, you're right! That heifer remains ours!"

The shepherd when he got home was downcast and sad. He had a daughter, a clever girl named Manka, who asked: "What is it, Father? What did the burgomaster say?"

The shepherd sighed. "I'm afraid I've lost the heifer. The burgomaster set us a riddle and I know I shall never guess it."

"Perhaps I can help you," Manka said.

So the shepherd gave her the riddle and the next day as he was setting out for the burgomaster's, Manka told him what answers to make.

When he reached the burgomaster's house, the farmer was already there rubbing his hands and beaming with self-importance.

The burgomaster again propounded the riddle and then asked the farmer his answers.

The farmer cleared his throat. "The swiftest thing in the world? Why, my dear sir, that's my gray mare, of course, for no other horse ever passes us on the road. The sweetest? Honey from my beehives, to be sure. The richest? What can be richer than my chest of golden ducats!"

And the farmer squared his shoulders and smiled triumphantly.

"H'm," said the young burgomaster, dryly. Then he asked: "What answers does the shepherd make?"

The shepherd bowed politely and said: "The swiftest thing in the world is thought, for thought can run any distance in the twinkling of an eye. The sweetest thing of all is sleep, for when a man is tired and sad what can be sweeter? The richest thing is the earth, for out of the earth come all the riches of the world."

"Good!" the burgomaster cried. "Good! The heifer goes to the shepherd!"

Later the burgomaster said to the shepherd: "Tell me, now, who gave you those answers? I'm sure they never came out of your own head."

At first the shepherd tried not to tell, but when the burgomaster pressed him he confessed that they came from his daughter, Manka. The burgomaster, who thought that he would like to make another test of Manka's cleverness, sent for ten eggs. He gave them to the shepherd and said: "Take these eggs to Manka and tell her to have them hatched out by tomorrow and to bring me the chicks."

When the shepherd reached home and gave Manka the burgomaster's message, Manka laughed and said: "Take a handful of millet and go right back to the burgomaster. Say to him: 'My daughter sends you this millet. She says that if you plant, grow it, and have it harvested by tomorrow, she'll bring you the ten chicks and you can feed them the ripe grain.'"

When the burgomaster heard this, he laughed heartily. "That's a clever girl of yours," he told the shepherd. "If she's as comely as she is clever, I'd like to marry her. Tell her to come to see me, but she must come neither by day nor by night, neither riding nor walking, neither dressed nor undressed."

When Manka received this message she waited until the next dawn when night was gone and day not yet arrived. Then she wrapped herself in a fishnet and, throwing one leg over a goat's back and keeping one foot on the ground, she went to the burgomaster's house.

Now I ask you: did she go dressed? No, she wasn't dressed. A fishnet isn't clothing. Did she go undressed? Of course not, for wasn't she covered with a fishnet? Did she walk to the burgomaster's? No, she didn't walk for she went with one leg thrown over a goat. Then did she ride? Of course, she didn't ride for wasn't she walking on one foot?

When she reached the burgomaster's house she called out: "Here I am, Mr. Burgomaster, and I've come neither by day nor by night, neither riding nor walking, neither dressed nor undressed."

The young burgomaster was so delighted with Manka's cleverness and so pleased with her comely looks that he proposed to her at once and in a short time married her.

"But understand, my dear Manka," he said, "you are not to use that cleverness of yours at my expense. I won't have you interfering in any of my cases. In fact if ever you give advice to any one who comes to me for judgment, I'll turn you out of my house at once and send you home to your father."

All went well for a time. Manka busied herself in her housekeeping and was careful not to interfere in any of the burgomaster's cases.

Then one day two farmers came to the burgomaster to have a dispute settled. One of the farmers owned a mare which had foaled in the marketplace. The colt had run under the wagon of the other farmer, and thereupon the owner of the wagon claimed the colt as his property.

The burgomaster, who was thinking of something else while the case was being presented, said carelessly: "The man who found the colt under his wagon is, of course, the owner of the colt."

As the owner of the mare was leaving the burgomaster's house, he met Manka and stopped to tell her about the case. Manka was ashamed of her husband for making so foolish a decision and she said to the farmer:

"Come back this afternoon with a fishing net and stretch it across the dusty road. When the burgomaster sees you, he will come out and ask you what you are doing. Say to him that you're catching fish. When he asks you how you can expect to catch fish in a dusty road, tell him it's just as easy for you to catch fish in a dusty road as it is for a wagon to foal. Then he'll see the injustice of his decision and have the colt returned to you. But you mustn't let him find out that it was I who told you to do this."

That afternoon when the burgomaster chanced to look out the window he saw a man stretching a fishnet across the dusty road. He went out to him and asked: "What are you doing?"

"Fishing."

"Fishing in a dusty road? Are you daft?"

"Well," the man said, "it's just as easy for me to catch fish in a dusty road as it is for a wagon to foal."

Then the burgomaster recognized the man as the owner of the mare, and he had to confess that what he said was true.

"Of course the colt belongs to your

[225]

mare and must be returned to you. But tell me," he said, "who put you up to this? You didn't think of it yourself."

The farmer tried not to tell, but the burgomaster questioned him until he found out that Manka was at the bottom of it. This made him very angry. He went into the house and called his wife.

"Manka," he said, "do you forget what I told you would happen if you went interfering in any of my cases? Home you go this very day. I don't care to hear any excuses. The matter is settled. You may take with you the one thing you like best in my house, for I won't have people saying that I treated you shabbily."

Manka made no outcry. "Very well, my dear husband, I shall do as you say. I shall go to my father's cottage and take with me the one thing I like best in your house. But don't make me go until after supper. We have been very happy together and I should like to eat one last meal with you. Let us part as friends."

The burgomaster agreed and Manka prepared a fine supper of all the dishes of which her husband was particularly fond. The burgomaster opened his choicest wine and pledged Manka's health. The supper was so good that he ate and ate and ate. And the more he ate, the more he drank, until at last he grew drowsy and fell sound asleep in his chair. Then without awakening him Manka had him carried out to the wagon that was waiting to take her home to her father.

The next morning when the burgomaster opened his eyes, he found himself lying in the shepherd's cottage. "What does this mean?" he roared.

"Nothing, dear husband, nothing!" Manka said. "You know you told me I might take with me the one thing I liked best in your house, so of course I took you! That's all."

For a moment the burgomaster rubbed his eyes in amazement. Then he laughed loud and heartily to think how Manka had outwitted him.

"Manka," he said, "you're too clever for me. Come on, my dear, let's go home."

So they climbed back into the wagon and drove home.

The burgomaster never again scolded his wife, but thereafter whenever a very difficult case came up he always said: "I think we had better consult my wife. You know she's a very clever woman."

FERNÁN CABALLERO

The Three Wishes

MANY years ago in Spain there lived an old couple, who, although poor, had worked diligently on their little piece of ground. One winter's night they were seated in front of their comfortable hearth, but instead of giving thanks to God for the benefits they enjoyed, they spent the time in enumerating the good things possessed by their neighbors.

"Instead of my little hut, which is on bad soil, and only fit to house a donkey in, I would like to have the farm of old Polainas!" exclaimed the man.

"And I," added his wife, "would like to have our neighbor's house, which is nearly new."

"And I," continued her husband, "instead of our old donkey, which can scarcely carry an empty sack, would like to have Polainas' mule!"

"And I," exclaimed the wife, "would like to have such a fat porker as our neighbor has. Some people seem only to wish for a thing in order to get it. How I should like to see my wishes accomplished!"

Scarcely had she uttered these words, than they beheld a beautiful little woman standing in front of the fire. She was so small that her height could not have been more than eighteen inches, and she wore a crown like a queen's upon her head. Her tunic and veil seemed to be made of white smoke, while the sparks from the fire crackled like fireworks about her. In her hand she bore a little golden scepter, the end of which was formed by a gleaming ruby.

"I am the Lady Fortunata," said she. "I was passing when I heard your complaints, and I am here to grant you three wishes. One to you!" she said to the wife. "The other to you!" she spoke to the husband. "The third wish must be something you both desire. This last I will agree to in person tomorrow, when I return; and until then I leave you to think what it shall be."

With these words, the fairy sprang through the flames and disappeared in a cloud of smoke.

The delight of the old couple may be imagined. Their desires were so many that, not knowing which wishes to select, they determined not to make a definite decision until the following day. In a little while they again began to discuss their wealthy neighbors.

"I was at their house today," said the husband. "They were making black puddings. Ah, such puddings! It would have done you good to see them!"

"I wish I had one of them here," replied the wife, "to roast on the ashes for supper."

Scarcely had she uttered the words than there appeared upon the ashes the most delicious-looking black pudding. The woman stared at it with open mouth and eyes starting out of her head. Her husband jumped up in despair.

"You greedy woman," he said. "Through your gluttony, we have lost one of the wishes. Good heavens, what a woman this is. More stupid than a goose! It makes me desperate. You and your black pudding! I wish it were stuck onto your nose!"

No sooner had he spoken than there was the black pudding hanging from the place indicated.

Then was the old man struck with horror and his wife with desperation!

"You see what you have done, evil tongue!" exclaimed she, as she tried to tear the unwanted appendage from her nose. "If I employed my wish badly, at least it was to my own disadvantage, and not to the injury of anyone else. But your sin carries its punishment with it. I will not have any other wish, than that the black pudding be taken off my nose."

"Wife, for heaven's sake! What of the new house?"

"Nothing!"

"Wife, for heaven's sake, think of the farm!"

"It does not matter."

"My dear, let us wish for a fortune, and then we will have a golden case for the black pudding."

"I will not hear of it."

"Then you would have us left just as we were before?"

"That is all that I wish for."

And for all that the man could say, nothing could alter his wife's determination. She grew more and more enraged with her double nose, and the following night when the fairy appeared, she learned what the last wish of the old couple was to be.

"We see how blind and foolish it is," they said, "to fancy that the realization of our wishes will make us happy."

The Man with the Bag

ONCE UPON a time a man who had a beggar's bag on his back came to the door of a house that was hereabouts. He asked for shelter. "And if you let me take my rest here while I'm begging through the parish, I'll ask you for nothing else, ma'am," said he to the woman of the house. "A good beggar doesn't ask for food where he gets shelter and doesn't ask for shelter where he gets food. I know what a good beggar's conduct should be. My father was a beggar and his father was a beggar before him. I'm no upstart."

The woman of the house told him he could rest by the fire when he finished his round of begging in the evening. When she told him this, the man with the bag on his back turned from the door and went along the crooked lane that went from the house. The woman's daughter was there, and she looked after him as he went down the laneway. She thought that only for the grime that was on him and the ragged clothes that he wore he would be good-looking enough.

Let the beggarman go on while I tell you about the girl. She was named Liban, and well did she deserve the name which means "Beauty of Woman," for her eyes were beaming, her mouth was smiling, her cheeks were like roses, and her hair was brown as a cluster of nuts. But for all her beauty Liban had little chance of being wedded.

Young men came to ask for her in marriage, but if they did, her mother told them they were first to climb the tree that overhung the high cliff. There they would find a raven's nest, and from it they must take a pair of scissors that the raven had carried off. They must also bring back two of the raven's eggs. One young man and another young man would climb the tree. But when he came to the top branches that overhung the cliff and found them breaking under him, he would get down from the tree and not go to the house again.

So Liban stayed, and was likely to stay, beside her mother's hearth, spinning threads on her spindle while her mother spun them upon her wheel. And this was just what her mother wanted her to be doing, for she got a deal of silver for all the thread that she and Liban spun.

The beggarman came back in the evening and his bag hung as if there were nothing in it. All the same, he refused the cup of milk and the cut of bread that Liban offered him. "All that I'll take in your house," said he, speaking to her mother, "is the place to rest myself, and leave to put in your charge what I get on my travels."

And saying that he put his hand down into the bag, and searched and searched there, and brought up what he found. It was a pea. "I'll leave this in your charge and you'll be accountable for it," said he. "I'll take it back from you when I'm going."

She took the pea and put it on the corner of her spinning wheel. Then the beggarman put the bag under his head and went to sleep by the fire.

Liban and her mother came out of the sleeping room at the peep of day, and as they did the beggarman got up from where he was lying. He opened the house door, and went off on his rounds with the crooked lanes of the parish before him. Liban went to get ready the breakfast. The little speckled hen that was her own came in to pick up the crumbs that would be around the table. But when she came as far as the spinning wheel she saw the pea, and when she saw it she picked it and swallowed it.

"Mother," Liban said, "the pea that the beggarman left in your charge, my own little speckled hen has swallowed."

"He'll forget to ask about it," said her mother. "As for you, take the spindle and get some threads down while the breakfast porridge is cooling."

The first thing the beggarman said when he came in on the doorway was, "Where is the pea I left in your charge, woman of the house?"

"A hen ate it."

"Which is the hen that ate the pea I left in your charge?"

"The speckled hen that's before you."

"If the speckled hen ate the pea that was mine, the hen herself is mine."

"That cannot be."

"It can be and it is, ma'am. It's the law, and if a beggarman doesn't know the law, who would know it?"

And saying this he took up the hen that was picking from a dish on the floor and put her into his empty bag. The woman of the house believed what he said, for she had once stood in a court—the Court of Dusty Feet it was —and had heard a sentence passed on a man who had lost something that was left in his charge and that he was accountable for.

When he was going off the next morning, he took the speckled hen out of his bag. "I leave her in your charge," he said to Liban's mother.

Then he went off, facing the crooked lanes of the parish, his empty bag hanging on his back. And Liban, so that nothing might happen to her, made a little pen of wattles for the speckled hen, and tied her inside of it. Then she took up her spindle and her mother went to her wheel. "I wish that beggarman had come to ask you in marriage so that I might have made him climb the tree," she said.

Liban was looking out of the door. She saw the pig beside the pen of wattles. The pen was strange to the pig, and she went rooting around it. The speckled hen flew into her mouth. The pig ate her. All that was left of the little speckled hen was the white feathers on the pig's snout.

And the first thing that the beggarman said when he came in on the door was, "Where is the speckled hen that I left in your charge?"

"The pig ate her," said Liban's mother.

"Then the pig is mine. That's the law, and if a beggarman doesn't know the law, who'd know it?" He went out to the yard and took the pig by the leg and dragged her into the house. He put her into his bag and tied up the mouth of his bag. Then he went to sleep by the fire.

By the time the beggarman went out of her door next morning, Liban's mother had lost so much flesh through grief at the loss of her pig that she looked as if the weight of a pig had been taken out of her. She wasn't able to eat her porridge either. Liban took charge of the pig. She tied her to a bush under a wall of loose stones, thinking no harm could come to her there. Then she went back to her spinning. But before she had more than a few threads spun, the horse galloping toward the house threw the stones of the wall down upon the pig.

"Every misfortune has come on us since that beggarman came to the house for shelter," said the mother. "He'll want to take our horse now. If he does and rides away on him, I'll be content with my loss, so glad I'll be to see the last of the beggarman."

He came back in the evening with a corner of his bag filled. "Where's my pig?"

"Our horse has killed her."

"Your horse is mine."

"Take him and ride away, and may all my bad luck go with you."

"No. I never stay less than five days in any house. It's due to a promise I made to my father. He feared that I might become a vagabond, one day here and another day there, and he made me promise I'd stay the greater part of the week in any house I had been given shelter in. One day more I'll stay for the sake of the promise I made. Mind the horse for me. I put him in your charge."

He lay by the fire, his head on his bag, and he went to sleep. The next morning he went off, his bag on his back, and his face toward the crooked lanes of the parish. Liban put a halter on the horse and, so as not to let him get into any danger, went with him everywhere the horse went to graze. Along the cliff he went where the grass was sweetest. When they came to the tree that the raven's nest was in, Liban put her hands before her eyes so that she might look up and see how high the young men had to climb when they had asked for her. Not so high at all, she thought. And there was the raven on the branch above the nest, flapping its wings at her. As she looked, the horse, leaning out to get a mouthful of sweet grass, slipped and slithered down the cliff. And the raven with a croak flew down after him.

So poor Liban went back to her mother. "Our horse is gone now," she said. "Over the cliff he has fallen, and what will the beggarman take from us now?"

"Nothing at all can he take," said

her mother. "Let him take the horse's skin, and come near us no more."

When he came back that evening with only a corner of his bag filled, the beggarman said, "Where's my horse so that I can go riding tomorrow?"

"The horse fell over a cliff and the raven is upon him now."

"Who was minding my horse when he fell over the cliff?"

"My daughter was minding your horse."

"Then your daughter is mine. That's the law, and if you don't think it is the law I'll stand face to face with you about it in the Court of Dusty Feet."

Saying this the beggarman lifted up Liban (and, oh, but his arms were strong!) and thrust her into his bag. Then he put the bag on his back and ran from the house with her.

Her mother ran after him. The neighbors ran with the mother. But the beggarman's legs were long and strong and his back was broad and unbending. "Liban's in the bag, Liban's in the bag! Stop him! Stop him!" cried her mother and the neighbors. But their cries only made him go faster and faster. When he came to the cross-roads he laid the bag upon a bank, and he let Liban come out of it.

"Take me back to my mother," said Liban.

"Indeed, I'll do nothing of the kind," said the man. Now that he had taken off his ragged coat and had washed his face in the stream, he looked a handsome sort of a young man. "Here's a coach," he said. "It's waiting for you and me, and we'll go in it, not to the Court of Dusty Feet, but to the court in my father's castle where there will be one who will marry us. I put on the beggar's garb and carried this bag upon my back only to come to you, Liban, Beauty of Woman. There are many things I can do, but there are a few I can't do, and climbing a tree is one of them."

Then he put his arm around her and lifted her into the coach that was waiting there, with two black horses to draw it. They had just got into the coach when Liban's mother and the neighbors came up. The neighbors stopped to pick up the shower of silver that the coachman threw them, and the footman lifted Liban's mother and left her standing on the board beside him, and the coach went dashing on.

⟨[Padraic Colum's *books include:* Children of Odin, The Golden Fleece and the Heroes Who Lived Before Achilles, *and* The Bright Islands, *Hawaiian folk tales.*

The Piper at the Gates of Dawn

⟨ MOLE and Water Rat shared a home on the riverbank. The night our
tale begins, Rat had been having supper with his friends, the Otters. This
story is from THE WIND IN THE WILLOWS.

MOLE, I'M afraid they're in trouble," said the Rat. "Little Portly is missing again; and you know what a lot his father thinks of him, though he never says much about it."

"What, that child?" said the Mole lightly. "Well, suppose he is; why worry about it? He's always straying off and getting lost, and turning up again; he's so adventurous. But no harm ever happens to him. Everybody hereabouts knows him and likes him, just as they do old Otter, and you may be sure some animal or other will come across him and bring him back again all right. Why, we've found him ourselves, miles from home and quite self-possessed and cheerful!"

"Yes, but this time it's more serious," said the Rat gravely. "He's been missing for some days now, and the Otters have hunted everywhere, high and low, without finding the slightest trace. And they've asked every animal, too, for miles around, and no one knows anything about him. Otter's evidently more anxious than he'll admit.

I got out of him that young Portly hasn't learned to swim very well yet, and I can see he's thinking of the weir. There's a lot of water coming down still, considering the time of year, and the place always had a fascination for the child. And then there are—well, traps and things—you know. Otter's not the fellow to be nervous about any son of his before it's time. And now he *is* nervous. When I left, he came with me—said he wanted some air, and talked about stretching his legs. But I could see it wasn't that, so I drew him out and pumped him, and got it all from him at last. He was going to spend the night watching by the ford. You know the place where the old ford used to be, in bygone days before they built the bridge?"

"I know it well," said the Mole. "But why should Otter choose to watch there?"

"Well, it seems it was there he gave Portly his first swimming lesson," continued the Rat. "From that shallow, gravelly spit near the bank. And it was

[233]

there he used to teach him fishing, and there young Portly caught his first fish, of which he was so very proud. The child loved the spot, and Otter thinks that if he came wandering back from wherever he is—if he *is* anywhere by this time, poor little chap—he might make for the ford he was so fond of; or if he came across it he'd remember it well, and stop there and play perhaps. So Otter goes there every night and watches—on the chance, you know, just on the chance!"

They were silent for a time, both thinking of the same thing—the lonely, heartsore animal, crouched by the ford, watching and waiting, the long night through—on the chance.

"Well, well," said the Rat presently, "I suppose we ought to be thinking about turning in." But he never offered to move.

"Rat," said the Mole, "I simply can't go and turn in, and go to sleep, and *do* nothing, even though there doesn't seem to be anything to be done. We'll get the boat out, and paddle upstream. The moon will be up in an hour or so, and then we will search as well as we can—anyhow, it will be better than going to bed and doing *nothing*."

"Just what I was thinking myself," said the Rat. "It's not the sort of night for bed anyhow; and daybreak is not so very far off, and then we may pick up some news of him from early risers as we go along."

They got the boat out, and the Rat took the sculls, paddling with caution. Out in midstream there was a clear, narrow track that faintly reflected the sky; but wherever shadows fell on the water from bank, bush, or tree, they were as solid to all appearance as the banks themselves, and the Mole had to steer with judgment accordingly. Dark and deserted as it was, the night was full of small noises, song and chatter and rustling, telling of the busy little population who were up and about, plying their trades and vocations through the night till sunshine should fall on them at last and send them off to their well-earned repose. The water's own noises, too, were more apparent than by day, its gurglings and "cloops" more unexpected and near at hand; and constantly they started at what seemed a sudden clear call from an actual articulate voice.

The line of the horizon was clear and hard against the sky, and in one particular quarter it showed black against a silvery climbing phosphorescence that grew and grew. At last, over the rim of the waiting earth the moon lifted with slow majesty till it swung clear of the horizon and rode off, free of moorings; and once more they began to see surfaces—meadows widespread, and quiet gardens, and the river itself from bank to bank, all softly disclosed, all washed clean of mystery and terror, all radiant again as by day, but with a difference that was tremendous. Their old haunts greeted them again in other raiment, as if they had slipped away and put on this pure new apparel and come quietly back, smiling as they shyly waited to see if they would be recognized again under it.

Fastening their boat to a willow, the friends landed in this silent, silver kingdom, and patiently explored the hedges, the hollow trees, the tunnels and their little culverts, the ditches and dry waterways. Embarking again and crossing over, they worked their way up the stream in this manner, while the moon, serene and detached in a cloudless sky, did what she could, though so far off, to help them in their quest; till her hour came and she sank earthwards reluctantly, and left them, and mystery once more held field and river.

Then a change began slowly to declare itself. The horizon became clearer, field and tree came more into sight, and somehow with a different look; the mystery began to drop away from them. A bird piped suddenly, and was still; and a light breeze sprang up and set the reeds and bulrushes rustling. Rat, who was in the stern of the boat, while Mole sculled, sat up suddenly and listened with a passionate intentness. Mole, who with gentle strokes was just keeping the boat moving while he scanned the banks with care, looked at him with curiosity.

"It's gone!" sighed the Rat, sinking back in his seat again. "So beautiful and strange and new! Since it was to end so soon, I almost wish I had never heard it. For it has roused a longing in me that is pain, and nothing seems worthwhile but just to hear that sound once more and go on listening to it forever. No! There it is again!" he cried, alert once more. Entranced, he was silent for a long space, spellbound.

"Now it passes on and I begin to lose it," he said presently. "O, Mole! the beauty of it! The merry bubble and joy, the thin, clear, happy call of the distant piping! Such music I never dreamed of, and the call in it is stronger even than the music is sweet! Row on, Mole, row! For the music and the call must be for us."

The Mole, greatly wondering, obeyed. "I hear nothing myself," he said, "but the wind playing in the reeds and rushes."

The Rat never answered, if indeed he heard. Rapt, transported, trembling, he was possessed in all his senses by this new divine thing that caught up his helpless soul and swung and dandled it, a powerless but happy infant, in a strong, sustaining grasp.

In silence Mole rowed steadily, and soon they came to a point where the river divided, a long backwater branching off to one side. With a slight movement of his head Rat, who had long dropped the rudder lines, directed the rower to take the backwater. The creeping tide of light gained and gained, and now they could see the color of the flowers that gemmed the water's edge.

"Clearer and nearer still," cried the Rat joyously. "Now you must surely hear it! Ah—at last—I see you do!"

Breathless and transfixed, the Mole stopped rowing as the liquid run of that glad piping broke on him like a wave, caught him up, and possessed him utterly. He saw the tears on his comrade's cheeks, and bowed his head and understood. For a space they hung there, brushed by the purple loosestrife that fringed the bank; then the clear imperious summons that marched hand in hand with the intoxicating melody imposed its will on Mole, and mechanically he bent to his oars again. And the light grew steadily stronger, but no birds sang as they were wont to do at the approach of dawn; and but for the heavenly music all was marvelously still.

On either side of them, as they glided onward, the rich meadow grass seemed that morning of a freshness and a greenness unsurpassable. Never had they noticed the roses so vivid, the willow herb so riotous, the meadow-sweet so odorous and pervading. Then the murmur of the approaching weir began to hold the air, and they felt a consciousness that they were nearing the end, whatever it might be, that surely awaited their expedition.

A wide half-circle of foam and glinting lights and shining shoulders of green water, the great weir closed the backwater from bank to bank, troubled all the quiet surface with twirling eddies and floating foam streaks, and deadened all other sounds with its solemn and soothing rumble. In midmost of the stream, embraced in the weir's shimmering arm spread, a small island lay anchored, fringed close with willow and silver birch and alder. Reserved, shy, but full of significance, it hid whatever it might hold behind a veil, keeping it till the hour should come, and, with the hour, those who were called and chosen.

Slowly, but with no doubt or hesitation whatever, and in something of a solemn expectancy, the two animals passed through the broken, tumultuous water and moored their boat at the flowery margin of the island. In silence they landed, and pushed through the blossom and scented herbage and undergrowth that led up to the level ground, till they stood on a little lawn of a marvelous green, set round with Nature's own orchard trees —crabapple, wild cherry, and sloe.

"This is the place of my song dream, the place the music played to me," whispered the Rat, as if in a trance. "Here, in this holy place, here if anywhere, surely we shall find Him!"

Then suddenly the Mole felt a great awe fall upon him, an awe that turned his muscles to water, bowed his head, and rooted his feet to the ground. It was no panic terror—indeed he felt wonderfully at peace and happy—but it was an awe that smote and held him and, without seeing, he knew it could only mean that some august Presence was very, very near. With difficulty he turned to look for his friend, and saw him at his side, cowed, stricken, and trembling violently. And still there was utter silence in the populous bird-haunted branches around them; and still the light grew and grew.

Perhaps he would never have dared to raise his eyes, but that, though the piping was now hushed, the call and the summons seemed still dominant and imperious. He might not refuse, were Death himself waiting to strike him instantly, once he had looked with mortal eye on things rightly kept hidden. Trembling he obeyed, and raised his humble head; and then, in that utter clearness of the imminent dawn, while Nature, flushed with fulness of incredible color, seemed to hold her breath for the event, he looked in the very eyes of the Friend and Helper; saw the backward sweep of the curved horns, gleaming in the growing daylight; saw the stern, hooked nose between the kindly eyes that were looking down on them humorously, while the bearded mouth broke into a half-smile at the corners; saw the rippling muscles on the arm that lay across the broad chest, the long supple hand still holding the Panpipes only just fallen away from the parted lips; saw the splendid curves of the shaggy limbs

"Afraid! Of *Him?* Oh, never, never! And yet—and yet—O, Mole, I am afraid!"

Then the two animals, crouching to the earth, bowed their heads and did worship.

Sudden and magnificent, the sun's broad golden disc showed itself over the horizon facing them; and the first rays, shooting across the level water meadows, took the animals full in the eyes and dazzled them. When they were able to look once more, the Vision had vanished, and the air was full of

disposed in majestic ease on the sward; saw, last of all, nestling between his very hooves, sleeping soundly in entire peace and contentment, the little, round, podgy, childish form of the baby otter. All this he saw, for one moment breathless and intense, vivid on the morning sky; and still, as he looked, he lived; and still, as he lived, he wondered.

"Rat!" he found breath to whisper, shaking. "Are you afraid?"

"Afraid?" murmured the Rat, his eyes shining with unutterable love.

the carol of birds that hailed the dawn.

As they stared blankly, in dumb misery deepening as they slowly realized all they had seen and all they had lost, a capricious little breeze, dancing up from the surface of the water, tossed the aspens, shook the dewy roses, and blew lightly and caressingly in their faces, and with its soft touch came instant oblivion. For this is the last best gift that the kindly demigod is careful to bestow on those to whom he has revealed himself in their helping: the gift of forgetfulness. Lest the awful remembrance should remain and grow, and overshadow mirth and pleasure, and the great haunting memory should spoil all the afterlives of little animals helped out of difficulties, in order that they should be happy and lighthearted as before.

Mole rubbed his eyes and stared at Rat, who was looking about him in a puzzled sort of way. "I beg your pardon; what did you say, Rat?" he asked.

"I think I was only remarking," said Rat slowly, "that this was the right sort of place, and that here, if anywhere, we should find him. And look! Why, there he is, the little fellow!" And with a cry of delight he ran towards the slumbering Portly.

But Mole stood still a moment, held in thought. As one wakened suddenly from a beautiful dream, who struggles to recall it, and can recapture nothing but a dim sense of the beauty of it, the beauty! Till that, too, fades away in its turn, and the dreamer bitterly accepts the hard, cold waking and all its penalties; so Mole, after struggling with his memory for a brief space, shook his head sadly and followed the Rat.

Portly woke up with a joyous squeak, and wriggled with pleasure at the sight of his father's friends, who had played with him so often in past days. In a moment, however, his face grew blank, and he fell to hunting round in a circle with a pleading whine. As a child that has fallen happily asleep in its nurse's arms, and wakes to find itself alone and laid in a strange place, and searches corners and cupboards, and runs from room to room, despair growing silently in its heart, even so Portly searched the island and searched, dogged and unwearying, till at last the black moment came for giving it up, and sitting down and crying bitterly.

The Mole ran quickly to comfort the little animal; but Rat, lingering, looked long and doubtfully at certain hoofmarks deep in the sward.

"Some—great—animal—has been here," he murmured slowly and thoughtfully, and stood musing, musing, his mind strangely stirred.

"Come along, Rat!" called the Mole. "Think of poor Otter, waiting up there by the ford!"

Portly had soon been comforted by the promise of a treat, a jaunt on the river in Mr. Rat's real boat; and the two animals conducted him to the water's side, placed him securely between them in the bottom of the boat, and paddled off down the backwater. The sun was fully up by now, and hot on them, birds sang lustily and without restraint, and flowers smiled and nodded from either bank, but somehow—so thought the animals—with less of richness and blaze of color than they seemed to remember seeing quite recently somewhere, they wondered where.

The main river reached again, they turned the boat's head upstream, toward the point where they knew their friend was keeping his lonely vigil. As they drew near the familiar ford, the Mole took the boat in to the bank, and they lifted Portly out and set him on his legs on the towpath, gave him his marching orders and a friendly farewell pat on the back, and shoved out into midstream. They watched the little animal as he waddled along the path contentedly and with importance; watched him till they saw his muzzle suddenly lift and his waddle break into a clumsy amble as he quickened his pace with shrill whines and wriggles of recognition. Looking up the river, they could see Otter start up, tense and rigid, from out of the shallows where he crouched in dumb patience, and could hear his amazed and joyous bark as he bounded up through the osiers on to the path. Then the Mole, with a strong pull on one oar, swung the boat round and let the full stream bear them down again whither it would, their quest now happily ended.

"I feel strangely tired, Rat," said the Mole, leaning wearily over his oars as the boat drifted. "I feel as if I had been through something very exciting and rather terrible, and it was just over; and yet nothing particular has happened."

"Or something very surprising and splendid and beautiful," murmured the Rat, leaning back and closing his eyes. "I feel just as you do, Mole; simply dead tired, though not body tired. It's lucky we've got the stream with us, to take us home. Isn't it jolly to feel the sun again, soaking into one's bones! And hark to the wind playing in the reeds!"

"It's like music—faraway music," said the Mole, nodding drowsily.

"So I was thinking," murmured the Rat, dreamful and languid. "Dance music—the lilting sort that runs on without a stop—but with words in it, too—it passes into words and out of them again. I catch them at intervals, then it is dance music once more, and then nothing but the reeds' soft thin whispering."

"You hear better than I," said the Mole sadly. "I cannot catch the words."

"Let me try and give you them," said the Rat softly, his eyes still closed. "Now it is turning into words again, faint but clear. *Lest the awe should dwell—And turn your frolic to fret—You shall look on my power at the helping hour—But then you shall forget!* Now the reeds take it up—*forget, forget,* they sigh, and it dies away in a rustle and a whisper. Then the voice returns—

"*Lest limbs be reddened and rent—I spring the trap that is set—As I loose the snare you may glimpse me there—For surely you shall forget!* Row nearer, Mole, nearer to the reeds! It is hard to catch, and grows each minute fainter.

"*Helper and healer, I cheer—Small waifs in the woodland wet—Strays I find in it, wounds I bind in it—Bidding them all forget!* Nearer, Mole, nearer! No, it is no good; the song has died away into reed talk."

"But what do the words mean?" asked the wondering Mole.

"That I do not know," said the Rat simply. "I passed them on to you as they reached me. Ah! now they return again, and this time full and clear! This time, at last, it is the real, the unmistakable thing, simple—passionate—perfect—"

"Well, let's have it, then," said the Mole, after he had waited patiently for a few minutes, half-dozing in the hot sun.

But no answer came. He looked, and understood the silence. With a smile of much happiness on his face, and something of a listening look still lingering there, the weary Rat was fast asleep.

SALLY BENSON

Phaëthon and the Chariot of the Sun

❨ THE early Greeks and Romans worshiped many of the same gods. Jupiter, as the Romans called him, was believed to live on Mount Olympus and to rule the world. Neptune ruled the sea. Mercury was the messenger of the gods. Vulcan was the god of fire. Apollo, god of light, drove the chariot of the sun across the sky.

WHEN THE world was still very new, there lived a little boy named Phaëthon who was the son of Apollo and the nymph Clymene. He was very proud of his noble birth and boasted about it to his schoolmates. One of them laughed at the idea of an ordinary little boy being the son of a god, and Phaëthon, enraged by his companion's doubt, ran to his mother. "If," he said, "I am indeed of heavenly birth, give me, Mother, some proof of it."

Clymene stretched her arms toward the skies and swore, "I call to witness the Sun that I have told the truth. But it needs not much labor to go and inquire for yourself. The land whence the sun rises lies next to ours. Go and demand of him whether he will own you as his son."

Phaëthon was wild with delight. His mother prepared him for the journey and he traveled to India which lies directly toward the sunrise. Full of

hope, he neared the place where his father began his course each day.

The Palace of the Sun rested on columns of purest gold, set with glittering jewels. The ceilings were made of polished ivory and the doors were of silver. Vulcan had built it for Apollo, and it was the most magnificent thing he had ever made. On the walls the earth, the sea and the skies were represented. In the sea were the nymphs, playing in the waves, riding on the backs of fishes, or lying on rocks drying their soft green hair. The earth was complete in every detail; even the cities, forests and fields were carved out exactly and tinted in glorious colors. Above lay the beautiful heavens, while each door bore the twelve signs of the zodiac, six on each side.

Phaëthon climbed the steep ascent to the palace and entered the hall. He approached his father but was forced to stop, for the light was more than he could bear. Apollo, clad in royal purple robes, sat on a throne encrusted with diamonds. On either side of him stood the Day, the Month, the Year, and at regular intervals, the Hours. Spring was crowned with a garland of flowers. Summer stood with garments cast aside, a wreath made of spears of ripe grain around her neck. Autumn's feet were stained with the juice of purple grapes. And Winter stood stiff and icy, his hair thick with frost.

Apollo, seeing that the boy was dazzled by the splendor, asked him why he had journeyed so far from home.

Phaëthon replied: "O light of the boundless world, Apollo, my father, if you permit me to use that name, give me some proof, I beseech you, by which I may be known as yours."

His father, laying aside the beams that shone all around his head, bade him approach. Then, embracing the boy, he said, "My son, I gladly confirm what your mother has told you. To put an end to your doubts, ask what you will. The gift shall be yours."

It did not take Phaëthon long to think of what he wanted. "Let me for one day, my father," he begged, "drive the chariot of the sun across the sky."

Apollo, aghast at the boy's request, repented his promise. He shook his head in warning. "I have spoken rashly," he said. "This request I would fain deny. I beg you to withdraw it. It is not a safe boon, nor one, my Phaëthon, suited to your youth and strength. Your lot is mortal, and you ask what is beyond a mortal's power. In your ignorance you aspire to do that which not even the gods themselves may do.

None but myself may drive the flaming car of day. Not even Jupiter, whose terrible right arm heaves the thunderbolts."

Drawing the boy to him, he went on: "The first part of the way is steep, and such as the horses fresh in the morning can hardly climb. The middle is high up in the heavens, whence I, myself, can scarcely look down and behold the sea and earth stretched beneath me without alarm. The last part of the road descends rapidly, and requires most careful driving. Tethys, mother of the chief rivers of the earth, who is waiting to receive me, often trembles for me lest I should fall headlong. Add to all this, the heaven is all the time turning around and carrying the stars with it. I have to be perpetually on my guard lest that movement, which sweeps everything along, should hurry me away also.

"Suppose I should lend you the chariot, what would you do? Could you keep your course while the sphere was revolving under you? Perhaps you think that there are forests and cities, the abodes of the gods, and palaces and temples on the way. On the contrary, the road is through the midst of frightful monsters. You pass by the horns of the Bull, in front of the Archer, and near the Lion's jaws, and where the Scorpion stretches its arms in one direction and the Crab in another.

"Nor will you," he said in warning, "find it easy to guide those horses, with their lungs full of fire that they breathe forth from their mouths and nostrils. I can scarcely govern them myself when they are unruly and resist the reins. Beware, my son, lest I be the donor of a fatal gift. Recall your request while yet you may. Do you ask me for proof that you are sprung from my blood? I give my proof in my fears for you. Look at my face. I would that you could look in my heart. You would see all a father's anxiety.

"Finally," he continued, "look around the world and choose whatever you will of what earth and sea contain. Ask it and fear no refusal. This only I pray you not to urge. It is not honor, but destruction you seek. Why do you hang around my neck and still entreat me? You shall have it if you wish, the oath is sworn and must be kept, but I beg you to choose more wisely."

Apollo looked tenderly into his son's eyes, and saw that it was useless to plead with him. Taking him by the hand, he led him to the lofty chariot. It was of gold, the gift of Vulcan. Even the axle was gold, the poles and wheels of gold, while the spokes were made of shining silver. Along the seat, were rows of chrysolites and diamonds, which reflected the brightness of the sun.

Phaëthon, proud and daring, gazed on the chariot with admiration. As he stood there, early Dawn threw open the purple doors of the east, and a pathway lay before him strewn with roses. The stars moved slowly away. Apollo, when he saw the earth beginning to glow and the Moon fade, ordered the Hours to harness up the horses. They led the magnificent steeds forth from the stable full fed with ambrosia, and they attached the reins.

Then Apollo bathed his son's face with a powerful oil to protect him from the brightness of the flame. He set the rays on his head and with a sigh filled with foreboding, said: "My son, spare the whip and hold tight to the reins. The horses go fast enough of their own accord. The labor is to hold them in. You are not to take the straight road directly between the five circles, but turn off to the left. Keep within the limit of the middle zone, and avoid the northern and the southern alike. You will see the marks of the wheels, and they will serve to guide you. And, that the skies and the earth may each receive their due share of heat, go not too high or you will burn the heavenly dwellings, nor too low or you will set the earth on fire. The middle course is safest and best. And now I leave you to your chance, which I hope will plan better for you than you have done for yourself. Night is passing out of the western gates, and we can delay no longer. Take the reins."

Phaëthon sprang lightly into the chariot, stood erect, and grasped the reins. He laughingly shouted thanks to Apollo who stood by sadly. The horses snorted impatiently and stamped their feet. The bars were let down and the boundless plain of the universe lay before him. The horses sprang forward, cleaving the dense clouds, and they outran the morning breezes.

It was not long before the steeds realized that the load they carried was lighter than usual. As a ship without ballast is tossed about on the sea, so the chariot, without its accustomed weight, was dashed about as if empty.

[243]

They rushed headlong and soon left the traveled road. Phaëthon became alarmed and tugged at the reins. But his arms were not strong enough to pull in the maddened horses. Past the Great Bear and Little Bear they sped, scorching them so badly that they would have plunged into the water if that had been possible.

Phaëthon looked down at the earth and he grew pale and his knees shook with terror. He wished that he had never touched his father's horses, never learned his parentage, never begged to drive the chariot. He wanted to kneel and pray, but he did not dare loose the reins. He looked vainly around, back to the goal where he began his mad ride, and ahead to the realms of the sunset. He saw the Scorpion extending his two great arms, his tail and crooked claws stretching over two signs of the Zodiac. His courage failed at the sight of the creature menacing with its fangs, and the reins fell from his hands.

The horses, when they felt them slack on their backs, dashed off into the unknown regions of the sky in among the stars, hurling the chariot over pathless places, now high up in heaven, now down almost to the earth. The clouds began to smoke, and the mountaintops broke into flames. Below, the fields were parched and the plants withered, and the trees were ablaze. The fire spread, and great cities burned. People were trapped in their houses and perished in the flames.

Phaëthon beheld the whole world on fire. The heat was intolerable and the air he breathed was like the air of a furnace. Burning ashes filled the skies. Still the chariot dashed on. The people of Ethiopia became black because of the blood being forced so suddenly to the surface of their skins, and the Libyan desert was dried up to the condition in which it remains to this day. The Nile fled and hid its head in the desert, and there it still hides. The earth cracked open. The sea shrank up, and where there had once been water was now a dry plain; and the mountains beneath the waves lifted their heads and became islands. The fishes sought the lowest depths, and the dolphins no longer ventured to sport on the surface. Three times Neptune tried to raise his head above the water, and three times he was driven back by the heat. The Earth, surrounded by the boiling waters, looked up to heaven and with a voice parched with heat called upon Jupiter.

"O ruler of the gods," she cried, "is this the reward of my fertility, of my obedient service? Is it for this that I have supplied herbage for cattle and fruits for men? But if I am unworthy of regard, what has my brother Ocean done to deserve such a fate? Save yet what remains to us from the devouring flame. O, take thought for our deliverance in this awful moment!"

Overcome with heat and thirst, Earth could say no more. Jupiter, calling to witness all the gods, including Apollo who had lent the chariot, and, showing them that all was lost unless something was done immediately, mounted the high tower from which he sends the clouds abroad and hurls the forked lightnings. Looking about, he could not find a single cloud to interpose for a screen to the earth, nor was there a shower that had not been exhausted. He thundered, and brandishing a lightning bolt in his right hand, launched it against Phaëthon and struck him from the seat. Phaëthon, his hair on fire, fell headlong, like a shooting star. . . .

The earth burned more feebly and soon the fires abated. Apollo caught the reins of the runaway steeds and led them to their stable. Clouds gathered once more and the rain fell to refresh the rivers.

Apollo, sick at heart, mourned the fate of his reckless son. Phaëthon's sisters, the Heliades, mourned for their little brother and were turned into poplar trees on the banks of the river. And as their tears continued to flow they became amber as they dropped into the stream.

❨ THIS *story is from* STORIES OF GODS AND HEROES. *Sally Benson, the author, is also well known for her popular* JUNIOR MISS *stories.*

The Apples of Iduna

LONG AGO in the early days of the world, the gods of the Norsemen lived in a beautiful city called Asgard. It stood on a high plain, on top of a lofty mountain, in the very center of the universe. Its towers and battlements shone among the clouds. Odin, the strong and wise father of the gods, had built this shining city, and here he ruled over gods and men.

Many great palaces and halls rose in Asgard. One belonged to Odin. In this hall Odin had a high seat from which he could look out over the whole world. He looked across the highest mountains and into the deep valleys and beyond the distant seas, and saw all that took place among men. He watched men plowing in their fields and building their houses and fighting their wars.

Odin could look even beyond the realm of men to the dark edges of the world where the giants or Jotuns lived. Their land, which was called Jotunheim, was dark and gloomy, with great mountains and strange valleys. The Frost Giants and Hill Giants fought an unceasing war against the gods. The gods wished men well and strove to make life fair and good. But the giants loved evil and destruction. They wished to bring disaster to the whole world of gods and men.

Thor, the mighty god of thunder, was the son of Odin. Many other gods and goddesses lived in Asgard. There was only one among them who did not desire to bring beauty and healing to the world, and to make the ways of men pleasant and prosperous. This was Loki. He was pleasing to look upon, but in his heart he loved evil. The gods learned to their sorrow how little they could trust him.

Odin often traveled forth from Asgard to take part in the affairs of men and to see what was going on in all the wide expanse of the world. One day he set out on such a journey, taking Loki and Hoenir with him. They wandered a long way over mountains and wasteland, and at length they grew hungry. But food was hard to find in that lonely country. They had walked many miles when they saw a herd of oxen grazing in a valley.

"There is food for us at last," said Hoenir.

They went down into the valley and it was not long before they had one of the oxen roasting on a fire. While their meal cooked they stretched out on the ground to rest. When they thought the meat had cooked long enough they took it off the fire. But it was not yet ready. So they put it back over the embers and waited.

"I can wait no longer," cried Loki at last. "I am starving. Surely the meat is ready."

The gods scattered the fire once more and pulled forth the ox, but it seemed as though it had not even begun to cook. It was certainly not fit for eating. This was a strange thing and not even Odin knew the meaning of it. As they wondered among themselves, they heard a voice speak from the great oak tree above them.

"It is because of me," said the voice, "that there is no virtue in your fire and your meat will not cook."

They looked up into the branches of the tree and there sat a huge eagle. "If you are willing to give me a share of the ox, then it will cook in the fire," said the eagle.

There was little the gods could do but agree to this. The eagle let himself float down from the tree and alighted by the fire. In no time at all the ox was roasted. At once the eagle took to himself the two hindquarters and the two forequarters as well.

This greediness angered Loki. He snatched up a great pole, brandished it with all his strength, and struck the eagle with it. The eagle plunged violently at the blow and whirled into the air. One end of the pole stuck fast to to eagle's back and Loki's hands stuck fast to the other end. No matter how he tried, he could not free them. Swooping and turning, the eagle dragged Loki after him in his flight, flying just low enough that Loki's feet and legs knocked against stones and trees. Loki thought his arms would be torn from his shoulders. He cried out for mercy.

"Put me down! Put me down!" begged Loki. "Free me and you shall have the whole ox for your own."

"I do not want the ox," cried the eagle. "I want only one thing—Iduna and her apples. Deliver them into my power and I will set you free."

Iduna was the beautiful and beloved wife of the god Bragi. She guarded the most precious possession of the gods, the apples of youth. Unless they might eat of them the gods would grow old and feeble like mortal men. They kept the gods ever young. Iduna and her apples were priceless beyond words.

"Iduna and her apples! Such a thing cannot be done," shouted Loki.

"Then I will fly all day," screamed the eagle. "I will knock you against the rocks until you die." And he dragged Loki through rough tree branches and against the sides of mountains and over the rocky earth. Loki could endure it no longer.

"I will do as you ask," he cried. "I will bring Iduna to you, and her apples as well."

"Give me your oath," said the eagle. Loki gave his oath. A time was set when Loki should put Iduna in the eagle's power.

The eagle straightway made Loki free and flew off into the sky. A much-bruised Loki returned to his companions and all three set off on their homeward journey. But Odin and Hoenir did not know the promise which Loki had made.

Loki pondered how he could keep his word to the eagle, whom he now knew to be the giant Thjazi in disguise. When the appointed day came Loki approached Iduna.

"Iduna," he said, "yesterday I found a tree on which grow wondrous apples. It is in the wood to the north of Asgard. They are like your apples in color and shape. Surely they must have the same properties. Should we not gather them and bring them to Asgard?"

"There are no apples anywhere," said Iduna, "like to my apples."

"These are," said Loki. "Come and look for yourself. If you bring your apples we can put them side by side and you will see."

So Iduna went with Loki to the wood, taking her apples with her. While they were in the wood the giant Thjazi swooped down in his eagle's plumage and carried Iduna and her apples off to his abode.

The gods soon missed Iduna. They knew her apples were gone, for the signs of old age began to show among them. They grew bent and stiff and stooped.

Odin called a hasty council of the gods. They asked each other what they knew of Iduna.

"Where was she last seen?" asked Odin.

Heimdal had seen her walking out of Asgard with Loki. That was the last that was known of her.

Odin sent Thor to seize Loki and to bring him to the council. When Loki was brought the gods threatened him with tortures and death unless he told what he knew of Iduna. Loki grew frightened and admitted that Iduna had been carried off to Jotunheim.

"I will go in search of her," he cried, "if Freyja will lend me her falcon wings."

Freyja was more than willing. When Loki had put on the feather dress he flew to the north in the direction of Jotunheim. He flew for a long time before he came to the home of Thjazi, the giant. Then he circled slowly overhead and saw Iduna walking below. She carried in her arms her golden casket of apples. Thjazi was nowhere to be seen, for he had rowed out to sea to fish. Loki quickly alighted on the ground beside Iduna.

"Hasten, Iduna," he cried, "I will rescue you." And he changed Iduna into the shape of a nut and flew off with her in his claws.

Loki had no sooner gone than Thjazi arrived home. At once he missed Iduna and her precious apples. Putting on his eagle's plumage, he flew into the air. Far off in the distance he saw the falcon flying. Instantly he took after him. The eagle's wings beat powerfully, making a deep rushing sound like a great wind. Thjazi drew nearer and nearer to Loki. Loki flew with all his might, but the eagle was bearing down upon the falcon just as the towers of Asgard came into view. With a last burst of strength Loki hastened toward the shining battlements.

The gods were on watch for Loki's return. They saw the falcon bearing

·the nut between his claws, with the eagle in close pursuit. Quickly they built a great pile of wood shavings just outside the wall of Asgard. As Loki came near he swooped down low over the shavings. Thjazi swooped down too, hoping to seize the falcon before he reached the safety of Asgard. Just as the eagle came close to the pile the gods set fire to the shavings. Instantly the fire blazed up, but Thjazi could not stop himself. He plunged into the flames and the feathers of his wings took fire. Then he could fly no more and the gods slew him where he was.

There was great rejoicing within the walls of Asgard to have Iduna safe once more. And the gods grew young and bright again.

The Farmer Saint

([*"This is one of the tales,"* said the Japanese author, *"to which I listened as a little girl on long wintry evenings, as I sat snuggled up close to my grandmother. I can see Honorable Grandmother now, her black eyes smiling as she begins . . ."*

WHO DOES not know Omi Seijin, the youth who gave his best to the farmers of his country?

When Toji, for that was the boy name of the Saint of Omi, waked up at sunrise one winter morning, no one, least of all himself, dreamed that before sunset of that day he would have taken his first step on the long road that leads to lasting fame.

Soon after breakfast Toji was seated at his low desk busily studying.

"Clap—clap—clap!" sounded his uncle's "come" signal. Immediately Toji placed his pen brush in the upright bamboo tube on his desk and, pushing back the silk panel to his uncle's room, bowed low at the door.

Within, seated beside a bronze fire brazier was a man of perhaps forty years of age. He had a scholarly face with kindly eyes and a long beard that was beginning to turn gray. He was holding a partially unrolled letter scroll, the torn envelope of which was lying beside him on the floor.

"What may your errand be, Honorable Uncle?" asked Toji.

"No errand this time, Toji. A message has come from your mother."

Toji's heart gave a bound of joy. For two years he had not seen his mother, whom he loved above everything else on earth. But, as is the courteous Japanese way, Toji simply bowed and patiently waited.

"She speaks," said his uncle, glancing up and down across the page, "of the happiness she has in feeling that you are here and receiving knowledge. And she says that your honored father in the blessed realm beyond the western horizon is also glad."

Toji bowed with close-shut eyes, fearful that his throbbing heart might cause a tear to drop upon the matted floor. And that would make him ashamed.

"The weather must be cold at your home," continued his uncle, unrolling still further the letter scroll, "for your mother speaks of the unsmooth use of her brush pen because of chapped and bleeding fingers from the frost."

For a moment Toji could not hear his uncle's voice. His mother's fingers bleeding from frost? The room where her loom stood was bitter cold, he well knew, for she always had the wooden panels of the porch open in order to give her light. And it was those skillful fingers that gave him not only clothing, but books as well. Oh, would that he could see her! Would that he could help!

The uncle's voice read on. "She is counting much on your progress. She is weaving a new piece of silk that will provide for your new book of Chinese classics. That is all, Toji"; and he rolled up the letter. "You may retire now."

With a bow and a murmured "I thank you, Honorable Uncle," Toji slowly left the room.

As he passed along the narrow porch toward his warm comfortable room, he stopped to look out upon the tiny garden. The snow was falling gently upon the brushwood fence and on the curving branches of a bent pine where the white flakes were building long beautiful ranges of saw-tooth mountains.

"They look like the snowy hilltops of my home," he thought. "How cold indeed it must be there! And Honorable Mother—"

He closed his eyes and saw in thought the mended thatch of the humble farmhouse—the room with the big wooden loom and the paper doors. He could see clearly the snowflakes blowing through the cracks between the porch panels which threw shafts of light on his mother sitting at the loom weaving with her chapped and bleeding hands. He could not stand it! He could not *stand* it!

Quickly he reached his room and, tucking up his pleated skirt on both sides to a shortness which gave freedom for long strides, he put on an extra cotton coat. Then, wrapping in a square of cloth his precious book of Chinese classics, he threw the bundle diagonally over his shoulder and tied the ends in front.

Passing quietly through the rooms, he found the kitchen. His aunt was busy elsewhere with household duties. Taking some cold rice from the wooden rice bucket, he hastily rolled two large balls with a salted plum in each, and wrapping them in a small square of cloth, he tied it in his belt. Then, without saying good-by to anyone, he hurried noiselessly to the shoe-off vestibule. He slipped his bare feet into his straw sandals and tied them on with strips torn from the edge of a towel, thus making them into pilgrim sandals. Then opening his many-ribbed umbrella of oiled paper, he stepped out into the fast falling snow.

It was a long day's journey to the little village with its one long street of thatch-roofed homes. They squatted flatly at the foot of a dreary hillside of dry stubble-filled rice fields. But Toji's mind was bright with memories and anticipation. He was nine years old and he was going home to take care of his mother.

So busy were his thoughts he did not notice that the snow was falling faster. He found himself on a straight country road running through fields of many-shaped rice patches—swampy and empty. At first he overtook many straw-coated farmers pulling two-wheeled carts laden with large wooden buckets of fertilizer for the outlying farms. The men leaned far over the pulling bar as they pushed bare-sandaled feet through the thick wet snow, panting in breathless, regular "Ehs" and resting at intervals. Later on he passed through little one-street villages, the low huts almost buried beneath their top-heavy, wide-eaved thatch, heavy with snow. In one place of many small rice fields, a great lonely water wheel loomed against the sky, its wind-jogging steps piled high with snow.

By-and-by he stopped to rest on the low branch of one of the twisted pines that grew at intervals by the roadside. Wiping the clumps of snow off his bare feet, he knotted tighter his loosened sandal cords. Then, comfortably seated beneath his umbrella roof, he ate his rice-ball lunch, to which the juicy salted plums gave moisture and relish. Then on again he trudged toward the mother he longed to see more and more as each mile was passed. Never should her fingers bleed again! Fast as his brain planned, his hurrying feet went faster still, and the miles fell behind.

The white world was beginning to change to gray when he caught sight of Omi village. A man walking beside an ox wagon turned into the road from one of the four narrow cross streets. He looked at the boy curiously. Toji did not notice him, for just beyond was a low hut with a light shining between the half-closed porch panels, and he heard the steady *chan-kara-chan* of a loom. He forgot his wet garments and his aching feet, and stealing softly to the porch he pushed back a panel and called a soft "I have come!"

The sound of the shuttle ceased. There was a pause, then the paper doors opened and a lady of about thirty, with close-cut widow's hair, stood in the doorway. She was dressed in a gay kimono with a long narrow apron, and her sleeves were looped back with a twisted strip of cotton. With soft, grave eyes she gazed upon the boy standing out in the snow with eager, uplifted face. The flickering shadows and the gray whiteness were a floating mist that blinded her eyes. Her heart cried, "My son! My son!" but with her lips she made no sound. Instead, she turned and quietly took her place at the loom.

"Honorable Mother! Honorable Mother! Do you not recognize your son?" cried poor Toji. But in his heart he knew, suddenly, that he had done wrong.

For a moment his mother's hand held the shuttle a little tremblingly, ready to start it through its path of threads. Then her answer came.

"I have no son here," she said, in a low, steady voice. "My son has no time to come here. He is studying hard with his scholarly uncle in Kyoto. He made a promise to return to me when he completed his seven years of schooling. I am sorry," with a quick breath. "I have no son here."

There was a deep silence save for one jerky gasp. Toji was his mother's son and he understood. He cared much—much—for his mother, but his promise was broken.

For a moment he stood with his head bowed low. Then, without a word, without a glance, he turned, and with a determined look on his young face, walked into the grayness, through the falling snow, and steadily on—on—back to his uncle's distant home. The boy was nine years old.

The mother silently bent over her halted weaving and looked at the pattern through eyes dull with pain.

Seven years later Toji was well known in Kyoto as a tutor in literature. A few years more, and he bade a grateful farewell to his uncle and, declining many splendid offers of honor, made his way to the little Omi village. There he was received with a welcoming feast of red-bean rice and whole fish, served by a mother whose heart swelled with warm and loving pride.

"Here I shall remain," he said. "The worker of land requires not only patience and skill, but talent and thought as well. If knowledge has given me power, my first duty lies in using it for the country which gave me birth."

And so it was that, after years of earnest and intelligent zeal and untiring faithfulness, he brought to the discouraged land of Omi a practical system of irrigation. Like magic it changed the barren hillsides into terraces of fertile fields and rich harvests. Then it spread farther, and farther, carrying a blessing to distant waterless fields, until grateful hearts gave to their benefactor the title known to every schoolboy in Japan—Omi Seijin—the farmer saint.

❦ This story is from PICTURE TALES FROM THE JAPANESE. The author was born in the United States but within a few years was taken to the land of her ancestors. A charming account of her childhood in both countries may be read in her mother's book, A DAUGHTER OF THE SAMURAI.

Mondamin

IN TIMES past a poor Indian was living with his wife and children in a beautiful part of the country. He was not expert at procuring food for his family, and his children were too young to give him much help. His eldest son had now arrived at the proper age to undertake the ceremony of the Ke-ig-uish-im-o-win, or fast, to prove his fitness for manhood, and to see what manner of spirit would be his guide through life. Wunzh, for this was his name, was an obedient boy beloved by the whole family. When spring came they built him the customary little lodge some distance from their own, where he would not be disturbed during this solemn rite.

He immediately went into the lodge and commenced his fast. The first few days he amused himself by walking in the woods, examining the plants and flowers. In this way he prepared himself to enjoy his sleep, and stored his mind with pleasant ideas for his dreams.

He felt a strong desire to know how the plants, herbs, and berries grew without any aid from man, and why it was that some species were good to eat, and others possessed medicinal or poisonous juices. He recalled these thoughts after he became too languid to walk about, and wished he could dream of something that would prove a benefit to his family, and to all others.

"True," he thought, "the Great Spirit made all things, and it is to him that we owe our lives. But could he not make it easier for us to get our food than by hunting animals and taking fish? I must try to find out this in my visions."

On the third day he became weak and faint and kept to his bed. He fancied that he saw a handsome young man coming down from the sky and advancing toward him. He was richly dressed in garments of green and yellow, but differing in their deeper or lighter shades. He had a waving plume on his head, and all the motions were graceful.

"I am sent to you, my friend," said the celestial visitor, "by that Great Spirit who made all things in the sky and on the earth. He knows your motive in fasting. He sees that it is from a benevolent wish to do good to your people."

He then told the young man to arise, and prepare to wrestle with him, as it was only by this means that he could hope to succeed in his wishes. Wunzh was weak from fasting, but he felt his courage rising in his heart, and immediately got up, determined to die rather than fail. He commenced the trial, and after a protracted effort, was almost exhausted.

Then the beautiful stranger said "My friend, it is enough for once; I will come again to try you." Smiling on him, he ascended in the air.

The next day the celestial visitor reappeared and renewed the trial. Wunzh felt that his strength was even less than the day before, but the courage of his mind seemed to increase in proportion as his body became weaker. Seeing this, the stranger said, "Be strong, my friend, for this is the only way you can overcome me, and obtain the boon you seek."

On the third day he again appeared and renewed the struggle. The youth was faint in body, but determined to prevail. He exerted his utmost powers, and after the contest had been continued the usual time, the stranger declared himself conquered. Sitting down beside the youth, he told him in what manner he should proceed to take advantage of his victory.

"You have won your desire of the Great Spirit," said the stranger. "You have wrestled manfully. Tomorrow I shall meet you and wrestle with you for the last time. As soon as you have prevailed against me, you will strip off my garments and throw me down, clean the earth of roots and weeds, make it soft, and bury me in the spot. When you have done this, leave my body in the earth. Do not disturb it, but come occasionally to visit the place, to see whether I have come to life, and be careful never to let the grass or weeds grow on my grave. Once a month cover me with fresh earth. If you follow my instructions, you will accomplish your object of doing good to your fellow creatures by teaching them the knowledge I now teach you." He then disappeared.

In the morning the youth's father came with some slight refreshment, saying: "My son, you have fasted long enough. If the Great Spirit will favor you, he will do it now. It is seven days since you have tasted food, and you must not sacrifice your life. The Master of Life does not require that."

"My father," replied the youth, "wait till the sun goes down. I have a particular reason for extending my fast."

At the usual hour of the day the sky visitor returned, and the trial of strength was renewed. Although the youth had not availed himself of his father's offer of food, he grasped his angelic antagonist with supernatural strength, threw him down, and took from him his beautiful garments and plume. Finding him dead, he buried him on the spot, confident that his friend would again come to life.

He then returned to his father's lodge, and partook sparingly of the meal that had been prepared for him. But he never forgot the grave of his friend. He visited it throughout the spring, and carefully weeded out the grass, and kept the ground in a soft and pliant state. Soon he saw the tops of the green plumes coming through

[255]

the ground; and the more careful he was to keep the ground in order, the faster they grew.

Days and weeks passed. Summer was drawing toward a close, when one day, after a long absence in hunting, Wunzh invited his father to follow him to the quiet spot of his former fast. The lodge had been removed, but in its place stood a tall, graceful plant, with bright-colored silken hair, surmounted with nodding plumes and stately leaves, and golden clusters on each side.

"It is my friend," shouted the lad. "It is the friend of all mankind. It is Mondamin."

He then pulled an ear of corn. "See, my father," said he, "this is what I fasted for. The Great Spirit has listened to my voice, and sent us something new. We need no longer rely on hunting alone. As long as this gift is cherished and taken care of, the ground itself will give us a living."

He then communicated to his father the instructions given him by the stranger. The broad husks must be torn away, as he had pulled off the garments in his wrestling. Then the ear must be held before the fire till the outer skin became brown, while all the milk was retained in the grain.

The whole family then united in a feast on the newly grown ears, expressing gratitude to the Merciful Spirit who gave it.

Thus corn came into the world.

❨ THIS *legend of the Ojibway Indians is from* INDIAN TALES AND LEGENDS. *The author, more than a century ago, spent much time among the red men, studying their beliefs and collecting their myths. His writings were studied by Henry Wadsworth Longfellow, author of "Hiawatha."*

THE BOOK OF

Poetry

Introduction

❪ In the beginning, nearly every child likes poetry. He enjoys the measured flow of rhythmic sentences. The world is still new to him and, like the poet, he sees it with fresh eyes. He is fortunate if this enthusiasm is nourished by the introduction of many new poems into his reading as he grows older. His pleasure is keener, as it is for the older members of the household, if the reading is done aloud. Poetry is intended primarily to be heard, and there are many poems that provide a common meeting ground for listeners of varied ages.

This is true of some of our loveliest nature lyrics. A family may find a oneness of interest "under the open sky" of which William Cullen Bryant spoke. All the members can share in the wonder evoked by A. E. Housman's "cherry hung with snow," in the poignant beauty Edna St. Vincent Millay found in "God's World," and in the mystery of birds winging their way south in Rachel Field's "Something Told the Wild Geese." Parents and children alike feel a sweet concern for the little colt in "The Runaway," by Robert Frost, and they are touched with compassion for the "Four Little Foxes," movingly described by Lew Sarett.

Many poems which celebrate the triumph of the human spirit know no barriers of age. Young people and older ones alike respond to the courage of Helen Keller, blind and deaf since childhood, in her verses "In the Garden of the Lord." They thrill to the magnificent story of "The Creation," by James Weldon Johnson, and to the even more magnificent Psalms. The philosophies of Emily Dickinson or Sara Teasdale or Christina Rossetti may be sensed,

[259]

even if not fully understood. The vigorous, marching lines of Whit-man's "Miracles" are for everyone.

Even the poetry written for children is not limited to them. Some of the outstanding writers of recent years—Walter de la Mare, Rachel Field, Eleanor Farjeon, and Elizabeth Madox Roberts—succeeded in capturing that elusive quality of childhood that appeals to the child in each of us. Aileen Fisher, among others, has shown how a small girl's delight or a small boy's wonderings can touch the most ordinary happenings with a kind of magic. Robert Louis Stevenson's A Child's Garden of Verses *is replete with happy memories. When this book was first published nearly three-quarters of a century ago, the effect was that of a fresh wind blowing. Until that time, most of the verses intended for "the little ladies and gentlemen" of the day were very dull. Their purpose was to teach a lesson. Stevenson dared to express the joy that he felt was the rightful heritage of every child. To him, writing for children was fun. "You just indulge the pleasure of your heart; that's all," he said. He set an inspired precedent.*

A half century earlier Edward Lear had set another precedent. His first Book of Nonsense *was followed some years later by Lewis Carroll's* Alice in Wonderland, *which included some of the funniest rhymes in the English language. They knew, as did our own American Laura E. Richards, that even very small children like to hear funny words that can be rolled under the tongue. The new words coined by Ogden Nash and some of his highly original rhymes and rhythms have set readers of all ages to chuckling.*

We all need to laugh. We need to have our esthetic senses sharpened. We need to lose ourselves in the singing words of a lyric, to be stirred by an old ballad, to find inspiration in some poet's testament of courage. A good poem refreshes us. It says for us what we would like to say.

"All men are poets at heart," said Ralph Waldo Emerson. Poems lie deep within our thoughts, but most of us have no words to express them. The poets find the words for us. And the words are words that sing. If a poem lifts our spirits, that poem is for us. It adds a new dimension to our own world.

DARK-EYED LAD
COLUMBUS
Nancy Byrd Turner

When the dark-eyed lad, Columbus,
   Saw the white sails dip and gleam,
Slanting, swaying down the harbor,
   In his heart he dreamed a dream.

"I will some day be a sailor!
   I will have a ship!" he cried.
"I will sail and sail the ocean
   Till I reach the other side."

So he dreamed and so he waited,
   And the dream came true, we know.
Now we name his name with singing,
   Dark-eyed lad of long ago.

WASHINGTON
Nancy Byrd Turner

He played by the river when he was
   young,
He raced with rabbits along the hills,
He fished for minnows, and climbed
   and swung,
And hooted back at the whippoorwills.
Strong and slender and tall he grew—

And then, one morning, the bugles
   blew.

Over the hills the summons came,
Over the river's shining rim.
He said that the bugles called his
   name,
He knew that his country needed him,
And he answered, "Coming!" and
   marched away
For many a night and many a day.

Perhaps when the marches were hot
   and long
He'd think of the river flowing by
Or, camping under the winter sky,
Would hear the whippoorwill's far-off
   song.
Boy and soldier, in peace or strife,
He loved America all his life!

IN PHILADELPHIA, 1723
Marjorie Knapp

Young Deborah Reed stood at her
   father's door
And watched a strange young man
   come down the street.

[261]

She thought her eye had never chanced
    to meet
Anyone quite so singular before,
Awkward, ridiculous. A roll of bread
Was snugly tucked beneath each arm.
    A third,
The youth was busy eating. What she
    said
Low to herself, he certainly never
    heard.

Weary and hungry, he was too intent
On food to notice who might see him
    pass,
Delighted that with only threepence
    spent
He had three puffy rolls. Smile on, my
    lass!
Your laughter cannot fret this stalwart
    lad.
For seventeen years his eyes have
    opened wide
On all the world around him. He has
    had
More than a boy's experience. See his
    pride
Of bearing, all unconscious of your
    eyes!
His appetite is hearty? No mistaking
That he's a boy? You will find him wise
Beyond his years, a great man in the
    making.

O Deborah, you'll be learning after a
    while
Who the boy is and who will be his
    wife,

And so we watch, and smile to see you
    smile
The day Ben Franklin walks into your
    life.

LETTERS FROM DOROTHEA
Ethel Barnett de Vito

Dear Friend: Such strange things do
    occur!
My mother's boarder, Aaron Burr,
Hath said James Madison asked to be
Allowed to come and call on me.
Does this not seem to thee quite odd?
Thy true friend, Mrs. D. Payne Todd.

Dear Friend: He hath a courtly grace,
A merry wit, a handsome face;
And, friend, he asked to call again!
Thy dear friend, Dorothea Payne.

Dear Friend: He said I can beguile
And quite confuse him with a smile.
Imagine this from one who may
Be in the Cabinet one day!
He is indeed most kind to me.
Affectionately, Dolly P.

Dear Friend: He is so good, so wise,
And hath such twinkling merry eyes,
And such rare judgment, such fine wit,
I shall be quite content to sit
By him forever and anon.
Thy good friend, Dolly Madison

AMERICA! AMERICA!
Katharine Lee Bates

America! America!
God shed His grace on thee
And crown thy good with brotherhood
From sea to shining sea!

FROM "America the Beautiful"

ABRAHAM LINCOLN
Mildred Plew Meigs

Remember he was poor and country-
bred;
His face was lined; he walked with
awkward gait.
Smart people laughed at him sometimes and said,
"How can so very plain a man be
great?"

Remember he was humble, used to
toil.
Strong arms he had to build a shack,
a fence,
Long legs to tramp the woods, to plow
the soil,
A head chuck full of backwoods common sense.

Remember all he ever had he earned.
He walked in time through stately
White House doors;
But all he knew of men and life he
learned

In little backwoods cabins, country
stores.

Remember that his eyes could light
with fun;
That wisdom, courage, set his name
apart;
But when the rest is duly said and
done,
Remember that men loved him for
his heart.

THE FLOWER-FED BUFFALOES
Vachel Lindsay

The flower-fed buffaloes of the spring
In the days of long ago,
Range where the locomotives sing
And the prairie flowers lie low.

The tossing, blooming, perfumed grass
Is swept away by the wheat;
Wheels and wheels and wheels spin by
In the spring that still is sweet.

But the flower-fed buffaloes of the
spring
Left us long ago.
They gore no more, they bellow no
more,
They trundle around the hills no more

With the Blackfeet, lying low,

With the Pawnees, lying low,
Lying low.

THY NAME SHALL SHINE
Sidney Lanier

Long as thine art shall love true love,
Long as thy science truth shall know,
Long as thine eagle harms no dove,
Long as thy law by law shall grow,
Long as thy God is God above,
Thy brother every man below,
So long, dear land of all my love,
Thy name shall shine, thy fame shall
grow.

FROM "The Centennial Ode" (1876)

EARLY AMERICAN
Gail Brook Burket

He had five wives or was it seven? Who
Is certain now which tale is really true?
His tribe fought, lost, and yielded to
the one
Great paleface chieftain down in
Washington.
The stern commissioner told him
alone,
In what he hoped was an official tone,
"Our laws permit one wife to every
man.
Big Chief is now a good American,
So tell your wives that, starting from
today,
You must choose one and send the rest
away."
The brave put on a face benign and
mild.

"White man tell squaws himself," he
said, and smiled.

This poem is based on a true incident in
the life of a Comanche Indian chief and his
reply to the American commander who had
defeated him.

V. I. P.
Gail Brook Burket

He isn't any smarter, but
He puts his brains to use;
So he's the engine on the train,
Instead of the caboose.

ELETELEPHONY
Laura E. Richards

Once there was an elephant,
Who tried to use the telephant—
No! No! I mean an elephone

Who tried to use the telephone—
(Dear me! I am not certain quite
That even now I've got it right.)

Howe'er it was, he got his trunk
Entangled in the telephunk;
The more he tried to get it free,
The louder buzzed the telephee—
(I fear I'd better drop the song
Of elephop and telephong!)

A NEW SONG TO SING ABOUT JONATHAN BING
Beatrice Curtis Brown

O Jonathan Bing, O Bingathon Jon
Forgets where he's going and thinks
    he has gone.
He wears his false teeth on the top of
    his head,
And always stands up when he's sleep-
    ing in bed.

O Jonathan Bing has a curious way
Of trying to walk into yesterday.
"If I end with my breakfast and start
    with my tea,
I ought to be able to do it," says he.

O Jonathan Bing is a miser, they say,
For he likes to save trouble and put it
    away.
"If I never get up in the morning," he
    said,

"I shall save all the trouble of going to
    bed!"

"O Jonathan Bing! What a way to be-
    have!
And what do you do with the trouble
    you save?"
"I wrap it up neatly and send it by post
To my friends and relations who need
    it the most."

THE CROCODILE
Lewis Carroll

How doth the little crocodile
Improve his shining tail
And pour the waters of the Nile
On every shining scale.

How cheerfully he seems to grin,
How neatly spreads his claws,
And welcome little fishes in
With gently smiling jaws!

HOW TO GET WHAT YOU WANT FOR CHRISTMAS
Aileen Fisher

Once there was an antelope
who said, "I'll write to Santa Clope."
"You mean, my son, to Santa *Claus*,"
his mother told the antelaus.

[266]

"I know. But, Mom, it never rhymes—
I've tried it half a dozen times!"
And so he wrote: "Dear Santa Climes,
do you have skates for antelimes?"

"My son, see here, this will not do,"
his mother told the anteloo.
"It's Santa *Claus!* Now try again."
And so he wrote, "Dear Santa Clen,
I'd like some skates, I'd like a sled."
"No, no," said Mrs. Anteled,
"It's Santa *Claus,* not Clope or Cled,
Come, quit this joke, and go to bed!"

The outcome is that Santa Claus,
not hearing from the antelaus,
Forgot to think of sleds and skates
and just brought flannel-underwates!
Which makes me, friends, in your be-
    half
compose this final paragraph:
Sometimes it's best to stick to prose
in writing notes to Santa Close!

LIMERICKS
Edward Lear

There was a young farmer of Leeds,
Who swallowed six packets of seeds.
    It soon came to pass
    He was covered with grass,
And he couldn't sit down for the
    weeds.

There once was a boy of Bagdad,
An inquisitive sort of a lad.
    He said, "I will see
    If a sting has a bee."
And he very soon found that it had.

There was a young maid who said,
    "Why
Can't I look in my ear with my eye?
    If I give my mind to it,
    I'm sure I can do it.
You never can tell till you try."

THE HIPPOPOTAMUS
Ogden Nash

Behold the hippopotamus!
We laugh at how he looks to us,
And yet in moments dank and grim
I wonder how we look to him.
Peace, peace, thou hippopotamus!
We really look all right to us,
As you no doubt delight the eye
Of other hippopotami.

THE PANCAKE
Florence Page Jaques

Once there was a pancake
    Made in a house,
But it hid from the cook,
    And quick as a mouse

It slipped down the steps,
    It skipped down the walk,
It ran and it ran,
    And it didn't stop to talk!

[267]

It got itself some honey
  From a honeybee,
And butter from a buttercup,
  And treacle from a tree.

It found a little grassy place,
  Shaped like a cup,
And it sat right down and
  It ate itself up!

REFLECTION
Eunice Tietjens

I'm glad I'm not the President
And very glad I'm not a king.
There's something grand about them,
  but
They're blamed for everything.

WELCOME TO THE NEW YEAR
Eleanor Farjeon

Hey, my lad, ho, my lad!
   Here's a New Broom.
Heaven's your housetop
   And Earth is your room.

Tuck up your shirtsleeves,
   There's plenty to do—
Look at the muddle
   That's waiting for you!

Dust in the corners
   And dirt on the floor,
Cobwebs still clinging
   To window and door.

Hey, my lad, ho, my lad!
   Nimble and keen—
Here's your New Broom, my lad!
   See you sweep clean.

ST. VALENTINE
Eunice Tietjens

I'm sure I don't know who he was,
The saint whose name was Valentine;

Nor what he could have done to cause
A holiday like yours and mine.

But this I do know: he was kind
And people loved him near and far;
So when he died they had a mind
To keep him in the calendar.

He must have been a man who knew
A lot of secrets everywhere
But never told—just laughed and drew
A frilly pattern in the air.

And when at dusk he walked the town,
Shy lovers curtsied as he passed,
And children, as the dark came down,
Ran to his hand and held it fast.

PADDY BOY
Aileen Fisher

Oh, what's the smile for, Paddy boy,
that goes from ear to ear?
Sure, don't you know what day it is?
St. Patrick's Day is here!

And what's the green for, Paddy boy,
the wearing of the green?

[269]

It's tokening the Emerald Isle—
the greenest place you've seen.

And what's the shamrock, Paddy boy,
with leaves that come in three?
And don't you know that illustrates
the Holy Trinity!

And what's the song for, Paddy boy,

The lily straight and tall—
So like the flowers, dewy, still,
   In that old garden on a hill,
   The first Easter of all.

I think the light, that morning, fell
   In the same lovely way
On petal, leaf, and lifting bell,
   As the light falls today;

that sets the day apart,
'Tis just the Irish joy of me
a-bursting from my heart.

That violets looked gently up,
   Hearing the dawn-wind's call,
And dew was in a crocus cup
   And fragrance in a lily cup,
In that old garden long ago,
   That first Easter of all.

THE FLOWERS OF EASTER
Nancy Byrd Turner

They have come back to field and hill,
   To garden and to wood,
The crocus and the daffodil,
   The violet in her hood,
The mignonette, the pansy blue,

MAY DAY
Aileen Fisher

I'd like to spend May Day
Sitting on a hill

With a mushroom for a parasol,
And violets for a frill,

And the blossoms in the treetops
For gay balloons
And the wind for a violin
To play spring tunes.

ESCAPE AT BEDTIME
Robert Louis Stevenson

The lights from the parlor and the
    kitchen shone out
    Through the blinds and the windows
    and bars;
And high overhead and all moving
    about,
    There were thousands of millions of
    stars.

There ne'er were such thousands of
    leaves on a tree,
    Nor of people in church or the park,
As the crowds of the stars that looked
    down upon me,
    And that glittered and winked in the
    dark.

The Dog, and the Plough, and the
    Hunter, and all,
    And the Star of the Sailor, and Mars,
These shone in the sky, and the pail
    by the wall
    Would be half full of water and
    stars.

They saw me at last, and they chased
    me with cries,
    And they soon had me packed into
    bed;
But the glory kept shining and bright
    in my eyes,
    And the stars going round in my
    head.

THE LITTLE WHISTLER
Frances M. Frost

My mother whistled softly,
My father whistled bravely,
My brother whistled merrily,
And I tried all day long!
I blew my breath inwards,
I blew my breath outwards,
But all you heard was breath blowing
And not a bit of song!

But today I heard a bluebird,
A happy, young, and new bird,
Whistling in the apple tree—
He'd just discovered how!
Then quick I blew my breath in,
And gay I blew my breath out,
And sudden I blew three wild notes—
And I can whistle now!

A KITTEN
Eleanor Farjeon

He's nothing much but fur

And two round eyes of blue,
He has a giant purr
And a midget mew.

He darts and pats the air,
He starts and cocks his ear,
When there is nothing there
For him to see and hear.

He runs around in rings,
But why we cannot tell;
With sideways leaps he springs
At things invisible—

Then halfway through a leap
His startled eyeballs close,
And he drops off to sleep
With one paw on his nose.

BACK, BUSTER!
Dorothy Brown Thompson

Back, Buster, do!
School's not for you—
A pretty pass
With you in class!
Go in the gate,
You'll make me late!
I know it's hard—
Stay in that yard!
All summer long
It wasn't wrong
To go; but today
You've got to stay.
No, I'm not mad—
See, here's my hand—
Don't look so sad.
Please understand!
You just can't go—
No, Buster, NO!

WHAT DOES THE BEE DO?
Christina Rossetti

What does the bee do?
  Bring home honey.
What does Father do?
  Bring home money.
And what does Mother do?
  Lay out the money.
And what does Baby do?
  Eat up the honey.

HALLOWEEN
Marie Lawson

"Granny, I saw a witch go by,
I saw two, I saw three!
I heard their skirts go swish, swish,
    swish—"

"*Child, 'twas leaves against the sky,
And the autumn wind in the tree.*"

"Granny, broomsticks they bestrode,

Their hats were black as tar,
And buckles twinkled on their shoes—"

"You saw but shadows on the road,
The sparkle of a star."

"Granny, all their heels were red,
Their cats were big as sheep.
I heard a bat say to an owl—"

"Child, you must go straight to bed,
'Tis time you were asleep."

"Granny, I saw men in green,
Their eyes shone fiery red,
Their heads were yellow pumpkins—"

"Now you've told me what you've seen,
WILL you go to bed?"

"Granny?"
"Well?"
"Don't you believe—?"
"What?"
"What I've seen?
Don't you know it's Halloween?"

THEME IN YELLOW
Carl Sandburg

I spot the hills
With yellow balls in autumn.
I light the prairie cornfields
Orange and tawny gold clusters
And I am called pumpkins.

On the last of October
When the dusk is fallen
Children join hands
And circle around me
Singing ghost songs
And love to the harvest moon;
I am a jack-o'-lantern
With terrible teeth
And the children know
I am fooling.

A THANKSGIVING GRACE

For food and all Thy gifts of love
　　We give Thee thanks and praise,
Look down, O Father, from above,
　　And bless us all our days.

THANKSGIVING MAGIC
Rowena Bastin Bennett

Thanksgiving Day I like to see
Our cook perform her witchery.
She turns a pumpkin into pie
As easily as you or I
Can wave a hand or wink an eye.
She takes leftover bread and muffin
And changes them to turkey stuffin'.
She changes cranberries to sauce
And meats to stews and stews to broths,
And when she mixes gingerbread
It turns into a man instead
With frosting collar 'round his throat
And raisin buttons down his coat.

[273]

Oh, some like magic made by wands,
And some read magic out of books,
And some like fairy spells and charms
But I like magic made by cooks!

THE FRIENDLY BEASTS
Old Carol

Jesus our brother, strong and good,
Was humbly born in a stable rude,
The friendly beasts around him stood,
Jesus our brother, strong and good.

"I," said the donkey, shaggy and
brown,
"I carried His mother up hill and
down,
I carried her safely to Bethlehem town;
I," said the donkey, shaggy and brown.

"I," said the cow all white and red,
"I gave Him my manger for His bed,
I gave Him my hay to pillow His head,
I," said the cow all white and red.

"I," said the sheep with curly horn,
"I gave Him my wool for His blanket
warm,
He wore my coat on Christmas morn;
I," said the sheep with curly horn.

"I," said the dove, from the rafters high,
"Cooed Him to sleep, my mate and I
We cooed Him to sleep, my mate and I;
I," said the dove, from the rafters high.

And every beast, by some good spell,

In the stable dark was glad to tell,
Of the gift he gave Immanuel,
The gift he gave Immanuel.

CRADLE HYMN
Martin Luther

Away in a manger,
No crib for a bed,
The little Lord Jesus
Laid down His sweet head;
The stars in the heavens
Looked down where He lay,
The little Lord Jesus
Asleep on the hay.

The cattle are lowing,
The baby awakes,
But little Lord Jesus
No crying He makes.
I love Thee, Lord Jesus,
Look down from the sky,
And stay by my side
Till morning is nigh.

WHAT CAN I GIVE HIM?
Christina Rossetti

What can I give Him,
Poor as I am?
If I were a shepherd
I would bring a lamb,
If I were a Wise Man
I would do my part—
Yet what can I give Him,
Give my heart.

UNDER THE OPEN SKY
William Cullen Bryant

Go forth, under the open sky, and list
to Nature's teachings. . . .

FROM "Thanatopsis"

OUT OF THE MORNING
Emily Dickinson

Will there really be a morning?
Is there such a thing as day?
Could I see it from the mountains
If I were as tall as they?

Has it feet like water lilies?
Has it feathers like a bird?
Is it brought from famous countries
Of which I have never heard?

Oh, some scholar! Oh, some sailor!
Oh, some wise man from the skies!
Please to tell a little pilgrim
Where the place called morning lies!

ALL THINGS THAT LOVE THE SUN
William Wordsworth

There was a roaring in the wind all
    night;

The rain came heavily and fell in
    floods;
But now the sun is rising calm and
    bright;
The birds are singing in the distant
    woods;
Over his own sweet voice the stock
    dove broods . . .

All things that love the sun are out-of-
    doors;
The sky rejoices in the morning's birth;
The grass is bright with raindrops; on
    the moors
The hare is running races in her mirth;
And with her feet she from the plashy
    earth
Raises a mist that, glittering in the sun,
Runs with her all the way, wherever
    she doth run.

FROM "Resolution and Independence"

THE NIGHT WILL NEVER STAY
Eleanor Farjeon

The night will never stay,
The night will still go by,
Though with a million stars

[275]

You pin it to the sky;
Though you bind it with the blowing
    wind
And buckle it with the moon,
The night will slip away
Like sorrow or a tune.

THE LINNET
Walter de la Mare

Upon this leafy bush
    With thorns and roses in it,
Flutters a thing of light,
    A twittering linnet.
And all the throbbing world
    Of dew and sun and air
By this small parcel of life
    Is made more fair;
As if each bramble spray
    And mounded gold-wreathed furze,
Harebell and little thyme,
    Were only hers;
As if this beauty and grace
    Did to one bird belong,
And, at a flutter of wing,
    Might vanish in song.

CHILD'S SONG IN SPRING
E. Nesbit

The silver birch is a dainty lady,
    She wears a satin gown;

The elm tree makes the old church-
    yard shady,
    She will not live in town.

The English oak is a sturdy fellow,
    He gets his green coat late;
The willow is smart in a suit of yellow,
    While brown the beech trees wait.

Such a gay green gown God gives the
    larches—
    As green as He is good!
The hazels hold up their arms for
    arches
    When Spring rides through the
    wood.

The chestnut's proud, and the lilac's
    pretty,
    The poplar's gentle and tall,
But the plane tree's kind to the poor
    dull city.
    I love him best of all.

THE CLOUD
Percy Bysshe Shelley

I bring fresh showers for the thirsting
    flowers,
    From the seas and the streams;
I bear light shade for the leaves when
    laid
    In their noonday dreams.
From my wings are shaken the dews
    that waken

The sweet buds every one,
When rocked to rest on their mother's
  breast
As she dances about the sun.
I wield the flail of the lashing hail,
  And whiten the green plains under,
And then again I dissolve it in rain,
  And laugh as I pass in thunder. . . .

FOUR LITTLE FOXES
Lew Sarett

Speak gently, Spring, and make no sudden sound;
For in my windy valley, yesterday I
  found
Newborn foxes squirming on the
  ground—
  Speak gently.

Walk softly, March, forbear the bitter
  blow;
Her feet within a trap, her blood upon
  the snow,
The four little foxes saw their mother
  go—
  Walk softly.

Go lightly, Spring, oh, give them no
  alarm;
When I covered them with boughs to
  shelter them from harm,
The thin blue foxes suckled at my
  arm—
  Go lightly.

Step softly, March, with your rampant
  hurricane;
Nuzzling one another, and whimpering with pain,
The new little foxes are shivering in
  the rain—
  Step softly.

LOVELIEST OF TREES
A. E. Housman

Loveliest of trees, the cherry now
Is hung with bloom along the bough,
And stands about the woodland ride
Wearing white for Eastertide.

Now, of my threescore years and ten,
Twenty will not come again,
And take from seventy springs a score,
It only leaves me fifty more.

And since to look at things in bloom
Fifty springs are little room,
About the woodlands I will go
To see the cherry hung with snow.

A DAY IN JUNE
James Russell Lowell

And what is so rare as a day in June?

[277]

Then, if ever, come perfect days;
Then Heaven tries earth if it be in
tune,
And over it softly her warm ear lays;
Whether we look or whether we listen,
We hear life murmur, or see it glisten;
Every clod feels a stir of might,
An instinct within it that reaches and
towers,
And, groping blindly above it for light,
Climbs to a soul in grass and flow-
ers . . .
We sit in the warm shade and feel
quite well
How the sap creeps up and the blos-
soms swell;
We may shut our eyes, but we cannot
help knowing
That skies are clear and grass is grow-
ing.

FROM "The Vision of Sir Launfal"

PUCK'S SONG
William Shakespeare

Where the bee sucks, there suck I;
In a cowslip's bell I lie;
There I couch when owls do cry,
On the bat's back I do fly
After summer merrily;
Merrily, merrily shall I live now,
Under the blossom that hangs on the
bough.

[278]

FIREFLY
Elizabeth Madox Roberts

A little light is going by,
Is going up to see the sky,
A little light with wings.

I never could have thought of it,
To have a little bug all lit
And made to go on wings.

SEPTEMBER
Helen Hunt Jackson

The goldenrod is yellow;
The corn is turning brown;
The trees in apple orchards
With fruit are bending down.
The gentian's bluest fringes
Are curling in the sun;
In dusty pods the milkweed
Its hidden silk has spun.

The sedges flaunt their harvest
In every meadow nook;
And asters by the brookside
Make asters in the brook.
From dewy lanes at morning
The grapes' sweet odors rise;
At noon the roads all flutter
With yellow butterflies.

By all these lovely tokens
September days are here,

With summer's best of weather
And autumn's best of cheer.

GOD'S WORLD
Edna St. Vincent Millay

O World, I cannot hold thee close
    enough!
    Thy winds, thy wide gray skies!
    Thy mists that roll and rise!
Thy woods, this autumn day, that ache
    and sag
And all but cry with color! That gaunt
    crag
To crush! To lift the lean of that black
    bluff!
World, World, I cannot get thee close
    enough!

Long have I known a glory in it all,
    But never knew I this;
    Here such a passion is
As stretcheth me apart. Lord, I do fear
Thou'st made the world too beautiful
    this year.
My soul is all but out of me—let fall
No burning leaf; prithee, let no bird
    call.

SOMETHING TOLD THE WILD GEESE
Rachel Field

Something told the wild geese

It was time to go.
Though the fields lay golden
    Something whispered, "Snow."
Leaves were green and stirring,
    Berries, luster-glossed,
But beneath warm feathers
    Something cautioned, "Frost."
All the sagging orchards
    Steamed with amber spice,
But each wild breast stiffened
    At remembered ice.
Something told the wild geese
    It was time to fly—
Summer sun was on their wings,
    Winter in their cry.

THE RUNAWAY
Robert Frost

Once when the snow of the year was
    beginning to fall,
We stopped by a mountain pasture to
    say, "Whose colt?"
A little Morgan had one forefoot on
    the wall,
The other curled at his breast. He
    dipped his head
And snorted at us. And then he had
    to bolt.
We heard the miniature thunder when
    he fled,
And we saw him, or thought we saw
    him, dim and gray,
Like a shadow against the curtain of
    falling flakes.

"I think the little fellow's afraid of the snow.
He isn't winter-broken. It isn't play
With the little fellow at all. He's running away.
I doubt if even his mother could tell him, 'Sakes,
It's only weather.' He'd think she didn't know!
Where is his mother? He can't be out alone."

Ought to be told to come and take him in."

WINTER
Robert Louis Stevenson

In rigorous hours, when down the iron lane
The redbreast looks in vain
For hips and haws,
Lo, shining flowers upon my window-

And now he comes again with clatter of stone,
And mounts the wall again with whited eyes
And all his tail that isn't hair up straight.
He shudders his coat as if to throw off flies.
"Whoever it is that leaves him out so late,
When other creatures have gone to stall and bin,

pane
The silver pencil of the winter draws.

When all the snowy hill
And the bare woods are still;
When snipes are silent in the frozen bogs,
And all the garden garth is whelmed in mire,
Lo, by the hearth, the laughter of the logs—
More fair than roses, lo, the flowers of fire!

WRITTEN WITH STARS
Gail Brook Burket

World beyond shining world,
Inscribing ancient space,
The book of night confounds
The fragile human race.

Yet he who scans the sky
Is greater than a star.
Each page of night proclaims
How glorious we are.

BEAUTY
E Yeh-Shure (Louisa Abeita)

Beauty is seen
In the sunlight,
The trees, the birds,
Corn growing and people working
Or dancing for their harvest.

Beauty is heard
In the night,
Wind sighing, rain falling,
Or a singer chanting
Anything in earnest.

Beauty is in yourself.
Good deeds, happy thoughts
That repeat themselves
In your dreams,
In your work,
And even in your rest.

This poem by a Pueblo Indian girl, whose name means "blue corn," was written when she was twelve years old.

A JOY FOREVER
John Keats

A thing of beauty is a joy forever:
Its loveliness increases; it will never
Pass into nothingness; but still will
    keep
A bower quiet for us, and a sleep
Full of sweet dreams . . .

FROM "Endymion"

THE COIN
Sara Teasdale

Into my heart's treasury
    I slipped a coin

[281]

That time cannot take
　　Nor a thief purloin—
Oh, better than the minting
　　Of a gold-crowned king
Is the safe-kept memory
　　Of a lovely thing.

MOTHER TO SON
Langston Hughes

Well, son, I'll tell you:
Life for me ain't been no crystal stair,
It's had tacks in it,
And splinters,
And boards torn up,
And places with no carpet on the
　　floor—
Bare.
But all the time
I'se been a-climbin' on,
And reachin' landin's,
And turnin' corners,
And sometimes goin' in the dark
Where there ain't been no light.
So, boy, don't you turn back.
Don't you set down on the steps
'Cause you finds it kinder hard.
Don't you fall now—
For I'se still goin', honey,
I'se still climbin',
And life for me ain't been no crystal
　　stair.

[282]

THE SECRET HEART
Robert P. Tristram Coffin

Across the years he could recall
His father one best way of all.

In the stillest hour of night
The boy awakened to a light.

Half in dreams he saw his sire
With his great hands full of fire.

The man had struck a match to see
If his son slept peacefully.

He held his palms each side the spark
His love had kindled in the dark.

His two hands were curved apart
In the semblance of a heart.

He wore, it seemed to his small son,
A bare heart on his hidden one.

A heart that gave out such a glow
No son awake could bear to know.

It showed a look upon a face
Too tender for the day to trace.

One instant, it lit all about,
And then the secret heart went out.

But it shone long enough for one
To know that hands held up the sun.

FLOWER IN THE
CRANNIED WALL
Alfred, Lord Tennyson

Flower in the crannied wall,

I pluck you out of the crannies;
I hold you here, root and all, in my
hand,
Little flower—but if I could understand
What you are, root and all, and all in
all,
I should know what God and man is.

TO A WATERFOWL
William Cullen Bryant

Whither, midst falling dew,
While glow the heavens with the last
steps of day,
Far, through the rosy depths, dost thou
pursue
Thy solitary way? . . .
There is a Power whose care
Teaches thy way along that pathless
coast—
The desert and illimitable air—

Lone wandering but not lost.
All day thy wings have fanned,
At that far height, the cold thin at-
mosphere,
Yet stoop not, weary, to the welcome
land,
Though the dark night is near.
And soon that toil shall end;
Soon shalt thou find a summer home
and rest,
And scream among thy fellows; reeds
shall bend
Soon, o'er thy sheltered nest.

Thou'rt gone, the abyss of heaven
Hath swallowed up thy form; yet, on
my heart
Deeply hath sunk the lesson thou hast
given
And shall not soon depart.
He who, from zone to zone,
Guides through the boundless sky thy
certain flight,
In the long way that I must tread
alone,
Will lead my steps aright.

BE LIKE THE BIRD
Victor Hugo

Be like the bird, who
Halting in his flight
On limb too slight
Feels it give way beneath him,
Yet sings
Knowing he hath wings.

MIRACLES
Walt Whitman

Why, who makes much of a miracle,
As to me I know of nothing else but
    miracles,
Whether I walk the streets of Manhat-
    tan
Or stand under trees in the woods . . .
Or watch honeybees busy around the
    hive of a summer forenoon,
Or animals feeding in the fields,
Or birds, or the wonderfulness of in-
    sects in the air,
Or the wonderfulness of the sundown,
    or of the stars shining so quiet and
    bright,
Or the exquisite delicate thin curve of
    the new moon in spring;
These with the rest, one and all, are to
    me miracles . . .
To me every hour of the light and dark
    is a miracle . . .
What stranger miracles are there?

IN THE GARDEN OF
THE LORD
Helen Keller

The word of God came unto me,
Sitting alone among the multitudes;
And my blind eyes were touched with
    light,
And there was laid upon my lips a
    flame of fire.

I laugh and shout, for life is good,
Though my feet are set in silent ways.
In merry mood I leave the crowd
To walk in my garden. Even as I walk
I gather fruits and flowers in my hands.
And with joyful heart I bless the sun
That kindles all the place with radiant
    life.

I run with playful winds that blow the
    scent
Of rose and jessamine in eddying
    whirls.
At last I come where tall lilies grow,
Lifting their faces like white saints to
    God.
While the lilies pray, I kneel upon the
    ground;
I have strayed into the holy temple of
    the Lord.

THE CREATION
James Weldon Johnson

And God stepped out on space,

[284]

And he looked around and said:
I'm lonely—
I'll make me a world.

And far as the eye of God could see
Darkness covered everything,
Blacker than a hundred midnights
Down in a cypress swamp.

Then God smiled,
And the light broke,
And the darkness rolled up on one side,
And the light stood shining on the
    other,
And God said: That's good!

Then God reached out and took the
    light in his hands,
And God rolled the light around in his
    hands
Until he made the sun;
And he set that sun a-blazing in the
    heavens.
And the light that was left from mak-
    ing the sun
God gathered it up in a shining ball
And flung it against the darkness,
Spangling the night with the moon and
    stars.
Then down between the darkness and
    the light
He hurled the world;
And God said: That's good!

Then God himself stepped down—
And the sun was on his right hand,

And the moon was on his left;
The stars were clustered about his head,
And the earth was under his feet.
And God walked, and where he trod
His footsteps hollowed the valleys out
And bulged the mountains up.

Then he stopped and looked and saw
That the earth was hot and barren.
So God stepped over to the edge of
    the world
And he spat out the seven seas—
He batted his eyes, and the lightnings
    flashed—
He clapped his hands, and the thunders
    rolled—
And the waters above the earth came
    down,
The cooling waters came down.

Then the green grass sprouted,
And the little red flowers blossomed,
The pine tree pointed his finger to the
    sky,
And the oak spread out his arms,
The lakes cuddled down in the hollows
    of the ground,
And the rivers ran down to the sea;
And God smiled again,
And the rainbow appeared,
And curled itself around his shoulder.

Then God raised his arm and he waved
    his hand
Over the sea and over the land,
And quicker than God could drop his
    hand,

Fishes and fowls
And beasts and birds
Swam the rivers and the seas,
Roamed the forests and the woods,
And split the air with their wings.
And God said: That's good!

Then God walked around,
And God looked around
On all that he had made.
He looked at his sun,
And he looked at his moon,
And he looked at his little stars;
He looked on his world
With all its living things,
And God said: I'm lonely still.

Then God sat down—
On the side of a hill where he could
    think;
By a deep, wide river he sat down;
With his head in his hands,
God thought and thought,
Till he thought: I'll make me a man!

Up from the bed of the river
God scooped the clay;
And by the bank of the river
He kneeled him down;
And there the great God Almighty
Who lit the sun and fixed it in the sky,
Who flung the stars to the most far
    corner of the night,

Who rounded the earth in the middle
    of his hand;
This Great God,
Like a mammy bending over her baby,
Kneeled down in the dust
Toiling over a lump of clay
Till he shaped it in his own image;

Then into it he blew the breath of life,
And man became a living soul.
Amen. Amen.

PSALM 121

I will lift up mine eyes unto the hills,
    from whence cometh my help.
My help cometh from the Lord, which
    made heaven and earth.
He will not suffer thy foot to be moved;
    he that keepeth thee will not
    slumber.
He that keepeth Israel shall neither
    slumber nor sleep.
The Lord is thy keeper; the Lord is thy
    shade upon thy right hand.
The sun shall not smite thee by day,
    nor the moon by night.
The Lord shall preserve thee from all
    evil; he shall preserve thy soul.
The Lord shall preserve thy going out
    and thy coming in from this time
    forth, and even for evermore.

THE BOOK OF

Wisdom

Introduction

⟨[CULTURE, IN *the words of Matthew Arnold, is to know "the best that has been said and thought in the world." It is in the human being's capacity to* know *that he differs from the lower animals. No other creature, no matter how remarkable its intuitive powers, can pass on to its descendants the benefits of an ancestor's experience. With man it is different. He has been learning through more thousands of years than we can count, each generation slowly building on the knowledge of those who have gone before.*

Since the invention of printing, the process has been greatly accelerated. No longer are we solely dependent on what our immediate forebears can tell us. We have the wisdom of the ages to draw on. Anyone who reads can seek guidance through the pages of a good book. And any book is a good book if it helps us to see and feel and understand, if we are wiser for having read it.

"Happy is the man that findeth wisdom," said one of the Proverbs. Yet to different people wisdom means different things. It means to know more and more—and to understand what we have learned. It involves a never-ending search for truth. Many think of it in terms of conduct, wise conduct that enables us to get along with our fellowmen and to live more happily in the world. As a source of wisdom men have long looked to sayings of their great leaders, especially to the teachings of their religious prophets. From early times they have depended on storytelling.

Some of the stories called fables packed a truth or moral into a few words. Fables were popular in India centuries ago. Travelers probably carried them to Greece, where a witty slave, Aesop, is supposed to have lived about 600 B. C. He—or someone like him—retold them in a way that made people chuckle. Some thousand years later de la Fontaine, the Aesop of France, summed up the appeal of the fable in an amusing rhyme:

> *"We yawn at sermons, but we gladly turn*
> *To moral tales, and so amused we learn."*

"A bridge to truth" was the Arab description of a fable, which would apply equally to a parable or an allegory. The simple tales told by Jesus, to impress on His followers certain great moral and spiritual truths, are even more widely loved and quoted today than during His lifetime. Many rabbis used such stories to make their teachings easier to understand.

The world's most famous allegory is undoubtedly Pilgrim's Progress. *It was written in prison by a lowly tinker turned preacher who had dared to preach the truth as he saw it. Although his story reads like a fast-moving adventure tale, the characters and the happenings all have a deeper meaning. It has probably been read by more people than any other book except the Bible.*

Fables, parables, and allegories have been a source of joy and inspiration for generations. The sayings of some of the wise men of Europe and the Americas have helped many of us to grow in understanding, and understanding is a large part of wisdom. Never have we been in greater need of wisdom. Never has it been so important that we understand our neighbors, now that our neighbors include everyone on earth. We need to know more about them—the stories they like, the heroes they admire, and the religious leaders who have influenced them.

The founders of the most widely known religions believed and taught many of the same great fundamental truths. In "Man's Search for God" Genevieve Foster has summarized these teachings briefly and eloquently. The prophets, in their wisdom, knew that mankind was one. If we can partake of that wisdom—especially if young readers come to see its truth—the problems of our fast-shrinking globe may still be solved.

LAURA E. RICHARDS

The Golden Windows

([THE author's own favorites among her many books were two volumes of fables. This story was written at the turn of the century.

ALL DAY long the little boy worked hard, in field and barn and shed, for his people were poor farmers, and could not pay a workman; but at sunset there came an hour that was all his own. Then the boy would go up to the top of a hill and look across at another hill that rose some miles away. On this far hill stood a house with windows of clear gold and diamonds. They shone and blazed so that it made the boy wink to look at them. But after a while the people in the house put up shutters, as it seemed, and then it looked like any common farmhouse. The boy supposed they did this because it was suppertime; and then he would go into the house and have his supper of bread and milk, and so to bed.

One day the boy's father called him and said, "You have been a good boy, and have earned a holiday. Take this day for your own; but remember that God gave it, and try to learn some good thing."

The boy thanked his father and kissed his mother. Then he put a piece of bread in his pocket, and started off to find the house with the golden windows.

It was pleasant walking. His bare feet made marks in the white dust, and when he looked back, the footprints seemed to be following him and making company for him. His shadow, too, kept beside him, and would dance or run with him as he pleased; so it was very cheerful.

By-and-by he felt hungry; and he sat down by a brown brook that ran through the alder hedge by the roadside and ate his bread and drank the clear water. Then he scattered the crumbs for the birds, as his mother had taught him to do, and went on his way.

After a long time he came to a high green hill. When he had climbed the hill, there was the house on the top; but it seemed that the shutters were up, for he could not see the golden windows. He came up to the house, and then he could well have wept, for the windows were of clear glass, like any others, and there was no gold anywhere about them.

A woman came to the door, and looked kindly at the boy, and asked him what he wanted.

"I saw the golden windows from our hilltop," he said, "and I came to see them, but now they are only glass."

The woman shook her head and laughed.

"We are poor farming people," she said, "and are not likely to have gold about our windows; but glass is better to see through."

She bade the boy sit down on the broad stone step at the door, and brought him a cup of milk and a cake, and bade him rest. Then she called her daughter, a child of his own age, and went back to her work.

The little girl was barefooted like himself, and wore a brown cotton gown. But her hair was golden like the windows he had seen, and her eyes were blue like the sky at noon. She led the boy about the farm, and showed him her black calf with the white star on its forehead, and he told her about his own at home, which was red like a chestnut, with four white feet. Then when they had eaten an apple together, and so had become friends, the boy asked her about the golden windows. The little girl nodded, and said she knew all about them, only he had mistaken the house.

"You have come quite the wrong way!" she said. "Come with me, and I will show you the house with the

golden windows, and then you will see for yourself."

They went to a knoll that rose behind the farmhouse, and as they went the little girl told him that the golden windows could only be seen at a certain hour, about sunset.

"Yes, I know that!" said the boy.

When they reached the top of the knoll, the girl turned and pointed. There on a hill far away stood a house with windows of clear gold and diamonds, just as he had seen them. And when they looked again, the boy saw that it was his own home.

Then he told the little girl that he must go; and he gave her his best pebble, the white one with the red band, that he had carried for a year in his pocket. She gave him three horse chestnuts, one red like satin, one spotted, and one white like milk. He promised to come again, but he did not tell her what he had learned; and so he went back down the hill, and the little girl stood in the sunset light and watched him.

The way home was long, and it was dark before the boy reached his father's house; but the lamplight and firelight shone through the windows, making them almost as bright as he had seen them from the hilltop. When he opened the door, his mother came to kiss him, and his little sister ran to throw her arms about his neck, and his father looked up and smiled from his seat by the fire.

"Have you had a good day?" asked his mother.

Yes, the boy had had a very good day. "And have you learned anything?" asked his father.

"Yes!" said the boy. "I have learned that our house has windows of gold and diamonds."

⁋ *Laura E. Richards' books include* CAPTAIN JANUARY, WHEN I WAS YOUR AGE, *her autobiography* STEPPING WESTWARD, *and* TIRRA LIRRA, *a volume of her nonsense verse.*

Aesop's Fables

ANDROCLES AND THE LION. A slave named Androcles once escaped from his master and fled to the forest. As he was wandering about there he came upon a Lion lying down moaning and groaning. At first he turned to flee, but finding that the Lion did not pursue him, he turned back and went up to him. As he came near, the Lion put out his paw, which was all swollen and bleeding. Androcles found that a huge thorn had got into it, and was causing all the pain. He pulled out the thorn and bound up the paw of the Lion, who was soon able to rise and lick the hand of Androcles like a dog. Then the Lion took Androcles to his cave, and every day used to bring him meat on which to live.

Shortly afterwards both Androcles and the Lion were captured. The slave was sentenced to be thrown to the Lion, after the latter had been kept without food for several days. The Emperor and all his Court came to see the spectacle, and Androcles was led out into the middle of the arena. Soon the Lion was let loose from his den, and rushed bounding and roaring toward his victim. But as soon as he came near Androcles he recognized his friend, and fawned upon him, and licked his hands like a friendly dog. The Emperor, surprised at this, summoned Androcles, who told him the whole story. Whereupon the slave was pardoned and freed, and the Lion let loose to his native forest.

Gratitude is the sign of noble souls.

THE BALD MAN AND THE FLY. There was once a Bald Man who sat down after work on a hot summer's day. A Fly came up and kept buzzing about his bald pate, and stinging him from time to time. The Man aimed a blow at his little enemy, but—*whack*—his palm came on his head instead. Again the Fly tormented him, but this time the Man was wiser and said:

"You will only injure yourself if you take notice of despicable enemies."

THE FROG AND THE OX. "Oh Father," said a little Frog to the big one sitting by the side of a pool, "I have seen such a terrible monster! It was as big as a mountain, with horns on its head, and a long tail, and it had hoofs divided in two."

"Tush, child, tush," said the old Frog, "that was only Farmer White's Ox. It isn't so big either; he may be a little bit taller than I, but I could easily make myself quite as broad. Just you see." So he blew himself out, and blew himself out, and blew himself out. "Was he as big as that?" asked he.

"Oh, much bigger than that," said the young Frog.

Again the old one blew himself out, and asked the young one if the Ox was as big as that.

"Bigger, Father, bigger," was the reply.

So the Frog took a deep breath, and blew and blew and blew, and swelled and swelled and swelled. And then he said, "I'm sure the Ox is not as big as —" But at this moment he burst.

Self-conceit may lead to self-destruction.

&

THE BOY WHO CRIED "WOLF!" There was once a young Shepherd Boy who tended his sheep at the foot of a mountain near a dark forest. It was rather lonely for him all day, so he thought upon a plan by which he could get a little company and some excitement. He rushed down toward the village calling out "Wolf! Wolf!" and the villagers came out to meet him, and some of them stopped with him for a considerable time. This pleased the boy so much that a few days afterwards he tried the same trick, and again the villagers came to his help.

Shortly after this a Wolf actually did come out from the forest, and began to worry the sheep, and the boy of course cried out, "Wolf! Wolf!" still louder than before. But this time the villagers, who had been fooled twice before,

thought the boy was again deceiving them, and nobody stirred to come to his help. So the Wolf made a good meal off the boy's flock, and when the boy complained, the wise man of the village said:

"A liar will not be believed, even when he speaks the truth."

&

THE GOOSE THAT LAID GOLDEN EGGS. One day a countryman going to the nest of his Goose found there an egg all yellow and glittering. When he took it up it was as heavy as lead and he was going to throw it away, because he thought a trick had been played upon him. But he took it home on second thought, and soon found to his delight that it was an egg of pure gold. Every morning the same thing occurred, and he soon became rich by selling his eggs. As he grew rich he grew greedy. Thinking to get at once all the gold the Goose could give, he killed it and opened it only to find—nothing.

Greed oft overreaches itself.

&

THE WIND AND THE SUN. The Wind and the Sun were disputing which was the stronger. Suddenly they saw a traveler coming down the road, and the Sun said: "I see a way to decide our dispute. Whichever of us can cause that traveler to take off his cloak shall be regarded as the stronger. You begin." So the Sun retired behind a cloud, and the Wind began to blow as hard as it could upon the traveler. But the harder he blew the more closely did the traveler wrap his cloak round him, till at last the Wind had to give up in despair. Then the Sun came out and shone in all his glory upon the traveler, who soon found it too hot to walk with his cloak on.

Kindness effects more than severity.

The Plowman and His Sons

A wealthy plowman drawing near his
    end,
Called in his sons apart from every
    friend,
And said, "When of your sire bereft,
The heritage our fathers left
Guard well, nor sell a single field.
A treasure in it is concealed.
The place, precisely, I don't know,
But industry will serve to show.
The harvest past, Time's forelock take,
And search with plow and spade and
    rake,
Turn over every inch of sod,

Nor leave unsearched a single clod."
The father died. The sons—and not in
    vain—
Turned o'er the soil and o'er again;
That year their acres bore
More grain than e'er before,
Though hidden money found they
    none,
Yet had their father wisely done,
To show by such a measure,
That toil itself is treasure.

The farmer's patient care and toil
Are oftener wanting than the soil.

Fables from India

⟨ ABOUT *the time that Aesop lived in Greece, the Buddha ("the Enlight-*
ened One") lived and taught in India. His followers, who believed that
the soul passes from one body to another until it becomes purified, called
him "the Bodisat" in his previous existences. Some of the stories told of
the Bodisat were adapted from earlier Indian fables.

THE FLIGHT OF THE ANIMALS. Not far from the Bay of Bengal, in a grove of coconut palms and carob trees, lived a short-eared rabbit so timorous that he searched for food at night and rarely left his burrow in the daytime.

One day the rabbit came hesitantly out of his dwelling, looking quickly to the right and to the left of him for any sight or sign of an enemy. Reassured that there was nothing dangerous in the neighborhood, he stretched out to bask in the sun near a tall carob tree.

He lay there contentedly looking up at the oval leaves so densely interwoven that not even a pinpoint of sky could be seen through them. Here and there upon the branches hung the ripening dark-brown, sickle-shaped seed pods, swaying in the breeze. They were a pleasant sight to the rabbit, for he well knew how honey-sweet their pulp was when they began to fall to the ground.

Suddenly, as he lay there, an alarming thought struck the faint-hearted rabbit: What would happen to him if the earth began to cave in? Where would he go for safety? The more he thought of it, the more alarmed he became, until his heart nearly burst with terror.

Just then, behind his head, a ripe coconut fell upon a dry palm leaf with a thundering crash. The rabbit jumped up in panic. Without a single look behind he scampered off as fast as his legs could carry him.

As he ran he passed a long-eared hare.

"Where are you running so fast?" called out the hare.

But the rabbit dared not pause to answer. The hare caught up with him and ran alongside, repeating his question.

The fleeing rabbit panted, "The earth is caving in behind us!"

The hare, just as frightened, followed the short-eared rabbit, and soon they were joined by thousands of other hares and rabbits, all fleeing from the place where the earth was caving in.

A doe and deer in a clearing were startled by the sight of so many hares and rabbits in flight and asked the cause of their alarm. And when they were told that the earth was caving in, they too joined the stampede.

As they fled on their way, they encountered a rhinoceros, who asked the same question and received the same answer. And he, too, joined them.

Before long the stampede included bears and elks, wild oxen and gnus, jackals and monkeys, tapirs and camels, tigers, and even elephants.

A young lion at the foot of a mountain saw the animals in flight. He climbed to the top of a high rock and roared a clap of thunder. All the animals stopped in their tracks. They were more frightened by the roar of their king than by the fear of the earth breaking up behind them.

"Why are you all running away?" asked the king of the beasts (who was really the Bodisat in the form of a young lion).

"The earth is caving in behind us," they all replied together.

"Who saw it caving in?" asked the lion.

"Ask the tigers, they know," replied the elephants.

But the tigers said, "We didn't see it, but the wild boars told us so."

And the wild boars said, "We didn't see it, but the camels know all about it."

And the camels pointed to the tapirs, who pointed to the deer, who pointed to the hares, who pointed to the rabbits.

When the lion questioned the rabbits one by one, he finally came to the short-eared rabbit. "Are you the one that saw the earth cave in?" asked the lion, fixing his fierce eyes upon the little rabbit, who was now more terrified than ever.

"Y-y-yes, Your Majesty," stuttered the rabbit.

"Where did you see this?" asked the lion.

"Near my home, in a grove of coconut palms and carob trees. I was lying there in the sun, thinking of what would happen to me if the earth suddenly began to cave in, and just then I heard the crash of the earth breaking up right behind me. And I fled."

"Come, show me the spot where you heard the earth breaking up," said the lion.

"Your Majesty, I am afraid to go near it," said the rabbit.

"Do not fear anything when you are with me," said the lion. "Jump upon my back and I will carry you there."

Together they returned to the spot where the rabbit had basked in the sun. And there upon the palm frond the lion saw the coconut that had fallen and frightened the rabbit.

The lion returned to the other animals to tell them what he had discovered. Then each returned peacefully to his home.

But had it not been for the young lion, the Bodisat, the stampeding animals would surely have rushed into the ocean, and all would have perished.

THE TALKATIVE TORTOISE. In a pond in the Himalaya Mountains there once lived a handsomely marked young tortoise. He was not vicious like his cousin, the snapping turtle, but he had the failing of liking to talk too much. Two wild ducks came to the pond in search of food one day, and the tortoise started to talk to them almost as soon as they alighted on the water.

Nevertheless the ducks and the tortoise became great friends, and the ducks said one day: "We have a fine home on Mount Beautiful in the Himalayas. Why don't you come and live with us?"

"How can I, a tortoise, get up to your place?"

"We thought of that," said the wild ducks. "We can take you to our home, if only you can keep from talking and not say a single word until we get there. Do you think you can do that and keep your mouth closed all that time?"

"I certainly can do that!"

The ducks took a sturdy stick and asked the tortoise to bite hard on the center. Then they each took hold of an end of the stick with their strong bills and rose into the air, swiftly flying toward the mountains.

As they flew over the palace of the King of Benares, a number of village children saw the wild ducks in flight, carrying a tortoise on a stick.

"Look! Look! Two wild ducks are carrying a tortoise on a stick!" they shouted excitedly to their parents.

Their outcries angered the tortoise, and he wanted to shout back at them:

"If my friends want to carry me like this, what affairs is that of yours!"

But when he opened his mouth to speak, he let go of the stick and fell with great force into the open courtyard of the palace; and he split in two.

The king's attendants came running up in excitement, shouting, "A tortoise has fallen out of the sky into the courtyard!"

Everyone, including the king and his Brahman, gathered around the spot where the dead tortoise lay.

The king asked the Brahman: "Teacher! What made this creature fall here?"

Now, this king was very talkative and no one could ever get a word in edgewise. The Brahman answered: "My king, his tongue killed him."

The king looked at him in amazement. And he asked, "How could his tongue bring him to his death?"

"O king, this tortoise held secure
A stick between his teeth;
But when he tried to chatter
He quickly met this fate.

"Behold him, O excellent of strength,
And speak not out of season!
You see how this tortoise fell—
He talked too much and that's the reason!"

The king asked, "Are you referring to me, Teacher?"

And the teacher (who was the Bodisat born as a Brahman) replied: "O Great King! Be it you, or be it another. Whoever talks too much sooner or later meets with disaster."

Why the Old Man Planted Trees

A NOBLEMAN WAS once riding along the road and saw a very old man digging in his garden. Beside the old man on the ground lay a sapling tree, ready to be planted. The nobleman stopped to watch, and after a few minutes called out to the old man, "What kind of tree are you planting there, my good man?"

The old man wiped his brow and picked up the sapling. "This is a fig tree, sir," he said.

"A fig tree?" cried the astonished nobleman. "Why, how old are you, may I ask?"

"I am ninety years old," said the other.

"What!" cried the nobleman. "You are ninety years old, and you plant a tree that will take years and years to give fruit?"

"Why not?" replied the old man.

The nobleman pointed to the tree. "Surely, you don't expect to live long enough to get any benefit from the hard work you are doing with this sapling."

The old man leaned on his shovel and looked around the garden. Then he smiled and said, "Tell me, sir, did you eat figs when you were a boy?"

"Certainly." The nobleman sounded puzzled. "Why?"

The old man smiled again. "Then tell me this," he said, "who planted the trees from which those figs were picked?"

The nobleman hesitated. "Why—why, I don't know."

"You see, sir," the old man continued, "our forefathers planted trees for us to enjoy, and I am doing the same for those who come after me.

How else can I repay my debt to those who lived before me?"

The nobleman was silent for a moment and then said, "You are very wise, old man, and I have been foolish."

"Thank you, sir," said the old man. "May I ask your name?"

"It doesn't matter," said the nobleman. "You are far more important than I am. Good-by."

The old man nodded his head in farewell and began to dig again, while the nobleman clucked to his horse and rode off, one arm raised in salute to the wise old man.

JOHN BUNYAN

Christian Meets Apollyon

⟨ THE allegory of PILGRIM's PROGRESS, told as if it were a dream, is about
the spiritual life of Christian who set out from the City of Destruction to
find the Celestial City. In this story he encounters the demon Apollyon.

THEN I SAW in my dream that Christian rose to take his leave of Discretion, and of Prudence, Piety, and Charity, but they said that he must stay till the next day, that they might show him The Delectable Mountains; so they took him to the top of the house, and bade him look to the south, which he did, and lo, a great way off, he saw a rich land, full of hills, woods, vines, shrubs, and streams.

"What is the name of this land?" said Christian.

Then they told him it was Immanuel's Land. "And," they said, "it is as much meant for you, and the like of you, as this hill is; and when you reach the place, there you may see the gate of The Celestial City." Then they gave him a sword, and put on him a coat of mail, lest he should meet some foe in the way; and they went with him down the hill.

"Of a truth," said Christian, "it is as great a toil to come down the hill as it was to go up."

Prudence: "So it is, for it is a hard

thing for a man to go down to The Vale of Humiliation, as thou dost now, and for this cause have we come with you to the foot of the hill." So, though he went with great care, yet he caught a slip or two.

Then in my dream I saw that when they got to the foot of the hill, those good friends of Christian's gave him a loaf of bread, a flask of wine, and a bunch of dry grapes; and then they left him to go on his way.

But now in this Vale of Humiliation poor Christian was hard put to it, for he had not gone far, ere he saw a foe come in the field to meet him, whose name was Apollyon. Then did Christian fear, and he cast in his mind if he would go back or stand his ground. But Christian thought that as he had no coat of mail on his back, to turn round might give Apollyon a chance to pierce it with his darts. So he stood his ground, for, thought he, "if but to save my life were all I had in view, still the best way would be to stand."

[303]

So he went on, and Apollyon met him with looks of scorn.

Apollyon: "Whence come you, and to what place are you bound?"

Christian: "I am come from The City of Destruction, which is the place of all sin, and I am on my way to Zion."

Apollyon: "By this I see you are mine, for of all that land I am the Prince. How is it, then, that you have left your king? Were it not that I have a hope that you may do me more good, I would strike you to the ground with one blow."

Christian: "I was born in your realm, it is true, but you drove us too hard, and your wage was such as no man could live on."

Apollyon: "No prince likes to lose his men, nor will I as yet lose you; so if you will come back, what my realm yields I will give you."

Christian: "But I am bound by vows to the King of Kings; and how can I, to be true, go back with you?"

Apollyon: "You have made a change it seems, from bad to worse; but why not give Him the slip, and come back to me?"

Christian: "I gave Him my faith, and swore to be true to Him; how can I go back from this?"

Then when Apollyon saw that Christian was stanch to his Prince, he broke out in a great rage, and said, "I hate that Prince, and I hate His laws, and I am come out to stop you."

Christian: "Take heed what you do. I am on the King's highway to Zion."

Apollyon: "I am void of fear, and to prove that I mean what I say, here on this spot I will put thee to death." With that he threw a dart of fire at his breast, but Christian had a shield on his arm, with which he caught it. Then did Christian draw his sword, for he saw it was time to stir; and Apollyon as fast made at him, and threw darts as thick as hail; with which in spite of all that Christian could do, Apollyon gave him wounds in his head, hand and foot.

This made Christian pause in the fight for a time, but Apollyon still came on, and Christian once more took heart. They fought for half a day, till Christian, weak from his wounds, was well nigh spent in strength. When Apollyon saw this, he threw him down with great force; on which Christian's sword fell out of his hand. Then said Apollyon, "I am sure of thee now!"

But while he strove to make an end of Christian, that good man put out his hand in haste to feel for his sword and caught it. "Boast not, O Apollyon!" said he, and with that he struck him a blow which made his foe reel back as one that had had his last wound. Then Apollyon spread out his wings and fled, so that Christian for a time saw him no more.

Then there came to him a hand which held some of the leaves of the tree of life; some of them Christian took, and as soon as he had put them to his wounds, he saw them heal up . . .

MANY were the trials and adventures that awaited Christian on his journey toward the Celestial City. He passed through the Valley of the Shadow and came to the town called Vanity, where he attended Vanity Fair. Later he was joined by a companion named Hopeful, but both of them were captured by Giant Despair and imprisoned in Doubting Castle. They escaped and, finally, after a long and dangerous journey, they reached the gate of the Celestial City—a journey of which you may read in all its colorful details in the book, *Pilgrim's Progress*.

Now while they thus drew up to the gate, lo, a host of saints came to meet them, to whom the two Bright Ones said: "These are men who felt love for our Lord when they were in the world, and left all for His name; and He sent us to bring them far on their way, that they might go in and look on their Lord with joy."

Then the whole host with great shouts came round on all sides (as it were to guard them); so that it would seem to Christian and Hopeful as if all Zion had come down to meet them.

Now, when Christian and Hopeful went in at the gate a great change took place in them, and they were clad in robes that shone like gold. There were bright hosts that came with harps and crowns, and they said to them, "Come ye, in the joy of the Lord." And then I heard all the bells in Zion ring.

Now, just as the gates were flung back for the men to pass in, I had a sight of Zion, which shone like the sun; the ground was of gold, and those who dwelt there had love in their looks, crowns on their heads, and palms in their hands, and with one voice they sent forth shouts of praise.

Man's Search for God

⟨[IN the following stories of the world's great religions, the leaders are presented in the order in which they appeared in history.

IKHNATON, THE FIRST TO BELIEVE IN ONE GOD. In the beginning, all early people everywhere worshiped many gods. They felt a Power in the world about them that they did not understand. Spirits seemed to be everywhere in lightning, thunder, wind and water, fire, trees, and stones. To bribe or persuade these spirits to be friendly, people thought up magic formulas, developed rules and laws to live by, as if binding themselves into a bargain. The Romans called what they did *religio*, from their word meaning to bind fast.

As people grew more civilized their ideas changed. From time to time in various lands, great prophets or teachers arose with such clear vision and understanding that, instead of many gods, they spoke of One God—a God in whose sight all people were equal, and who could be found within a man's own heart if his heart was pure. That belief is expressed in all the great religions in the world today.

The first person in the world to believe in One God and to think of all men as brothers was a young Pharaoh

of Egypt who ruled three thousand years ago and gave himself the name of Ikhnaton. Egypt was even then an ancient land. For thousands of years Egyptian farmers had been planting wheat and barley in the rich valley of the Nile. The life-giving river and the glorious sun had been their earliest gods. Each morning as they saw the sun god, Ra, rising over their fields of grain, they pictured him as a golden falcon or hawk soaring across the heavens. As the centuries passed and the gods increased in number, they also were pictured as birds and animals. Every city, every tribe, had its own special gods, but none was thought to be so powerful as the ancient sun god Ra.

In the year 1388 B.C., when Ikhnaton was born, Thebes was the royal city, and its god was Amen. So this newborn son of the Pharaoh was named Amenope, meaning "pleasing to Amen." At thirteen, the boy became Pharaoh and also priest in the temple of the sun god, Amen-Ra. The old priests of Amen were rich and powerful. They were also worldly and corrupt, and the young Pharaoh who loved truth and beauty above all things, lost faith in them and in their god, Amen, and in all the other gods of Egypt.

As he studied the sun and pondered and thought about it, it came to this young Egyptian that, just as there was only one sun in the world, there could be but one God! And as the sun did not shine upon any one land alone, but warmed and lighted the whole world, so God must not belong to any one race or nation. A life-giving spirit, radiant like the sun, he belonged equally to all people and creatures everywhere.

The young Pharaoh called this one God Aton, and changed his own name to Ikhnaton, meaning "beloved of Aton." Then he sent stone masons to chip the name Amen from the temple walls and also to cut out the plural word "gods" wherever it appeared.

Few people, however, could understand his teaching. The old priests were hostile. And when Ikhnaton died, the next Pharaoh returned to the old ways and to the worship of the old gods. Ikhnaton was spoken of as "that criminal," and in time his name was forgotten. More than three thousand years passed before his tomb was discovered. There at his feet, on a roll of papyrus, was found this beautiful prayer which he had written:

Ikhnaton's Prayer

O living Aton, Beginning of Life!
Thy dawning is beautiful on the horizon of heaven.

Thou fillest every land with thy beauty;
  thou bindest them
    With Thy love. How manifold are
    Thy works!
O thou sole God, whose power no
  other possesseth.
Thou didst create the earth according
  to thy desire,
Men and all cattle, large and small,
All that go upon their feet—all that
  fly with wings,
The foreign countries of Syria and
  Kush (as well as)
This land of Egypt.
Thou settest every man in his place.
  Thou suppliest their needs
(Though) their tongues differ in
  speech, their forms likewise
And the color of their skins (thou art)
Lord of them all.
How excellent are Thy designs,
  O Lord of Eternity!
Thou art in my heart, for Thou art the
  duration of Life.
By Thee men live.

MOSES, THE GREAT LAWGIVER. Moses, the great prophet who taught the Hebrews to worship one God, was born in Egypt less than a hundred years after Ikhnaton died. His people, the Hebrews, were then slaves of the Pharaoh Rameses II. They had lived in Egypt for many generations, although that was not their original home.

The earliest Hebrews had been half-savage shepherds roaming the Arabian desert, worshiping the strange spirits which they thought peopled the rocks and stones of their desert home. About eight hundred years before Moses was born, these ragged shepherds had begun to push north out of the barren desert into the fertile valley of the Babylonians and from there into the land of Canaan, later called Palestine. In that fertile green land, the Hebrews discarded their old desert gods for the gods of the Canaanites.

Then, when famine drove them from Canaan down into Egypt, they found and adopted the gods of the Egyptians. In Egypt the Hebrews multiplied and prospered, even under oppression. Finally, in fear that they might grow too strong, the Pharaoh Rameses II decreed that every son born to a Hebrew mother should be cast into the River Nile. One child was saved, hidden in a basket by the river's edge. There he was found by Pharaoh's daughter, who adopted him and gave him the Egyptian name of Moses, meaning son.

One day when Moses was grown, he saw an Egyptian master smiting a Hebrew slave. Moses killed the Egyptian and hid him in the sand and then fled for his life into the desert. There he lived as a shepherd for many years until he believed that the Lord's voice bade him return and bring forth the Hebrew people out of Egypt and back into the land of Canaan. But the Pharaoh was hard of heart and refused to let them leave.

The Bible tells of the horrible plagues that then befell the land. Finally there came that night in April, later to be called the Passover. On that night when the eldest born in every Egyptian household was killed, the Angel of Death "passed over" the houses of the Hebrews. Pharaoh then called for Moses to come. "Rise up," said he, "and get you forth from among my people, both ye and the children of Israel; and go serve the Lord as ye have said. Also take your flocks and your herds and be gone." The night when Pharaoh let the Hebrew people go— that strange and wonderful night of the Passover—is still celebrated in the world today.

As Moses led the Hebrew people out of Egypt, across the Red Sea into the wilderness of Sinai, he taught them the worship of One God, whose name was Javeh (Jehovah) and whose dwelling place was the volcano, Mount Sinai. In the third month of their journey, they camped before the mount. There, according to the Bible story, "the Lord Javeh called Moses," and Moses went up and was there with the Lord forty days and forty nights. And the Lord said unto Moses, "Hew these two tablets of stone," and Moses wrote upon them the words of the Ten Commandments which God spoke.

The Ten Commandments

I. I am the Lord thy God, Thou shalt have no other gods before me.

II. Thou shalt not make unto thee any graven image.

III. Thou shalt not take the name of the Lord thy God in vain.

IV. Remember the Sabbath day to keep it holy.

V. Honor thy father and thy mother.

VI. Thou shalt not kill.

VII. Thou shalt not commit adultery.

VIII. Thou shalt not steal.

IX. Thou shalt not bear false witness against thy neighbor.

X. Thou shalt not covet they neighbor's house or anything that is thy neighbor's.

THE SACRED BOOKS OF THE HEBREWS. Moses led the Hebrews to the border of the promised land of Canaan. There he died and the Hebrews passed on into the land of the Canaanites without him. In time the wandering Hebrew tribes were united into a nation by their great king, David; and Jerusalem, the old Canaanite stronghold, became their city. There Solomon, David's son, built a great Temple to the One God of whom Moses had spoken in the First Commandment.

The Hebrews, however, often forgot that commandment, and fell to worshiping the gods of the Canaanites. Again and again prophets arose and tried to bring the people back to their One God. At last in despair, one of the later prophets cried, "Behold, the eyes of the Lord are on this sinful nation and He will destroy it. Jerusalem shall become a ruin and the hill of the Temple as a place in the forest."

In time what the prophet foretold came to pass. Into the land of Canaan with the sound of thundering hoofs rode the Assyrian warriors, who conquered and carried the Hebrews off to captivity in Babylon. There "by the rivers of Babylon they sat down and wept" until comforted by another prophet who predicted that in time they would be cleansed of their sins and return to Jerusalem under a Saviour King anointed by God.

As a guide to live by until that great day came and to keep them from further sin, the scribes or rabbis wrote down the Laws that Moses had given them to follow and which they called the *Torah*. They also wrote down the sayings of the other great prophets. These treasured scrolls—the Law and the Prophets—were carried back to Jerusalem when the exile came to an end, and the Hebrews were allowed to return and rebuild their Temple.

From then on the sacred scrolls were read aloud in the synagogues on the Sabbath day. They are still read aloud whenever the scattered descendants of those early Hebrews gather today in synagogues and temples.

ZOROASTER'S GOD OF LIGHT AND GOODNESS. To the east of Egypt and Palestine, lay the land of Persia, which we now call Iran, a high plateau, ringed round with shining, snowcapped mountains rising out of dark ravines. There, about six hundred years after Moses died, a great Persian prophet lived and taught, whose name was Zoroaster.

The Persians still worshiped their early gods, spirits in the world about them—the sky, earth, thunder, but especially the sun, which they called Mithra, on whose altars the magi or priests kept constant fires burning. Then there came the prophet Zoroaster who taught his people to worship One God, a Spirit of Light and Goodness whom he called Ahura Mazda.

Little is known of Zoroaster's early life, although many legends have been told about him. As a youth he wandered far and wide over the high plateau, looking up at the shining mountain peaks and down into the dark valleys, pondering on the similar contrast between good and evil and seeking the meaning of life. When understanding came to him, he began to teach. All the world, said Zoroaster, was a battleground between light and darkness, good and evil. Every man born into this world must choose on which side of the battle he will fight, that of Ahura Mazda and his angels of light and goodness, or that of Angra Mainyu, the devil, and all that was darkness and evil.

Good Thoughts, Good Works, and Good Deeds were the weapons of those soldiers who would fight for the Good Spirit. Work was the way in which they could serve him best. A man's daily work was his prayer, and every act of his life was part of his religion, as all living should be.

Zoroaster was killed by jealous magi or priests of the old religion which he tried to purify. Lacking the pure vision of the prophet, the priests let the religion slip from the high standards Zoroaster had set. They brought back the worship of Mithra, the old god of the sun. Mithra was then spoken of, however, as being the son of Ahura Mazda, who had been sent to earth to help win the war against Evil and to save mankind from being overcome by Darkness and Death. Mithra was pictured as a man, and seemed nearer and more real to ordinary people than the pure Spirit, Ahura Mazda.

And so Mithraism spread beyond the borders of Persia. It was the leading religion of the Romans until the time when they accepted the later religion of Christianity. Even then the early Christians kept Sunday as their sacred day, the one on which they were used to worshiping the Persian sun god. December 25, the day on which the Persians celebrated the birthday of the sun, became Christmas.

In the *Avesta*, the sacred book of the Persians, may still be read the teachings of the great prophet Zoroaster. Although his followers today are few in number, his words, like those of all prophets everywhere who have the vision of One God, can never be entirely lost or forgotten.

BRAHMA, THE HINDU NAME FOR GOD. Long ago, about 2000 B.C. when the early Hebrews were pushing up out of the Arabian desert, another race of wandering shepherd people left their old home in central Asia. Some of them traveled west into Europe, where they became known as Europeans. Others traveled south into the valley of the Indus River, where they became known as Hindus. Wherever they went they carried with them their belief in the gods or spirits of nature which they had worshiped in their homeland. They found that the native inhabitants had gods of their own, many of which the Hindus also adopted.

The newcomers in the Indus valley began to wonder about these many gods. Which had come first? And how? "Who truly knows? Who can declare it?" These questions come from the *Rig Veda*, written about 1000 B.C. by those early Hindus. It is the oldest sacred book, or Bible, still used in the world today.

About two hundred years later, although ordinary Hindu people were still content to worship many gods, the Hindu philosophers were not. They had come to believe that there was but One God—one Great Self or Spirit in the Universe, whom they called Brahma. In sacred books called *Brahmana*, they said:

"When people sacrifice to this or that god, each god is but a way in which Brahma is made known, for he is all gods in One. He is imagined in the heart. The Great Self is always settled in the hearts of men. The wise who find Him within themselves, to them belongs eternal happiness, eternal peace."

Centuries passed. The Indus valley had become so crowded that the Hindus had to move on down into the hotter, moister valley of the Ganges River. There they found themselves among the dark-skinned natives of the jungle. To keep them apart, the Hindu priests, or Brahmans, shut off the natives because of their "caste," or color, into a class of slaves.

To satisfy the people, the wily priests used a myth to show that the caste system was sacred, saying that Brahma had not created all men equal. From the mouth of Brahma, they said, had sprung the highest caste, the Brahmans or priests. From Brahma's chest had come the caste of rajahs and soldiers. From his legs had come a third caste, the farmers and tradesmen; and from his feet, the slaves. The system

grew rigid. The castes multiplied in number. The priests loaded the religion with endless laws, rites, and regulations.

The philosophers were discouraged. How, they asked, could one live in such a world and be happy? Many reformers also protested. They tried to free India from customs and beliefs which they looked upon as harmful and false.

But the majority of people went on as always, worshiping many gods, erecting idols and shrines, offering sacrifices, and bathing in the sacred Ganges.

So India continued to be, and still is today, a land of many and widely varying beliefs and practices for all kinds of people, from the most primitive and ignorant to the most intellectual and pure in heart. All these forms and practices make up the religion known as Hinduism. In one of the later sacred books of India are to be found these words of understanding:

"As one can ascend to the top of a house by means of a ladder or a bamboo or a staircase or a rope, so varied are the ways and means to approach God. Every religion in the world shows one of these ways."

BUDDHA, THE ENLIGHTENED ONE. One of the reformers who arose in India about 500 B.C. was a prince, Gautama, who led such a holy life that he came to be called Buddha, "The Enlightened One." He had been born in a splendid palace by the Ganges, sacred river of the Hindus. As a boy all sorrowful sights and knowledge of misery had been kept from him by his

[311]

royal father, who wished his son to be happy.

The prince was well grown before he learned that there was evil in the world. Then his heart was saddened. Giving up his kingdom, he exchanged his rich robe for a mean cloak, the color of the ground, and set forth to seek a way of Truth that would free the world from misery and evil. He sought out the philosophers, he consulted the priests in the temple, and he fasted with the monks, seeking true wisdom, which would give him perfect peace. But he did not find it.

Then he directed his steps to a blessed banyan tree, where he was to end his search. There beneath its shade he gave himself up to meditation. Pondering on life and death, he saw this truth: that perfect peace, which he called Nirvana, can dwell only in a heart where all vanity and thought of self have disappeared.

"Blessed is he who has conquered all selfishness and pride," he said. "He has reached Nirvana. He has become the Buddha, the Enlightened One." And he thought: Now I desire to give light to those who are in darkness, and to found the kingdom of truth upon earth. So the Blessed One set the wheel of truth rolling.

To the Brahmans, the Buddha spoke of caste: "Who is an outcast? Who is a Brahman? An outcast is one who is angry and bears hatred, who does not fear to commit a wrong. He in whom there is truth and righteousness, he is a Brahman; not by his family or birth does one become an outcast, or a Brahman, but by his deeds. Our good and evil deeds follow us continually like shadows. It is impossible to escape the result of what we do.

"Let us then guard our thoughts that we do no evil, for as we sow, so shall we reap. That which is most needed is a loving heart. To all men, whatever they do, and whether they be artisans, merchants, priests or officers of the king, if they can struggle in life without cherishing any envy or hatred; if they can live in the world, not a life of self but a life of truth; then surely joy, peace and bliss will dwell in their hearts."

And those who heard him gladly said: "Truly, the Buddha, Our Lord, has set the wheel of Truth to rolling, which no one in the universe can ever turn back. The kingdom of Truth will spread; righteousness, goodwill and peace will reign among mankind."

Buddha was a Hindu. He had no intention of founding a new religion but to free the old one of evil ideas and practices. At first his teachings were passed on by word of mouth. Then, about 250 B.C. King Asoka ordered them put into writing.

The teachings of Buddha were known as the *Tri Pitaka*, or "Three Baskets" of Wisdom. By the year 1 A.D. they had been carried eastward by missionaries to the borders of China. And though Buddhism eventually died out in India, the religion that grew up about the life and teachings of Buddha became one of the leading religions of China, Japan and south-eastern Asia. It has many million followers in the world today.

LAO-TZE AND THE WAY OF HEAVEN. In the days of Buddha, far to the east by the Yellow River of China, two other great teachers were seeking to free their world from evil: the gentle old philosopher Lao-Tze and the vigorous master-teacher Confucius.

China, like India, was an ancient land. For more than three thousand years the black-haired people had tilled the fertile soil along *Huang Ho*, the Yellow River. Like other early people, they had felt the world about them to be full of unseen spirits. In the great winding river, whose water gave life to their fields, there seemed to be a friendly dragon. In the gathering clouds of the summer sky, the Chinese farmer looking up could see the good sky dragon who sent the gentle rain.

In the yearly return of the sun and the orderly passing of the seasons, the Chinese felt the Divine Law and order of the universe. The ancient sages spoke of it as *Tao*, or the Way of Heaven. If men would live in harmony with the great Way of Heaven, they said, all would be well upon earth. How could one do this? By following the rules of right behavior toward every person on every occasion. These rules the Chinese called The Law or *Li*. Needless to say, since people everywhere are much alike, the teaching of the ancient wise men was not always lived up to as the centuries passed.

In the days of Lao-Tze and Confucius, who were both state officials, China was divided among many landowning warrior chiefs. Their constant fighting, corrupt rule, and evil ways brought misery to the people. This was regretted by Lao-Tze, who was the state historian and keeper of the secret archives for the emperor at Loyang, strongest ruler of his day.

"If princes and kings would but follow the Way of Heaven," said Lao-Tze, "all things of themselves would be right. A man who understands *Tao* thinks of all people as himself. He gives and the more he gives to others, the more he has for himself. He does not force his power upon others or contend with arms. The strength of his goodness is like that of water. Nothing is so yielding. Yet it can wear away the hardest stone. Thus can the gentle overcome the strong. And he who fights with love will win the battle. Let us have sound knowledge to walk on the great way."

Lao-Tze was sad that men would not accept the Way of Life. He was old and discouraged with the evil ways of men. One day he left Loyang and rode away alone on a water buffalo, through the last gate in the great wall into the desert, and was seen no more. Before he left, the warden at the gate begged him not to depart without leaving some of his wisdom behind. So there in the gatehouse, the old Philosopher wrote a book of five thousand words, containing eighty-one of his sayings. It is known as the *Tao Teh Ching: Ching*, meaning text; *Tao*, the Way of Heaven; and *Teh*, the good life for man.

The teaching of Lao-Tze, so pure and simple that it seemed a mystery, was seized upon and degraded by ignorant priests into the religion of Taoism. It became a mixture of magic tricks and superstitious rites, exactly

[313]

the opposite of what Lao-Tze had taught: that pure goodness comes from within.

CONFUCIUS, SAGE OF CHINA. Lao-Tze was about fifty years old when to the eastward, in the province of Shantung, Confucius was born, the youngest of eleven children. As a boy in school, Confucius loved to study the ancient Chinese books and the wisdom of the sages, especially the *Li*, the rules of good behavior.

As a young man, Confucius became Chief Justice of his state, which he promptly put into such good order that the envious ruler of a neighboring state plotted to discredit him. He succeeded so well that Confucius was obliged to resign. Then for many years he traveled from state to state with his pupils, teaching good morals. The last years of his life were spent gathering together all the wisdom of the ancient sages into five texts—or *Ching*. After his death, his pupils wrote four more books called *Shu*, about the sayings of their master. These nine books became the Bible of China.

The heart of his teaching, the best-known saying of Confucius, is one upon which all great teachers of every land agree. When he was about nineteen he was asked to settle a dispute between some herdsmen who could not understand the fine points of the law. He gave them a simple rule to go by: *Do not do to others what you would not have them do to you.* When that Great Principle of Law prevails, the whole world becomes a Republic. . . . By nature all men are much alike; by custom only they grow wide apart. Men of the four seas are brothers."

The teachings of Confucius, being exact rules of behavior, were easily understood and not easily changed, and they became the rule of life in China, for centuries to come.

JESUS, A BOY IN NAZARETH. It was a little more than five hundred years after the Hebrews had returned from captivity in Babylon, and had rebuilt their temple in Jerusalem, that Jesus of Nazareth was born. The Jews, as the Hebrews had come to be called, were then under the rule of the Romans; but they still looked forward to the long-promised Messiah, or Saviour King, who would rescue them.

As a boy, Jesus must have heard of this promise from his mother Mary and from Joseph, who was a peasant carpenter in the little village. He also must have learned how important it was to obey the Law. Every Sabbath he heard the Law of Moses and the words of the prophets read aloud in the synagogue and explained by those strict students of the Law who were known as Pharisees.

In the spring of the year when he was twelve, Jesus went for the first time with Mary and Joseph on the annual journey to Jerusalem for the celebration of the Passover. There he entered the great Court of the Temple and saw the lamb sacrificed on the smoking altar. He ate of the Passover meal on the hillside at sunset, and joined in singing psalms of praise to the Lord for His goodness and mercy. The next morning he returned to the Temple to listen to the wise men who taught there each day in the Porch of Solomon answering questions and explaining the Law.

THE TEACHINGS OF HILLEL. One of those whom Jesus may have seen that morning was the great rabbi, Hillel, surrounded by a circle of pupils, and may have heard him say: "One must study the Torah constantly to learn the will of God."

All the years of his life Hillel had been studying the Law of Moses, seeking to extract from it all that was truly important, but never placing the letter of the Law above the Spirit, as many of the Pharisees did.

One day a Roman, interested, but puzzled about the endless number of laws and rules the Pharisees insisted upon, approached Hillel, saying, "I am ready to accept your religion, if you can tell it to me simply."

Hillel replied: "Our religion can be put into one sentence: What is hateful to thyself, do not unto thy neighbor. That is the whole Law, the rest is but explanation."

JESUS AND THE KINGDOM OF HEAVEN. Nothing is known of the life of Jesus after the first visit to Jerusalem, until he was about thirty years old. Then, according to the Bible: "Jesus came to Nazareth, where he had been brought up: and, as his custom was, he went into the synagogue on the Sabbath day, and he stood up for to read . . . [from the] prophet Isaiah . . . where it was written, 'The Spirit of the Lord is upon me, because he hath . . . sent me to heal the brokenhearted . . .'

"And he closed the book, and began to say unto them, 'This day is the scripture fulfilled in your ears.' And all . . . wondered at the gracious words . . . And they said, 'Is this not Joseph's son?' . . . And . . . they . . . were filled with wrath, and rose up, and thrust him out of the city, and led him unto the brow of the hill . . . that they might cast him down headlong. But he passing through the midst of them went his way."

His preaching and healing troubled the Pharisees, especially on the Sabbath, when they held that even to tie a knot was to commit a sin against the Fourth Commandment. When they saw Jesus heal a sick man on the Sabbath day, they held a council how they might prove his teachings false and be rid of him. And he was asked: "Master, which is the commandment in the law?"

"Jesus said unto him, 'Thou shalt love the Lord with all thy heart, and with all thy soul, and with all thy mind.' This is the first and great commandment. And the second is like unto it, 'Thou shalt love thy neighbour as thyself.' On these two commandments hang all the law and the prophets . . ."

"And when he was demanded of the Pharisees, when the kingdom of God should come, he answered them and said, 'The kingdom of God cometh not with observation: Neither shall they say, "Lo here! or, lo there!" for, behold, the kingdom of God is within you!'"

It was in the spring of the year 30 A.D. that Jesus went for the last time to Jerusalem for the celebration of the Passover, accompanied by his disciples.

[315]

As he entered the city, many seeing in him the long-awaited Messiah, or Saviour King, went before him crying, "Hosanna! . . . Blessed is he that cometh in the name of the Lord."

The chief priests, however, and the captain of the Temple were alarmed. The next morning the elders and scribes and the whole council of judges declared Jesus guilty of blasphemy against the Lord. They brought him to the Roman governor, and the governor delivered him to be crucified . . .

In the New Testament it is told how Jesus rose from the dead and appeared at different times to his disciples. "And he said to them, 'Go ye into all the world, and preach the gospel to every creature.'"

The belief that Jesus was the Messiah, or Christ, though it died out among his own people, spread in ever-widening circles through the Roman world. His life and teachings became the heart of a new religion, Christianity. In spite of torture and persecution, the number of Christians continued to increase, until three hundred years later they included the Roman emperor himself. The Emperor Constantine, in 312, made Christianity the official religion of the Roman Empire.

MOHAMMED, THE PROPHET OF ALLAH. About five hundred years after Jesus lived, a boy was born in Arabia, who came to be called Mohammed "The Praised One," and who taught his people of the One God, whom he called Allah. He founded the religion known as Islam.

In Arabia, that desert land from which the ancient Hebrew shepherds had originally come, the Arab tribesmen were still worshiping the same kinds of rocks and stones and tribal gods as had the early Hebrews.

Mohammed's birthplace was the city of Mecca on the edge of the desert. To this city of crowded bazaars and countless idols, tribesmen from the desert came once each year to buy and sell and especially to worship a small black sacred stone, known as the Kaaba. Mohammed belonged to the priestly caste who guarded the sacred Kaaba, but his branch of the family had been crowded out of power and had become poor. As an orphan he grew up without education and was unable to read or write.

When he was twenty-five, Mohammed became a camel driver and then a merchant, traveling by camel caravan along the Red Sea north to Jerusalem and Damascus. In those cities he heard people speak of One God, instead of many. He talked with both Jews and Christians and learned of their belief. He thought about it, using the Arab word for God, which was Allah. He went into the desert and prayed for understanding. And one day, there in the windy desert, it came to him, as in a vision, the way of life that he must preach. It was Islam, meaning submission—submission to the will of Allah, the one and only God.

"They who set their faces with submission toward God, and do what is right, no fear shall come to them; neither shall they be grieved." Those are the words of Mohammed. There had been many prophets, he said. There was but One God. The God of whom they all spoke was Allah, the One and only God, creator of all mankind.

So spoke the prophet Mohammed, denouncing the many tribal gods of the Arabs and their worship of idols. His words so alarmed the priestly guardians of the sacred Kaaba, and also the merchants who profited from the yearly pilgrimage to Mecca, that they drove the prophet from the city. Mohammed and his few poor converts fled from Mecca in the year 622. That was the Hegira or Flight of the Prophet. And it was the turning point. During the last ten years of his life, Mohammed became a warrior. He conquered, converted, and enlisted the tribes of the desert in a holy war and made himself master of all Arabia, its "prophet, priest and king."

The teachings of Mohammed, passed on at first by word of mouth, were later recorded in the *Koran*, the sacred book of Islam.

By 750, only one hundred years after Mohammed's death, the Arabs had conquered an empire that reached as far east as the Indus River. It extended westward across northern Africa and up into Spain. It is still the leading religion in those lands, except in Spain, where the Moslems were finally driven out in 1492. In that same important year Christopher Columbus sailed westward from Spain and planted the cross and the religion of Christianity in the New World.

· · · · · · ·

And so the belief in One God, who is to be found in the heart of every man, revealed to many prophets, and worshiped in various ways, spread around the world. Wherever and by whatever name He may be called, "the Lord Our God is One."

⟨[THIS story was adapted by the author from her books AUGUSTUS CAESAR'S WORLD and BIRTHDAYS OF FREEDOM. Among Mrs. Foster's other books are GEORGE WASHINGTON'S WORLD, ABRAHAM LINCOLN'S WORLD, and THE WORLD OF CAPTAIN JOHN SMITH, each of which presents a dramatic slice of history—a horizontal slice—as it was being made by the leaders who lived at the same time.

The Beatitudes

Blessed are the poor in spirit: for theirs is the kingdom of heaven.

Blessed are they that mourn: for they shall be comforted.

Blessed are the meek: for they shall inherit the earth.

Blessed are they which do hunger and thirst after righteousness: for they shall be filled.

Blessed are the merciful: for they shall obtain mercy.

Blessed are the pure in heart: for they shall see God.

Blessed are the peacemakers: for they shall be called the children of God.

Blessed are they which are persecuted for righteousness' sake: for their's is the kingdom of heaven . . .

—From The Sermon on the Mount (Matthew 5:3-10).

NATHAN AUSUBEL

The Preacher of Dubno

⟨[RABBI JACOB KRANTZ *of Dubno, Poland, who lived in the late 1700's, wandered from town to town preaching. Vast crowds gathered to hear him, for he was much loved for the homely wisdom of his parables.*

THE VENEER OF SILVER. A rich but stingy man once came to his rabbi to ask for his blessing. The rabbi suddenly arose, took his hand, and led him to the window looking out on the street.

"Tell me, what do you see?" asked the rabbi.

"I see people," answered the puzzled rich man.

Then the rabbi drew him before a mirror. "What do you see now?" he again asked him.

"I see myself," answered the man, bewildered.

"Now, my son, let me explain to you the meaning of my two questions. The window is made of glass, as is also the mirror, only the glass of the mirror has a veneer of silver on it. When you look through plain glass you see people. But no sooner do you cover it with silver when you stop seeing others and see only yourself."

⁊

THE BLEMISH ON THE DIAMOND. A king once owned a great diamond of the purest water. He was very proud of it for it had no peer in the world. But one day an accident happened and the diamond became deeply scratched. The king then consulted with several diamond cutters, artists in their line. They told him that even if they were to polish the stone they would never be able to remove the imperfection.

Some time later, at the king's command, the greatest lapidary in the country arrived in the capital and undertook to make the diamond look even more beautiful than it was before the accident.

With the greatest art he engraved a delicate rosebud around the imperfection, and out of the deep scratch he cut a stem. When the king and the diamond cutters saw what he had wrought with so much ingenuity they were filled with admiration.

This next story about Rabbi Krantz has something of the same salty wisdom that characterized his own parables.

⁊

A RABBI FOR A DAY. The famous Preacher of Dubno was once journeying from one town to another delivering his learned sermons. Wherever he went he was received with enthusiasm and accorded the greatest honors. His driver, who accompanied him on this tour, was much impressed by all this welcome.

One day, as they were on the road, the driver said, "Rabbi, I have a great favor to ask of you. Wherever we go people heap honors on you. Although I'm only an ignorant driver I'd like to know how it feels to receive so much attention. Would you mind if we exchange clothes for one day? Then they'll think I am the great preacher and you the driver, so they'll honor me instead!"

Now the Preacher of Dubno was a man of the people and a merry soul, but he saw the pitfalls awaiting his driver in such an arrangement.

"Suppose I agreed, what then? You know the rabbi's clothes don't make a rabbi! What would you do for learning? If they were to ask you to explain some difficult passage in the Law you'd only make a fool of yourself, wouldn't you?"

"Don't you worry, Rabbi. I am willing to take that chance."

"In that case," said the preacher, "here are my clothes."

The two men undressed and exchanged clothes as well as their callings.

As they entered the town all the Jewish inhabitants turned out to greet the great preacher. They conducted him into the synagogue while the assumed driver followed at a distance.

Each man came up to the "rabbi" to shake hands and to say the customary: "*Sholom Aleichem,* learned Rabbi!"

The "rabbi" was thrilled with his reception. He sat down in the seat of honor surrounded by the scholars and dignitaries of the town. In the meantime the preacher from his corner kept his merry eyes on the driver to see what would happen.

"Learned Rabbi," suddenly asked a local scholar, "would you be good enough to explain to us this passage in the Law we don't understand?"

The preacher in his corner chuckled, for the passage was a difficult one.

"Now he's sunk!" he said to himself.

With knitted brows the "rabbi" peered into the sacred book placed before him, although he could not understand one word. Then, impatiently pushing it away from him, he addressed himself sarcastically to the learned men of the town: "A fine lot of scholars you are! Is this the most difficult question you can ask? Why, this passage is so simple even my driver could explain it to you!"

Then he called to the Preacher of Dubno: "Driver, come here a moment and explain the Law to these 'scholars'!"

The Parables of Jesus

THE GOOD SAMARITAN. A certain lawyer stood up and tempted him, saying, "Master, what shall I do to inherit eternal life?" He said unto him, "What is written in the law? how readest thou?" And he answering said, "Thou shalt love the Lord thy God with all thy heart, and with all thy soul, and with all thy strength, and with all thy mind; and thy neighbour as thyself." And he said unto him, "Thou hast answered right: this do, and thou shalt live."

But he, willing to justify himself, said unto Jesus, "And who is my neighbour?"

And Jesus answering said, "A certain man went down from Jerusalem to Jericho, and fell among thieves, which stripped him of his raiment and wounded him, and departed, leaving him half dead.

"By chance there came down a certain priest that way: and when he saw him, he passed by on the other side. And likewise a Levite, when he was at the place, came and looked on him, and passed by on the other side.

"But a certain Samaritan, as he journeyed, came where he was: and when he saw him, he had compassion on him, and went to him, and bound up his wounds, pouring in oil and wine, and set him on his own beast, and brought him to an inn, and took care of him. "And on the morrow when he departed, he took out two pence, and gave them to the host, and said unto him, 'Take care of him; and whatsoever thou spendest more, when I come again, I will repay thee.' Which now of these three, thinkest thou, was neighbour unto him that fell among the thieves?"

And he said, "He that shewed mercy on him."

Then said Jesus unto him, "Go, and do thou likewise."

&

THE PRODIGAL SON. A certain man had two sons: and the younger of them said to his father, "Father, give me the portion of goods that falleth to me." And he divided unto them his living.

And not many days after the younger son gathered all together, and took his journey into a far country, and there wasted his substance with riotous living. And when he had spent all, there arose a mighty famine in that land; and he began to be in want. And he went and joined himself to a citizen of that country; and he sent him into his fields to feed swine. And he would fain have filled his belly with the husks that the swine did eat: and no man gave unto him.

And when he came to himself, he said, "How many hired servants of my father's have bread enough and to spare, and I perish with hunger! I will arise and go to my father, and will say unto him, 'Father, I have sinned against heaven, and before thee, and am no more worthy to be called thy son: make me as one of thy hired servants.' "

And he arose, and came to his father. But when he was yet a great way off, his father saw him, and had compassion, and ran, and fell on his neck, and kissed him.

And the son said unto him, "Father, I have sinned against heaven, and in thy sight, and am no more worthy to be called thy son."

But the father said to his servants, "Bring forth the best robe, and put it on him; and put a ring on his hand, and shoes on his feet; and bring hither the fatted calf, and kill it; and let us eat, and be merry: for this my son was dead, and is alive again; he was lost, and is found." And they began to be merry.

Now his elder son was in the field:

and as he came and drew nigh to the house, he heard music and dancing. And he called one of the servants, and asked what these things meant.

He said unto him, "Thy brother is come; and thy father hath killed the fatted calf, because he hath received him safe and sound."

And he was angry, and would not go in: therefore came his father out, and entreated him. And he answering said to his father, "Lo, these many years do I serve thee, neither transgressed I at any time thy commandment: and yet thou never gavest me a kid, that I might make merry with my friends: but as soon as this thy son was come, which hath devoured thy living . . . thou hast killed for him the fatted calf."

And he said unto him, "Son, thou art ever with me, and all that I have is thine. It was meet that we should make merry, and be glad: for this thy brother was dead, and is alive again; and was lost, and is found."

The Wisdom of St. Paul

THE GREATEST OF THESE. Though I speak with the tongues of men and of angels, and have not charity, I am become as sounding brass, or a tinkling cymbal.

And though I have the gift of prophecy, and understand all mysteries, and all knowledge; and though I have all faith, so that I could remove mountains, and have not charity, I am nothing.

And though I bestow all my goods to feed the poor, and though I give my body to be burned, and have not charity, it profiteth me nothing.

Charity suffereth long, and is kind; charity envieth not; charity vaunteth not itself, is not puffed up.

Doth not behave itself unseemly, seeketh not her own, is not easily provoked, thinketh no evil;

Rejoiceth not in iniquity, but rejoiceth in the truth;

Beareth all things, believeth all things, hopeth all things, endureth all things.

Charity never faileth: but whether there be prophecies, they shall fail; whether there be tongues, they shall cease; whether there be knowledge, it shall vanish away.

For we know in part, and we prophesy in part.

But when that which is perfect is come, then that which is in part shall be done away.

When I was child, I spake as a child, I understood as a child, I thought as a child: but when I became a man, I put away childish things.

For now we see through a glass, darkly; but then face to face: now I know in part; but then shall I know even as also I am known.

And now abideth faith, hope, charity, these three; but the greatest of these is charity.

—First Epistle to the Corinthians

❧

WHATSOEVER THINGS ARE TRUE. Whatsoever things are true, whatsoever things are honest, whatsoever things are just, whatsoever things are pure, whatsoever things are lovely, whatsoever things are of good report; if there be any virtue, and if there be any praise, think on these things.

—From *Epistle to the Philippians*

Words to Remember

WITH MALICE TOWARD NONE. Fondly do we hope, fervently do we pray that this mighty scourge of war may soon pass away . . . With malice toward none; with charity for all; with firmness in the right, as God gives us to see the right, let us strive on to finish the work we are in; to bind up the nation's wounds; to care for him who shall have borne the battle, and for his widow and his orphan—to do all which may achieve and cherish a just and lasting peace among ourselves, and with all nations.

—Abraham Lincoln in "Second Inaugural Address" (1865)

᾿ᴥ

THE FOUR FREEDOMS. We look forward to a world founded upon four essential human freedoms.

The first is freedom of speech and expression—everywhere in the world.

The second is freedom of every person to worship God in his own way—everywhere in the world.

The third is freedom from want—which, translated into world terms, means economic understandings which will secure to every nation a healthy peaceful life for its inhabitants—everywhere in the world.

The fourth is freedom from fear—which, translated into world terms, means a world-wide reduction of armaments to such a point and in such a thorough fashion that no nation will be in a position to commit an act of aggression against any neighbor—anywhere in the world.

—Franklin D. Roosevelt, in "Message to Congress" (1941)

Prayers to Remember

Joy Is the Grace

There is only one way to get ready for immortality, and that is to love this life and to live it as bravely and cheerfully as we can. Take joy home and make a place in thy great heart for her and give her time to grow and cherish her. It is a comely fashion to be glad. Joy is the grace we say to God. Beloved Pan and all other gods who haunt this place, give me beauty in the inward soul, and may the outward and the inward man be as one.

—Socrates

Lord, Make Me a Channel of Thy Peace

Lord, make me a channel of Thy peace.
That where there is hatred, I may bring love;
That where there is wrong, I may bring the spirit of forgiveness;
That where there is discord, I may bring harmony;
That where there is error, I may bring truth;
That where there is doubt, I may bring faith;
That where there is despair, I may bring hope;
That where there are shadows, I may bring light;

That where there is sadness, I may bring joy.
Lord grant that I may seek rather
To comfort than to be comforted;
To understand than to be understood;
To love than to be loved . . .

—St. Francis of Assisi

Old Gaelic Blessing

May the roads rise with you,
And the wind be always at your back;
And may the Lord hold you
In the hollow of His hand.

Sioux Indian Prayer

O Great Spirit of my fathers, this is my prayer:
Help me to feel Thine urge and Thy message.
Help me to be just even to those who hate me; and at all times help me to be kind.
If mine enemy is weak and faltering, help me to the good thought that I forgive him.
If he surrender, move me to help him as a weak and needy brother.

—Translated by Ohiyesa (Charles Eastman)

Prayer for a Better World

Our Earth is but a small star in the

[325]

great universe. Yet of it we can make, if we choose, a planet unvexed by war, untroubled by hunger or fear, undivided by senseless distinctions of race, color, or theory.

Grant us brotherhood, not only for this day but for all our years—a brotherhood not of words but of acts and deeds. We are all of us children of earth—grant us that simple knowledge. If our brothers are oppressed, then we are oppressed. If they hunger, we hunger. If their freedom is taken away, our freedom is not secure.

Grant us a common faith that man shall know bread and peace—that he shall know justice and righteousness, freedom and security, an equal opportunity and an equal chance to do his best, not only in our own lands but throughout the world. And in that faith, let us march toward the clean world our hands can make.

—Stephen Vincent Benét

Inaugural Prayer

Give us, we pray, the power to discern clearly right from wrong, and allow all our words and actions to be governed thereby and by the laws of this land. Especially, we pray that our concern shall be for all the people, re-

gardless of station, race or calling. May cooperation be permitted and be the mutual aim of those who, under the concepts of our Constitution, hold to differing political beliefs, so that all may work for the good of our beloved country and Thy glory.

—Dwight D. Eisenhower (1953)

Benediction

The Lord bless thee and keep thee:
The Lord make his face shine upon thee, and be gracious unto thee:
The Lord lift up his countenance upon thee, and give thee peace.

Numbers 6:24-28

The Lord's Prayer

Our Father which art in heaven,
Hallowed be thy name.
Thy kingdom come. Thy will be done in earth, as it is in heaven.
Give us this day our daily bread.
And forgive us our debts, as we forgive our debtors.
And lead us not into temptation, but deliver us from evil:
For thine is the kingdom, and the power, and the glory, forever. Amen.

Matthew 6:9-13

TYPOGRAPHY BY CHARLES FARRELL